UNTIL
TOMORROW
COMES

UNTIL TOMORROW COMES

Orville E. Kelly

EVEREST HOUSE
Publishers   *New York*

Library of Congress Cataloging in Publication Data
Kelly, Orville E.
Until tomorrow comes.

1. Lymphoma—Biography.   2.   Cancer patients—
Rehabilitation.   3.   Kelly, Orville E., 1930-
I.   Title.
RC280.L9K44   1979   362.1´9´699409   [B]   78-74582
ISBN 0-89696-031-5

Dedication

THIS BOOK is dedicated to my wife, Wanda, and my children—Mark, Tammy, Lori, and Britton, and my son-in-law, Paul Vickers; Wanda's parents, Clyde and Lora Klossing, Sr., of Burlington, Iowa, who have been my own "Mom and Dad," too; Rosemary Randolph and all the hundreds of students at Macomb Senior High School, Macomb, Illinois, who have provided me with much support and friendship during the past five years; and to Dr. Norman Vincent Peale and Ruth Stafford Peale for their spiritual, emotional, and financial support of me through Guidepost's Outreach Ministries program.

Special thanks

A SPECIAL THANKS to my friend and secretary, Jeannie Kuster, for her efforts in helping me finish this book on time; Bill Gray of the National Cancer Institute for furnishing me with so much material for the book; the late Fred Iverson of San Diego, for his close friendship during difficult times; Dr. Fred Brunk and Mary Brunk, for their help; Marcie Weaton, our Make Today Count secretary; Dr. Carl Hulen for his never-to-be-forgotten assistance in helping Wanda and me purchase a home of our own; the Make Today Count board of directors—Rich Goughnour, Steve Fausel, John Vickers, Rodney Wittkamp, Donna Peebler, B. F. "Chuck" Lawley, Wanda Kelly, and Carl Hulen—for their tireless efforts in supporting my philosophies; Dr. David Peters of La Jolla, California, for his loyal friendship; Dr. John Hoak, chief of hematology/oncology, University of Iowa Hospitals, for believing in me from the beginning; Dr. Charles Garfield, clinical psychologist, University of California Cancer Research Center, San Francisco, for his unwavering support; Jerry Gross, my editor, for believing in this book even before the first page was written; Sally Wecksler, my agent in New York; and the thousands of cancer patients and their families who helped me make my dream of an international self-help organization for the seriously ill come true.

Contents

APPENDIXES

   1. Hot Lines For Information About Cancer
   2. Other Information Services
   3. Comprehensive Cancer Centers
   4. Support Groups
      a. International Association of Laryngectomees
      b. Reach to Recovery (Breast Surgery Patients)
      c. Ostomy Rehabilitation Program of the American Cancer Society, Inc.
      d. The United Ostomy Association
      e. Candlelighters (Childhood and Adult Cancer)
      f. Leukemia Society of America, Inc.
      g. Make Today Count, Inc.
   5. Financial Assistance to Individuals
      a. Social Security Disability Income
      b. Supplemental Security Income
      c. Veteran's Benefits
   6. Where to Find Information About Cancer
      a. National Cancer Institute Publications
      b. Booklets and Reports Available from Various Sources
      c. Magazine, Newspaper, and Journal Articles on: Cancer Cause and Prevention, Cancer Detection and Diagnosis, Cancer Treatment and Rehabilitation, Cancer Biology
      d. Reference Sources of Information About Cancer
      e. Cancer Teaching Aids
      f. Free Brochures on Various Types of Cancer
      g. Principal Medical Libraries in the United States
      h. Nutrition for the Cancer Patient
      i. Cancer Information Clearinghouse

Introduction

"I do not consider myself dying of cancer, but rather living despite it. I no longer think of each passing day as another day closer to death, but rather as another day of life."

My name is Orville Eugene Kelly. I am a cancer patient and founder of Make Today Count, a grass-roots, self-help organization for persons with life-threatening illnesses, their loved ones, and other interested persons. Make Today Count has grown from one chapter, organized in my home city of Burlington, Iowa, in January 1974, to over two hundred chapters, in 1978, in the United States, Canada, and Europe.

I received my diagnosis of cancer on June 15, 1973, from a surgeon in Burlington, Iowa, following the removal of one of three discernible tumors. Subsequent testing at the University of Iowa Hospital at Iowa City, Iowa, indicated that I had lymphocytic lymphoma, poorly differentiated type, in an advanced stage. Chemotherapy (chemical drug) treatment was begun in September 1973 and continued for three and a half years.

After about two years of treatment, I went into a state of remission, which meant that the cancer was stabilized, that there were not enough cancer cells in my body to measure microscopically, and that the tumors had dissolved.

In the early part of October 1978, I was taking a shower and checking beneath my arms as usual, feeling for any sign of enlarged nodes, as I had been doing for the past three years. When I felt something beneath my left arm, near the spot where two of the original three tumors were located, I immediately called an oncologist at the hospital, who said he wanted to examine me. A few days later, I drove to Iowa City and discovered that what I had felt was apparently an enlarged node, signaling that my remission had probably ended. This meant a possible resumption of my chemotherapy treatment.

A few days later, I returned to the University Hospital for another examination. The oncologist told me the node beneath my arm had not grown in size since my earlier visit. He said he was not as convinced I was losing my remission as he had been the previous visit. My blood counts were all within normal limits and there were no indications of new tumor growth. The doctor recommended chemotherapy be withheld for the present time. I was elated, but on the way home from the hospital I began to wonder what was happening to me. Was I losing my remission or was the enlarged node insignificant for the moment?

Once again, I found myself trying to cope with the old fears and frustrations of the past. Once more, I found myself remembering how my world fell apart the day I learned I had cancer. I recalled how I refused to discuss my emotional problems with my wife, Wanda, and how I chose not to inform my four children, Mark (twelve), Tammy (eleven), Lori (eight), and Britton (three), that I had cancer. When I learned then that my cancer could be treated, but that there was no cure rate, I gave up living. After leaving the hospital, I went home to die. I felt as if I had lost control of my life, and I suffered from constant depression because I had been "tapped on the shoulder" by what we all fear most—Death.

As time passed and the tests continued, I began to realize that the emotional problems associated with a serious illness such as cancer—depression, loneliness, rejection, anger, lack of communication, fear, isolation, and sexuality—are often more difficult to cope with than the illness itself.

When I returned home from the hospital to await my first chemotherapy treatment, I discovered I was entering a different world from the one I had left. It was a world where even relatives and old friends seemed uncomfortable around me, because they were afraid they might say or do the wrong thing. I also reminded them of their own mortality. As a cancer patient I represented a dying person. In this age of cancerphobia, cancer represents death to most of us.

Nothing during my nearly twelve years of service in the United States Army, nor the time I spent as a reporter, city editor, and editor of newspapers in Illinois prepared me for what happened to me following the diagnosis of cancer. At times, I felt as if I were being manipulated as I followed instructions and reported to various departments within the hospital for such tests as lymphangiograms, bone marrow biopsies, and berium dye examinations. I had no active part to play in my own destiny. I felt I had lost my dignity as doctors continued to probe, poke, and thump my body, and nurses shoved tubes where tubes were not meant to go. Often, when I did manage to fall asleep at night, I was awakened so I could take a sleeping pill that would make me sleep again. Early in the morning, I was awakened once again to eat breakfast so I would be prepared when the physicians made "grand rounds" four or five hours later!

I tried to pretend everything was all right, but I thought of my own funeral often and wondered what would happen to Wanda and the children after my death. After reaching the depths of depression I contemplated suicide because I felt I had become a burden to my family. But I did not stay at rock bottom. I became determined to find ways to live despite the cancer. After hiding from reality for several months, I decided to tell the children I had cancer and I asked for their help in coping with my problems. I began to talk with Wanda and told her of my fears, depression, and anger. I became concerned about the quality of my life, regardless of the time I had left to live. But I could find no support outside my family for what I was trying to do. I wanted to talk with someone else who was "walking through the valley," but I did not know how to contact other patients. Wanda, too, expressed a desire to share her thoughts with family members of other cancer patients who experienced what she was enduring.

I wrote an article for the newspaper in Burlington, telling what it was like to live with cancer, and what some of the misconceptions were surrounding the disease and of the stigmas attached to it. I also suggested that an organization be formed so patients and their families could come together informally and help each other find ways to live with a tragedy they had never anticipated.

The same night the article appeared, the telephone at my home began ringing, with calls coming from not only patients and family members but members of the health-care field such as nurses and doctors. Clergymen called, too. I suggested to all of them that we hold a meeting in Burlington to form my proposed organization. We met at the Elks Club in Burlington on the night of January 25, 1974. Eighteen persons were present. My dream became a reality. When I proposed three possible names for our group, "Make Today Count" was the unanimous choice.

There was an immediate media interest in what had taken place in our small Iowa city. The wire services scattered the story around the world. Hundreds of letters came to us from desperate patients looking for a glimmer of light at the end of their tunnel. Family members of patients wrote, seeking help in coping with a tragedy they found impossible to endure without support. Health-care professionals asked for help, too, in trying to recognize the needs of terminally ill persons and then meeting those needs, if possible. I turned to Wanda for help in answering most of these letters. She shared my compassion for the people who came to us for help. And I learned a great deal more about her than I had ever known in the past. Her inner strengths surfaced as she "helped *me* make it through the night" on so many occasions. Both of us came to realize that there is no better therapy than helping others. And we knew what it was like to suffer, believing no one else understood. It was like living in a private hell.

The time obviously was right for the birth and growth of an organization such as Make Today Count. But because I was unable to work, we could not meet the financial demands made upon us to ensure the survival of our group. We needed stationery, postage, brochures, and a part-time secretary. We converted a small room adjacent to our upstairs bedroom into a makeshift office. Mrs. Jeannie Kuster came to us, seeking the position of part-time secretary. She has been with us ever since. She and her husband, Tom, have become close friends of ours. After her arrival, we could respond more effectively to the pleas for help and inquiries about how our group functioned.

I received requests from producers of national television shows, asking me to appear and discuss Make Today Count. I was interviewed by Tom Snyder on the *Tomorrow* show and by Mike Wallace for a *60 Minutes* segment. Later, Wanda and I were on the *Today* show and we were interviewed by David Hartman on *Good Morning, America.* Articles about our work appeared in the *Reader's Digest, New York Times Magazine, Family Circle, McCall's, Guidepost, Catholic Digest,* and many other publications. During the year following the formation of Make Today Count, I traveled over 100,000 miles to lecture at medical schools, hospitals, nursing conventions, high schools, medical seminars, and at public meetings. While traveling, I found time to visit many terminally ill patients in hospitals.

I also found time to write a book entitled *Make Today Count,* describing how I organized the group of the same name. I also described my childhood in rural Iowa and some of my early experiences as a cancer patient.

One day I received a letter from Dr. Norman Vincent Peale of the Foundation for Christian Living, internationally known Christian leader, and author of the book *The Power of Positive Thinking.* Because of his belief in my philosophy and my work, he and his wife, Ruth, gave financial support to Make Today Count through the Guidepost Outreach Ministries program. That support continues today.

Make Today Count today is a nonprofit, tax-exempt organization. Our office is now located in a building in downtown Burlington. Rodney Wittkamp, an attorney, serves as our executive director. We have a staff consisting of one full-time and two part-time secretaries. We produce a monthly newsletter and continue to answer letters from persons seeking help. We conduct several seminars each year, attended by patients, family members, clergymen, social workers, and health-care professionals.

The Make Today Count organization is dedicated to improving the quality of life of those who have been afflicted with a serious illness such as cancer. Individual chapter meetings are open to those persons who have or have had life-threatening diseases. Family members and friends are welcome, too. Health-care professionals and other community members have also become a part of the chapter's organizational structure in most communities.

The Make Today Count goals are: to help seriously ill patients and family members cope with life-threatening illness through a self-help approach; to improve the quality of life for all persons, regardless of their race, creed, or age, with serious illnesses; to identify emotional problems associated with serious illnesses and help individuals cope with them; to promote openness and honesty in discussing and dealing with a serious illness; and to assist the health-care professional in communicating with and meeting the needs of the seriously ill patient, family members, and friends.

Patients are an integral part of the MTC chapters. Often, a patient and professional person serve side by side as chapter coordinators. Family members, too, help support and operate chapters. Often, survivors of a patient who has died will remain active in the chapter, helping others to cope with their own problems.

I was proud to be the 1978 recipient of the annual award from the Association of Community Cancer Centers in America because of my support of "the patient with cancer." I was also presented with the annual Community Service Award from Western Illinois University.

I have traveled over 400,000 miles to make nearly one

thousand appearances on behalf of Make Today Count. I have talked with thousands of patients, family members, doctors, nurses, clergymen, and other persons, and I have continued to struggle with my own problems as a cancer patient. I have learned much from my exposure, and in this book I make available to you, the reader, information that was not available to me, or my wife, when we needed it. Actually, I feel my simple philosophy should apply to *all of you*, because it is impossible to live your life without being touched by some sort of tragedy. I want to show you, though, that from tragedy can sometimes come new lives and new dreams. The diagnosis of a serious illness does not necessarily mean an immediate death sentence. Perhaps you will understand, after reading this book, why the specter of death has given so many cancer patients like myself a new awareness of life.

In this book, too, you will find commonsense answers to many of your questions. (After all, who knows better than a cancer patient what it is like to live with cancer?) What is cancer? What causes it? What treatments are available? Should I seek a second opinion? Is laetrile effective? Are there any cures for cancer on the horizon? What rights do I have as a patient? Is there ever a time when a patient should refuse treatment? Will there be any help available in the event my finances become depleted? Can a seriously ill person be cared for at home? How can I cope with depression and fear? Should we tell the children? How important is faith? What side effects might I suffer from chemotherapy and/or radiation therapy? How many cancer patients suffer from intense pain? What can I say to someone who is dying of cancer? Should I make my own funeral arrangements? How can I face death when there seems to be no hope left?

It is often difficult to obtain honest, straightforward

answers to questions about cancer. When the diagnosis is cancer, we pretend, deceive, and resort to dishonesty in order to avoid facing reality. We think we are protecting those we love when we shield them from the truth. But we generally cause unintended harm and deny the patient an opportunity to express openly his thoughts and feelings which are so difficult to hide.

You will also find both practical advice and inspiration. The inspiration comes from the many persons I have known who endured a serious illness or watched a loved one suffer, or cared for them in their time of need.

No matter how serious your illness may be, you will find it is not necessary for you to walk through the valley alone, without human friendship. There are fellow travelers willing to hold your hand, people who care.

My hope is that this book will show them *how* to care—effectively, compassionately, realistically.

June, 1979
Burlington, Iowa   *Orville E. Kelly*

PART I
I
THE
BEGINNING

1

Diagnosis: Cancer

"**W**HAT IS CANCER?" someone asked me in a recent letter. "My mother died of it and I don't even understand what causes it or anything about it."

I have found that few people possess even a layman's knowledge of the most feared disease in the world and the number two killer of Americans. We live in an age of cancerphobia, but there are indications that most people do not want to know *too* much about cancer. Who wants to be reminded, for example, that cancer touches two out of every three families in America? Who wants to be told that the probability of having cancer during one's lifetime is one out of four? In the years ahead, about 54 million Americans who are alive now will have cancer and 34 million of them, or two out of every three patients, will eventually die of the disease. During 1977, for example, nearly 700,000 persons were newly diagnosed as having cancer. There were more deaths from cancer during the same year in America (approximately 390,000) than all U.S. casualties during the fifteen years of involvement in World War II (292,131 battle deaths), the Korean Conflict and Vietnam (46,397), a total of 372,157.

I have quoted these figures to stress the importance of treating cancer as an international problem, which it is. Any general will tell you it is important to identify and understand your enemy, but don't let these statistics prohibit you from going on with the business of living. No matter what we do, we are not going to stop nature from having its way. And if you were to isolate yourself from all cancer-causing agents in our world, you would have to live in a plastic, germ-free tent of some sort (and I doubt if you would be safe then, because the plastic itself would probably contain a chemical suspected of causing cancer!). What we should strive for is a more effective means of controlling the use of carcinogens.

What is the nature of this disease that has plagued mankind for centuries? (Evidence of cancer has been found in 5,000-year-old Egyptian mummies from between the third and fifth dynasties.) Why do we refer to cancer as an "extended," "prolonged," or "lengthy" illness in many newspaper obituaries? Why are most people reluctant to talk or even think about their personal involvement with cancer? What causes cancer and why don't we have a cure for it after years of research and billions of dollars spent on this research? I hope to be able to answer these and other questions in this book.

Perhaps we can understand why we hide our personal involvememt with cancer from the experience of a young attorney who belonged to one of our Make Today Count chapters. A victim of cancer, he was still able to practice law. He decided to be honest about his illness, not hiding it from anyone. But he told me his openness about cancer caused him to lose clients. It became obvious that people did not want an attorney who they thought might either be incapable of making proper decisions or not be around when needed.

Perhaps, too, there is an indication of the public's attitude toward cancer in the letter I received from a corporation executive who swore me to secrecy about his cancer. "If the board of directors were to learn about my illness, I would be retired early," he told me. "I should know, because I watched it happen to a fellow executive."

A nationwide Gallup poll survey of Americans showed cancer to be the most feared affliction, with blindness next and heart disease third.

A lady approached me once after one of my lectures and told me that the doctors had once thought her husband might have cancer.

"Thank God, it *wasn't* cancer!" she exclaimed.

"What was it?" I asked curiously.

"Heart disease," she replied.

"How is he doing?" I asked.

"Oh, he died later of a heart attack," she said.

Cancer strikes not only humans but animals and plant life, too. Cancer occurs in sunflowers, clover, and many other common plants. Dogs are afflicted with cancer of the breast. One type of cancer affects the eyelids of cows. Since this disease occurs frequently in mice, they are used for laboratory experimentation with cancers that can be transplanted.

It is possible that some animals were victims of cancer long before history was recorded.

What is cancer? It is a large group of diseases caused by

5

rapidly multiplying cells which can develop in any part of the body. Each of the billions of cells in your body has a job to do—skin cells give your body protection, bone cells build the skeleton, red blood cells carry oxygen. During childhood, these cells multiply as rapidly as they are needed, but when you become an adult, they divide and replace dead cells only as necessary, or they help to repair wounds in your body. Cancer cells appear to be runaway cells that multiply rapidly without purpose or restraint. As the cancer cells continue to grow, they consume food needed by the normal cells.

The cancer cells build up into tumors that compress, invade, and destroy surrounding healthy tissues. When the cancer cells spread through the blood system or lymph system to other parts of the body to form new growths of cancer, the process is called metastasis. (The lymph system is the circulatory network of vessels and nodes carrying an almost colorless fluid that cleanses our body's cells and helps protect us against infection.)

The parts of the body most often affected by cancer are the skin, female breasts, and the organs of the respiratory, digestive, reproductive, blood-forming, lymphatic, and urinary systems. The occurrence of cancer in these sites varies from country to country. For example, cancer of the stomach is more prevalent in Japan than in the United States.

The four major categories of cancer are the carcinomas, sarcomas, leukemias, and lymphomas.

The carcinomas are solid tumor cancers originating in the nerve tissue, glandular organs, bronchial tubes, intestines, urogenital tract, and skin. Carcinomas include cancer of the uterus, prostate, lung, stomach, breast, and colon and constitute by far the majority of cancers.

The sarcomas are solid cancers originating in fat, bone,

connective tissue or muscle tissue. They are the rarest of all cancers, but often among the most deadly.

The leukemias, or "blood cancers," are malignancies that start in the bone marrow and lymph glands and cause increased growths of white blood cells.

The lymphomas are solid tumor cancers related to leukemias. These cancers result in the growth of large numbers of immature lymphocytes in the lymph glands and other organs.

Skin cancer occurs more often in America than any other type of malignancy. However, most skin cancers grow slowly and can be successfully treated.

Breast cancer strikes both sexes, but occurs far more in women than in men. It is the major cause of cancer deaths among American women.

Lung cancer is by far the most common type of cancer affecting the respiratory system. The death rate among lung cancer patients is very high. This type of cancer kills more men in America than any other kind.

Cancers of the digestive system include colon and rectal cancer, and cancer of the esophagus, liver, pancreas, and stomach. These cancers are the second most common ones in America, after skin cancers.

Cancers of the reproductive system most often affect the prostate gland in men and the uterus in women. These cancers occur at a relatively high rate in America.

Cancers of the urinary system are rare. The bladder is the organ most often affected. Most victims of bladder cancer are men.

Cancers of the blood-forming and lymphatic systems include leukemia and lymphoma. One of the most common forms of leukemia is acute leukemia. It strikes more children in the United States than any other kind of cancer. The most common type of lymphoma is Hodgkin's disease. More young adults in America are attacked by Hodgkin's disease than by any other type of cancer.

What causes cancer? When I was young, many Americans assumed cancer was a stroke of bad luck, unavoidable and unpredictable. Some persons thought it to be the work of the Devil, while still others considered it a form of punishment inflicted by God upon sinners who deserved no less.

Today, we are beginning to learn, somewhat reluctantly, that man himself may be causing most of the cancers in the world. Almost everything around us is a suspected carcinogen, or cancer-causing agent—the air we breathe, the food we eat, the chemicals we produce, the water and other liquids we drink, the radiation we absorb, the sunshine we use to tan our bodies, and the cigarettes we smoke. The occurrence of cancer seems to be influenced by our environment, heredity, and life-style.

Even our workplaces are suspect as potential cancer-causing areas, with the Occupational Safety and Health Administration making public a study in 1978 which contends at least 20 percent and perhaps as many as 38 percent of cancer cases are related to workplace exposures. (See Appendix B for listing of suspected agents in the workplace.)

Occupational exposure to asbestos alone may cause two million premature deaths from cancer in the United States during the next thirty years, according to Health, Education, and Welfare Secretary Joseph A. Califano, Jr., in a speech before an AFL-CIO National Conference on Occupational Safety and Health in Washington, D.C., on September 11, 1978. Mr. Califano was quoting from a report prepared by the National Cancer Institute and the National Institute of Environmental Health Sciences. From eight to eleven million workers, the majority of them employed in government shipyards, have been exposed to asbestos fibers since World War II.

The same report also indicated that high excesses of cancer were found among leather and shoe, cadmium production, coke oven, and metal mine workers.

Chemicals that may contribute to 1 to 3 percent of cancers in America are benzene, coal tar pitch, vinyl chloride, and arsenic. More than one million workers will face an increased risk of lung cancer from arsenic exposure alone during the next three decades, with an estimated five thousand potential cases annually.

Industry representatives have attacked these reports, saying the government doesn't have the data to support their findings. I have to wonder whether industry is more concerned about profits or the safety of human beings. I think the answer is obvious. A reasonable doubt has been established and the protection of the American worker should be more important than industrial profits.

We may not know it or like it, but the world around us is filled with chemicals. The clothes we wear, the magazines we read, the food we eat, the cars we drive, and almost every part of our present-day civilization is made possible by the use of chemicals. To answer the question "How many chemicals are there?" is difficult, but the American Chemical Society's Abstract Service, as of November 1977, shows 4,039,907 distinct entities. The number of chemicals in the register has been growing at the rate of about 6,000 per week, including new combinations of old chemicals. About 63,000 of these chemicals are in common use as part of our everyday life. For instance, there are about 1,500 different active ingredients in pesticides. The Food and Drug Administration estimates there are about 4,000 active ingredients in drugs and about 2,000 other compounds used as excipients to promote stability and cut down on growth of bacteria.

About 2,500 additives are used for nutritional value and flavoring in the food industry.

Saccharin, Tris, aerosols, hair dyes, food additives, pesticides, cancer-causing substances in drinking water—we never know from one day to the next what the government will inform us is unsafe for us. The problem is that the federal government has made little progress toward any reliable system for identifying and regulating carcinogens. Much of the time no one knows what is unsafe or in what quantities it becomes unsafe. With the influx of new products and new chemicals entering the national market daily, how can we, as citizens, protect ourselves from hazardous carcinogens unless the federal government organizes its efforts and shows more interest in controlling hazardous substances *before* they reach the market, instead of warning us *after* we have lived with these hazards for extended periods of time? There is no doubt that the control of so many chemicals and carcinogens is a huge task, but more and more people would like answers about why it takes so long to remove a dangerous carcinogen from our midst, and how it got there in the first place.

During 1977, the U.S. Government spent $207 million in an effort to discover how chemicals cause cancer, lung and heart disease. The results of this effort produced little new information on the problems pertaining to the cause of these diseases in relation to carcinogens, but did indicate evidence of environmental association.

As the turn of the century, lung and heart disease and cancer accounted for about 12 percent of deaths annually in the United States. Today, these diseases cause an estimated 60 percent of total deaths annually. Even though this is due partly to medical advances in controlling death from infectious illnesses and accidents, we should not ignore evidence that indicates 60 to 90 percent of all cancers may be caused by carcinogens in the workplace, the air we breathe, the water we drink, and in our environment. The list of suspected carcinogens is growing. Cancers of the lung, skin, bladder, liver, some leukemias and mesotheliomas have been associated with occupational exposure in the workplace. Because of this growing evidence, isn't it time physicians routinely asked patients if they have ever been exposed to radiation and other carcinogens, making this information a part of the patient's permanent medical record?

Another known cause of cancer is cigarette smoking. The U.S. Public Health Service, after studying data from the United States, Europe, Canada, and Japan, has concluded that cigarette smoking is the main cause of lung cancer in men and a major cause of this type of cancer in women.

The risk of developing lung cancer increases with the number of cigarettes one smokes, and there seems to be more danger from high "tar" cigarettes than from those with a lower tar content.

A risk of developing lung cancer is greater for pipe and cigar smokers than for nonsmokers, but much less than for cigarette smokers. However, pipe smoking can cause cancer of the lip.

Cigarette smoking has also been associated with cancers of the larynx, mouth, esophagus, kidney, bladder, and perhaps pancreas.

Ultraviolet radiation from the sun is the major cause of skin cancer. Skin cancer occurs most often in people who have fair or freckled skin and who are exposed to a great amount of sunlight. Most skin cancers can be successfully treated.

There is growing evidence that man-made radiation causes cancer, too. There is an increasing use of radioactive materials in industry and medicine, as well as fallout from testing of nuclear weapons. Radiation may produce many different types of malignancy depending on the nature of the exposure. The early radium workers developed skin cancers and leukemias; later, osteogenic sarcomas (a form of bone cancer) developed in radium-dial painters. Radiologists exposed before the dangers were known and protective measures were taken have had above-average mortality from leukemia. Uranium mine workers have developed lung cancer at higher rates than the general population. Survivors of the atomic bombings of Hiroshima and Nagasaki experienced a high rate of acute leukemia, especially in the first ten years following the war; and elevated risks of other forms of cancer have become increasingly evident among the survivors since 1950.

There is evidence that radiation of the neck in infants, once a common treatment for enlargement of the thymus, is associated with an increased incidence of thyroid cancer. Irradiation of the spine for ankylosing spondylitis (an inflammatory disease of the vertebrae) resulted in above-average rates of leukemia and lung cancer, as well as increases in other forms of cancer. There is some evidence that exposing expectant mothers to diagnostic X rays increases the occurrence of leukemia and other forms of cancer among their children.

I am personally involved in the burgeoning controversy among government agencies, scientists, physicists, and doctors over whether low-level radiation can cause cancer in human beings. I served as a soldier at Eniwetok Atoll in

1957 and 1958, during the U.S. Government's testing of twenty-two nuclear devices. I was less than ten miles away from these blasts when they occurred.

In 1974 I applied to the Veterans Administration for a service-connected disability, claiming my cancer had been caused by my duty at Eniwetok Atoll. I received a terse reply from an adjudication officer, dated August 13, 1974, reading as follows:

We have carefully reviewed your claim of service-connection for your lymphoma condition based upon all the evidence of record, including your service records. The records show that you were exposed to a total of 3.15 roentgens. However, there were no abnormalities noted at discharge. There is no evidence in file to indicate there is any relationship between your service and your current condition. Therefore, service-connection must be denied.

I realized there was little I could do except continue accumulating information leading to a correlation between cancer and exposure to radiation and reapply at a later date. I did write a brief account of my duty at Eniwetok in my first book, *Make Today Count*, in 1975. And I kept scanning newspapers and magazines for articles about radioactivity and cancer. I noted that the original inhabitants of the Marshall Islands were not allowed to return to Eniwetok for nearly twenty years and I asked myself, "If the islands were safe for habitation during the tests in 1957 and 1958, why did we wait so long to allow the islanders to return?"

I have since reapplied twice for veteran's benefits and have been turned down twice by the Veterans Administration. As of this writing, my case is on the way to the Board of Veterans Appeals in Washington, D.C. I will probably choose to appear in person before this board, when my case is heard. My supporters include Dr. John Gofman, professor emeritus, University of California, San Francisco, the discoverer of uranium 233; Dr. Karl Morgan, professor of nuclear engineering, Georgia Institute of Technology; and Dr. Thomas Mancuso, research professor, University of Pittsburgh. The National American Legion will be my counsel.

Some scientists believe that the high cancer death rates in urban areas are at least partly due to air pollution, but there is no valid evidence to substantiate this claim at the present time. It is a fact that the atmosphere of all large cities and many adjoining areas is polluted by industrial fumes and smoke, automobile exhaust, and combustion products from home heating. The polluted air often contains chemicals known to cause cancer in laboratory animals.

The air in such places as mines or industrial plants is sometimes polluted by such substances as chromate dust. If these substances are inhaled or absorbed in enough concentration over a period of time, the result may be cancer.

In communities where lead, copper, or zinc smelters are located, the air may contain arsenic, an airborne product of the smelting operations. Since there is an above-average cancer death rate in these areas, it may be due in part to this air pollutant. (See list of cancer-causing agents associated with various occupations, Appendix B.)

Recent studies have disclosed several forms of cancer that may be linked to diet in certain groups of people. Overweight women have an above-average risk of cancer of the endometrium, gallbladder, pancreas, and breast. Scientists have not decided whether this increased risk is due to diet,

14

weight-affecting hormones, or the interaction of these and other factors.

Changes in food habits, so far unidentified, seem to be an influencing factor in the decrease of stomach cancer in America. The relationship of stomach cancer and foods preserved or pickled in salt has been studied closely, as has the possible link between colon cancer and beef.

The high incidence of mouth, throat, and esophageal cancers in northern Sweden and Finland could be related to multiple dietary deficiencies. Iodine deficiency may be related to development of thyroid cancer. Malnutrition may contribute to the high frequency of cirrhosis of the liver and the later development of liver cancer in some groups of Chinese, Japanese, and Africans.

Regarding alcohol and cancer, there is a well-established association between excessive alcohol consumption and cancers of the throat, mouth, and esophagus. Alcohol also enhances the cancer-causing effects of cigarette smoking. Mormons and Seventh-day Adventists who observe the rules of their faiths and neither smoke nor drink have a cancer death rate of about half that of the general population of the United States.

Pushing the alarm button on the potential cancer-causing effects of some food and food additives may cause even more harm because many people may turn to food cults and health-food faddism, believing they are making themselves healthier. For instance, widely publicized reports of the benefits of vegetable fibers in preventing cancer are overrated. Not enough studies have been conducted to substantiate the use of vegetable fibers as a cancer-preventing dietary tool. What we need are more scientific studies to determine the relationship between the foods we eat and their possible cancer-causing effects, and foods we eat that may prevent cancer.

The fact is that there does seem to be a place for nutrition in the prevention of cancer, but cancer quacks quickly take advantage of this by offering such remedies as "vitamin therapies" for cancer. If you feel you have a need for vitamins, check with your doctor. Everyone needs vitamins, but not everyone needs to obtain them in pill form. Most people get all the vitamins they need through their daily diets. But there is a tendency for most Americans to consume more vitamins than they need, thereby wasting money and even endangering their health on occasion. Some of us even feel that the more vitamins we consume, the healthier we will be. This is not true. The body can only use a certain amount of vitamins and excesses are not only unnecessary, but sometimes harmful.

Another recently suspected cause of cancer is the hormone estrogen, which is taken by some women to alleviate the physical and psychological effects of menopause. Studies indicate that long-term users of the hormone (five years or more) are up to fifteen times more likely to contract uterine cancer. Investigators stress that estrogen can be valuable in treating patients for a short period of time in the most severe cases of menopause, but they should always be taken in the lowest effective dose.

Have you ever worried about getting cancer? Don't. Even worry and stress can trigger the growth of cancer in some people, according to a group of researchers. Emotions can be a contributing factor, they say, and a factor often ignored by doctors. What seems to happen is that extreme stress makes people more vulnerable to illness.

If you, as a member of the public, are confused about what causes cancer, or how it can be prevented, perhaps it will be of some small comfort to know that there's no agreement among the experts about what causes it or how we can prevent it.

What *can* you do to protect yourself from getting cancer? First of all, don't smoke, particularly if you work in a place where you are exposed to fumes or dust. Eat a prudent, well-rounded diet, low in animal fat and low enough in calories from carbohydrates so that you will maintain your ideal weight.

Avoid too much sunlight, especially if you are fair-skinned or freckle easily.

If you are working at a job requiring safety clothing and safety equipment, wear it.

Have an annual physical examination. Women should have Pap tests and breast examinations by a physician annually. For women over age forty, a breast X ray may be necessary. Every woman past the age of fifty should have an annual proctoscopic examination of the lower bowel. For men, there should be an annual prostate examination. Men aged forty-five and over should have an annual proctoscopic examination.

Women should frequently perform breast self-examinations and men should check their testicles at least once every three months for signs of unusual lumps.

There are some unproven ways to prevent cancer, used by some people, which I might mention to you. Some persons feel that a glass of orange juice or a green salad at every meal may help to protect you against stomach cancer, and one or two slices of rye bread at meals may reduce the risk of colon cancer. Some people take increased amounts of vitamin C to help prevent cancer, but I would suggest you check with your doctor regarding amounts to be taken.

Perhaps you feel as some experts do—that cancer is genetically determined and that diet or environment may just "trigger" cancer, not cause it. This would mean there is very little we can do to prevent cancer. Perhaps, too, we all have a potential for cancer, but some immune system within our bodies prevents some of us from getting it.

If you are diagnosed as having cancer, what methods of treatment may be used by doctors in curing or controlling the disease?

A cancer patient may be treated by one or a combination of the following methods: surgery, irradiation by X ray or radioactive materials, or one or more anticancer drugs. The type of treatment depends on the site and type of cancer, the stage of the disease, and the age and general health of the patient.

A combination of treatment methods is often more effective than any single method. Also, a second or third course of treatment is frequently helpful if the primary treatment fails to cure or halt the growth of the cancer.

A fourth form of treatment, still being tested, is immunotherapy, which means using the body's natural defense system to control cancer. I have talked with some patients who swear this form of treament helped to keep them alive. Some physicians feel more research in this field will perhaps lead to an immunological approach to cancer prevention and treatment.

Surgery is successful in the treatment of many cancer patients. There have been improvements in operating procedures and care of the patient before and after surgery. New antibiotics administered before, during, and after surgery decrease the risk of infections. Emphasis has been placed on improving the patient's health prior to and after surgery and on increasing the survival rate.

If cancer is discovered in an early stage, the surgeon may hope to remove all the malignant tissue. Surgery is the main form of treatment for cancer of the lung, the cancer that claims the most lives in the United States.

Surgery is also the most effective method today for treating cancer of the rectum and intestine, the second leading type of cancer in the nation.

Cancer of the breast is mainly treated by surgery.

Sometimes surgery is performed to alleviate pain or to treat complications associated with cancer, such as intestinal perforations, abscesses, intestinal obstructions, and tumor-related bone fractures.

There is criticism of some cancer surgery, other than the risks involved. Some scientists feel that cancer cells may be released at the time of surgery, allowing them to move through the body, causing tumors to recur months after the operation.

Research is being conducted to discover whether drugs or radiation given before, during, or after surgery will destroy tumor cells, so that if they do migrate to other parts of the body, they cannot grow at a new site.

A relatively new technique called cryosurgery destroys tumors by freezing them. This method is used in the treatment of superficial cancers, but research may show this approach effective against other cancers.

Radiation treatment for cancer was initiated after scientists, late in the nineteenth century, discovered that radiation could damage body tissues, and that an amount of radiation tolerated by normal tissue could cause damage to cancer tissue or even destroy the cancer.

The radiation used to treat cancer tissues can be produced by X rays, atomic particles from radioactive materials, and gamma rays from radioactive isotopes.

Approximately one third of the cancer patients with localized cancer cannot be cured by gamma-ray of X ray treatments. Research has led to the development of accelerators which produce fast neutrons. These neutrons seem to be effective against cancer tissue that is resistant to other forms of radiation therapy.

Today, some form of radiation therapy is used to treat between 50 and 60 percent of all cancer patients during their treatment stage.

Meanwhile, scientists are seeking new ways to increase the effectiveness of radiation therapy. Total body radiation is used for some widespread cancers. This means the radiation is administered in repeated small doses, allowing normal tissues time to recover from damage.

Chemotherapy treatment for cancer was developed in the mid-1940s. Since then, over forty drugs have been approved for use, while thousands of new materials continue to be tested each year. These materials include antibiotics, chemicals, and plant extracts. About one out of every one thousand of these materials shows enough promise and safety to be tested on patients. Some seem to be effective against cancer tissues, but the side effects are too hazardous to allow their use with human beings.

Chemotherapy treatment produces cures in approximately 15 percent of the cases of clinical cancer; in the remainder, the drugs may stop the growth of cancer temporarily, relieve pain, and help to produce a more comfortable life for the patient.

The drugs sometimes lose their effectiveness against cancer. And there are side effects, causing some patients to refuse further treatment. Not all patients suffer from various side effects, and each drug produces different effects in different people. The gastrointestinal effects include nausea, heartburn, ulceration, vomiting, diarrhea, and constipation. There can be muscle and nerve effects, such as weakness and a tingling feeling, or numbness. Bone marrow effects cause many problems because of bruising or actual bleeding, and infections result because of decreased white cells and anemia.

There can be a loss of scalp and body hair, either partial or complete, during chemotherapy treatment, but the hair grows back again.

The drugs can also cause sterility.

Some patients suffer from a variety of rashes and itching associated with the administration of the drugs.

Some other drugs may affect chemotherapy. You should tell your physician if you take antibiotics, anticoagulants or blood medications, barbiturates, anticonvulsant pills, blood pressure pills, cough medicines, sleeping pills, diabetic pills, birth control pills, tranquilizers, or water pills. (See Appendix B.)

Generally, patients receiving chemotherapy need not restrict their diets. However, a light breakfast should be eaten on the day of the treatment. Also, patients should drink two to four more glasses of water each day, before, during, and after treatment.

Patients undergoing chemotherapy may be able to drink alcoholic beverages in moderation; however, a physician should be consulted beforehand, because in some cases it may be essential that no alcohol at all be consumed.

Many patients continue to work during the treatment period and some engage in activities such as tennis, swimming, fishing, and golf.

Most patients do not have to be hospitalized during their treatments. But in some cases doctors prefer to check the effects of the drugs more closely, requiring hospitalization.

The drugs may be given to patients by mouth or by injection into a muscle or vein. The intravenous administration of some of the drugs may cause a burning sensation in the veins, and a mild pain may remain for a few days.

It is difficult to predict the length or frequency of the chemotherapy treatment, because this depends upon the type of cancer being treated, the drug chosen to be used, the body's response to the drugs, and the tolerance to the side effects. Generally, treatments are given at weekly or monthly intervals, and sometimes on a daily basis for short periods of time.

Patients should never compare treatments because no two people respond the same, even if they have the same type of cancer and receive similar drugs.

During the treatment period, some patients may be worried by various symptoms. There should be no hesitation about calling a doctor about anything that concerns a patient, especially if there is a fever of 100° or higher, a rash, any pain of unusual intensity, a persistent bleeding, or a shortness of breath.

I received my first chemotherapy treatment in September 1973. I could not sleep the night before. I was exhausted the next day when Wanda, Britty, and I left for Iowa City. The other three children were in school.

We spoke little on the way to the hospital. There wasn't much for me to say.

Normally, I would have prayed, but during the past few weeks I had begun to blame God for my cancer, and I found little strength or comfort in religion.

At the hospital, a nurse took blood from my body, and after the counts came from the laboratory, I was assigned to a treatment room in the Specialty Medicine Clinic. Another nurse brought me two pills to prevent nausea. Still another nurse brought a tray of assorted vials, tubes, and needles. A bottle full of clear liquid, with a rubber tube extending from it, hung suspended from the ceiling.

A physician entered the room.

"Lie down and we'll begin," he told me.

"How long does all of this take?"

"Oh, about five to seven minutes."

A needle was injected into a vein in my arm, taped to hold it steady, and the cytoxan and vincristine sulfate began to flow into my body. Soon, I felt a strange taste in my mouth and my nose itched, like I had to sneeze.

"Is it over yet?"

"Not quite. We've lost the vein. We're going to have to find another one. Just relax now."

I tried to concentrate on the ceiling tiles. How many holes were in each tile? I wondered. But I couldn't fool myself. I was afraid.

Then the physician was untaping the needle, wiping away some blood, and it was over.

"You just lie there a few minutes while I write you a prescription for the prednisone," he said.

"Can I drive my car home?"

"Is your wife with you, and does she drive?"

"Yes."

"You had better see how you feel. Don't take any chances."

Wanda and Britty were still in the waiting room.

"Are you all right, honey?" Wanda asked.

"Yes, I'm okay."

But I still couldn't talk about it. I had to think about it first.

I continued to travel to the University of Iowa Hospitals and Clinics for my chemotherapy treatments. The heavy dosages of prednisone prevented me from sleeping many nights, and the intravenous shots of cytoxan and vincristine sulfate did cause some nausea and vomiting. I also noticed my arms and hands would "fall asleep" often.

Prior to and during my chemotherapy, many people offered me various "cures" and treatments, not accepted by the medical profession.

Ask yourself these questions before resorting to any treatments for a disease:

Is the remedy being promoted in sensational newspapers or magazines?

Does the person promoting the "cure" have a degree such as N.D. (doctor of naturopathy) or Ph.N (philosopher of naturopathy)?

Does the person make the claim he is battling the medical profession, which doesn't accept his marvelous treatment?

Is the treatment being offered as a secret cure?

Many patients are willing to try anything that offers a glimmer of hope for survival. And people close to the patients find it impossible to accept a verdict of advanced cancer without trying anything that offers hope. The fact that this false hope sometimes costs several thousand dollars and requires patients to travel while not feeling well does not seem to be an effective argument against quackery because the persons who turn to unorthodox treatments see it as a "freedom of choice" issue. They do not understand that a true cure for cancer could not be kept hidden. The whole problem becomes an emotional issue and those persons promoting quack cures manage to inflame patients and their loved ones by turning them against the "bureaucracy" (the American Cancer Society, Food and Drug Administration, and the National Cancer Institute).

When the issue becomes a matter of life and death, tempers get out of control and emotions prevail over common sense.

"Are you going to let them kill your husband?" a proponent of an unorthodox treatment for cancer may ask the wife of a cancer patient.

The truth is that there is no cure for most types of cancer, except when diagnosed early, and there is no overall cure on the horizon, according to many experts. Cancer is a vicious, horrible disease in many cases, but it *can* sometimes be treated successfully. There is no doubt that there is often the question of which is worse—the disease or the treatment. But conventional medical treatment is the only true hope we have at the present time. And we can do things to help the patient live with a life-threatening disease—and the patient can do things to help himself. I discuss many of these things throughout this book: faith, hope, caring, love, and a determination to live.

I received several hundred letters containing information about the asparagus therapy for cancer patients. This activity stemmed from an article written in the form of a letter to the editor of *Prevention* magazine and appeared in the February 1974 edition. Written by a biochemist, the letter recommended that patients cook asparagus (either canned or fresh) and then liquefy it at high speed in a blender to make a puree. The substance is then stored in a refrigerator.

"Give the patient four full tablespoons twice daily," the biochemist recommended. He pointed out that "patients usually show improvements in from two to four weeks." A very lenient person, the biochemist stated that his dosage was based on personal experience, "but certainly larger amounts can do no harm and may be needed in some cases."

"As a biochemist I have made an extensive study of all

aspects of cancer," the letter writer concluded. "As a result I am convinced that asparagus fits in better with the latest theories about cancer."

A very concerned friend sent me a blender and a case of asparagus shortly after this article appeared, and Wanda, not really knowing at that time very much about cancer and therapies, but wanting to do whatever possible for me, came into my bedroom one morning with a blender full of liquefied asparagus and a tablespoon.

"Get that stuff out of here!" I exclaimed, partly because I was nauseated and partly because of exasperation from having received so many recommended treatments for my cancer. (I did eat the asparagus, at mealtimes, and we still use the blender for other purposes; and I do thank my friend for caring enough to be concerned about me.)

Some of the more exotic "cures" were quite interesting, and my secretary, Jeannie, looked forward to letters similar to the one urging me to "go at once and get some cranberry juice and drink a half glass to start three times a day. Brother, don't give up before you try this juice for cancer. I hope to hear from you in a week or so after you try the juice."

The red beetroot juice cure for cancer attracted some attention during the 1960s and I think some patients still believe in its effectiveness. Some literature I received stated, "the anti-tumor effect of the beetroot juice may be explained by its high iron content, which acts as a regenerator and activator on red blood corpuscles. By their regeneration these corpuscles supply cancer cells with more oxygen, thus improving the impaired cell respiration and also activating respirator ferments. As a result of these happenings, hypertrophies break down and the tissues take up their natural structures, if the disease is not too far advanced."

As if this paragraph wasn't enough to discourage a person

from reading more, the next paragraph pointed out that "the juice of fresh beetroot may cause slight belching and it has a rather musty, beet-like taste [why *wouldn't* it have a beet-like taste, I wondered] which can be repulsive to patients who have to drink a tumblerful or more daily."

From faraway Serian, Sarawak, Malasia, came some advice for not only my cancer but any disease that I might face in the future. "What is the cure for influenza?" I was asked in the letter. I didn't know. But by reading on, I found that "only one injection of liver extract with a good massage of the injected muscle" would cure influenza. It also pointed out that the injection was effective "when there is a great deal of brain work to be done."

Then I was asked, in the letter, "How can a woman's menstruation be delayed by one or two days?" Once again, I did not know the answer. But, once more, by reading further I found that "three drops of eucalyptus oil in a teaspoon of sugar" was the answer. "It is also good for a bad cough," the letter continued.

Then the subject became more complicated. "You are in the jungle or in a village where there are no medical supplies. What can you do to heal a boil or a septic sore, wound, or a burn?" I was really baffled by that question. I knew that I would hate to be caught in such a predicament. But there was an answer. "Use a tamarind poultice, pour oil and toddy or wine into the wound, and cover a burn with minced onion."

It occurred to me that if I were in the jungle or in a native village, I might not have access to wine or minced onion, either.

At this point, the letter really got down to business. "For your cancer, three days of fasting and then drink hot water in abundance. Take large doses of vitamin B riboflavin. After fasting, follow a diet of one-half pound of liver a day."

27

"If you can reach a hot mineral spring, give yourself a good soak in it," the letter continued.

"Incidentally, the liver extract injection can also make you passionate with its introduction into the bloodstream," the letter suggested. "And if you follow all the instructions it should make it easy for you to cure all diseases, including cancer, encephalitis, etc., which you consider difficult to cure, and to remove mental deficiency and spasticity."

One well-meaning lady wrote me about a "miraculous grape wine cure, which will make you feel better instantly."

"I have felt like a different person since starting the grape wine treatment," the lady exclaimed. I could understand this after reading the prescribed dosage of wine, for it was quite evident by her intake of this liquid therapy that she was getting drunk daily.

For those who did not wish to drink wine, there was a "modified grape cure" which I received in the mail. "This cure is especially for busy people who must lead as close to a normal life as possible," the literature read. "A friend of our tells us that over two hundred cures have been reported using this treatment, with no failures. Eat nothing before noon. At 7 A.M. start sipping slowly a twenty-four-ounce bottle of unsweetened grape juice, finishing the bottle by 10 A.M. Occasionally there is a person who does not digest the twenty-four ounces and cuts back to fifteen or twelve ounces. (It would be my luck, I thought, to fall into this unfortunate category!) Lunch may be eaten at noon. Eat no pork. Follow sensible eating habits the rest of the day. Doing this each morning for six weeks usually wipes out an internal cancer. Prostate and bone cancers require more time."

Another interesting diet allowed patients the following menu for one year: 1,800 pounds of carrots, 1,300 pounds of apples, 350–400 pounds of liver (for juice), 45 heads of red cabbage, 400 heads of lettuce, 70 bushels of celery knobs, 55 bushels of parsley, and 125 pounds of green peppers.

From Dallas, Texas, came this cure: "In regard to cancer problems—suggest people to sop with bread one ounce whiskey per day or white Bicardi rum. After a while you can feel the rum enter the stomach and then you feel a burning. After nine months, this even cured my stomach gas. Also cured suspected lung hurt and damaged forehead. Why not try it?"

A handwritten letter from West Virginia opened with, "My happiness and joy knows no bounds as I write to you. I have become aware that the sometimes persistent and sometimes agonized question, 'Why was I born?' is beginning to be answered. I want to show the world, and you, that there is no such thing as an 'incurable disease.' Is it any wonder the Lord tells us, 'Woe to ye doctors, lawyers and hypocrites!' A very common weed, whose proper name is 'yarrow,' is a perfect cure for cancer. You boil the weed 30 to 45 minutes in water. Take a small bottleful, which will not be noticeable in your pocket. Put a sheet over your head and drink this beverage. If you cannot find the weed, contact the authorities who may make it possible for me to come to you. Do not be discouraged when you learn I have been a patient at a state mental hospital for treatment and that I'm accused of having hallucinations."

At least fifty persons wrote me about the psychic surgeons in the Philippines, who supposedly remove tumors from the bodies of cancer patients without the benefit of surgery. Even though this bloodless surgery has been condemned as a fraud, thousands of patients have visited Manila to have their tumors "removed." One of the psychic surgeons is a grammar school dropout who once jumped bail in Detroit to escape a federal grand jury indictment alleging that he had received thousands of dollars from Midwest residents with his phony "cures."

The psychic surgeons claim to be able to pierce the patient's skin with their bare hands, pluck out the tumors without the benefit of anesthetic, and then painlessly make the body whole again in less than half an hour. They claim to possess the power to cure cancer, coronaries, blindness, deafness, multiple sclerosis, diabetes, blood clots, and arthritis.

Day after day, the letters containing unproven cures and treatments for cancer arrived at my home. One lady told me she had suffered twenty-eight heart attacks and treated herself each time with a mixture of tea and honey. Her remedy for cancer was a combination of castor oil and olive oil. She wanted to build hospitals across the United States and pipe songs she had written into the room of each patient. All she needed was sufficient funds to finance her dream. She thought two hundred dollars might be a beginning.

One man wanted one hundred million dollars or he would not release his "secret cure for cancer." Some individuals came to my house, bringing their "cures" with them. One man presented me with a mixture of "fifteen secret ingredients" which his great-grandmother had discovered as a cure for cancer. It was wintertime when he arrived, and after he left I asked Wanda to set the bottle containing the "secret cure" on the top of a refrigerator located on our back porch. Later, the bottle froze and burst open. The "secret cure" removed part of the enamel from the side of my refrigerator. It may have been a great paint remover for all I know. Another man brought me three huge bottles of goat's milk and still another gentleman arrived at my doorstep with a goat, so I could have fresh milk every day. I am certain goat's milk is nutritional, but I don't like the taste of it. And I didn't want a goat running around in my front yard. It was bad enough to have cancer, without having to put up with a goat, too.

Laetrile, also known as vitamin B17 or amygdalin, was offered to me more than any other unorthodox treatment for my cancer. Laetrile is derived from apricot kernels. It has been around for over twenty-five years, but the Food and Drug Administration states there is no sound evidence to indicate it is safe or effective as a therapy for cancer. However, its use has been approved in a number of states, provided certain prerequisites are met, generally including the requirement that it be administered by a physician.

In the fall of 1978, the news media reported some laetrile "responses" by humans. The National Cancer Institute's nationwide search turned up six cases of "apparent" responses and three other cases where cancer patients who had received laetrile survived longer than normally expected for their type of cancer. In two of the cases of apparent responses, medical records indicated that all evidence of cancer had disappeared. In the other four cases, tumors that could be measured shrank by 50 percent or more. These responses were obtained from sixty-seven cancer patients who claimed some type of benefit from laetrile therapy.

National Cancer Institute officials said they could not dismiss the possibility that the six patients responded to laetrile, but the design of the study in no way allowed them to draw this conclusion. In other words, it was impossible to tell from the results whether laetrile or an unknown factor was responsible for patient improvement.

Since the laetrile issue was still in doubt, the National Cancer Institute agreed to further tests on the substance. Four sites were chosen for the studies. The purpose of the studies is to show, once and for all, whether or not laetrile is an effective therapy in the treatment of cancer. Since at

31

least 70,000 cancer patients have used laetrile during the past few years, the issue has become more a political than a scientific one.

Although I do not believe in the physical effectiveness of laetrile, nor am I convinced it is safe, I do feel that anything that *is* safe might help the patient because there is some evidence that patients who actually believe something will help them often benefit from the therapy, whether or not it is effective from a scientific standpoint. In other words, laetrile might be classified as a "mental" therapy.

What direction do we take now, in the field of cancer research and treatment? Cancer research is a complex, long-term program involving studies of life processes. Progress has been slow. Since the inception of the National Cancer Institute of National Institutes of Health in 1937, cancer research had grown into a controversial and sophisticated issue involving cell and tumor biology, molecular biology, genetics, immunology, virology, chemical carcinogenesis, chemotherapy, and immunotherapy. What we must do now is concentrate on rehabilitating those persons who already have cancer, as well as continuing our scientific research. So far, the emphasis has been placed on research, with few realistic support programs for the patient with cancer. Even if a successful treatment for all types of cancer was to be found tomorrow, which is highly unlikely, hundreds of thousands of persons already in the early stages of the disease would probably die in the years ahead.

Through improved treatments for cancer, survival rates for at least six of the ten most common forms of cancer in the United States have risen gradually since the early 1960s. These six cancers showing increased responses are bladder, breast, colon, prostate, rectum, and uterine corpus.

Rates remained relatively unchanged for cancers of the lung, cervix, pancreas, and stomach.

Twenty years ago, about one patient in four could expect to live free of cancer for five years or more. The figure today is one out of three. Chemotherapy drugs are credited with this improvement in survival rates. But looking at the other side of the coin, two out of every three cancer patients still die of the disease. Meanwhile, researchers continue to screen thousands of potential anticancer agents while trying new combinations of treatments utilizing the old drugs.

We must seek ways to improve the quality of life for the patient and family members during treatment periods when the patient is nauseated from the chemotherapy drugs. We must find more effective methods for controlling intractable pain, realizing that a percentage of advanced cancer patients suffer from extreme pain prior to death.

We must not ignore the warnings from reputable scientists and doctors who tell us that man himself is causing most of his own cancers through increased use of chemicals, nuclear weapons testing, excessive use of X rays, pollution, cigarette smoking, and dietary habits. We must ask ourselves if our standard of living and advanced technology have attached to it a price tag much too costly for us. Are we killing ourselves with comfort? Will the life of luxury we enjoy today cost future generations their lives? Will we reach a point in time when it will be too late to call a halt to the endless flow of carcinogens into the air, water, and land of this earth?

The questions are difficult. The answers even more so. But we must decide *now* about the quality of our lives or face ever-increasing dangers of an even higher cancer rate.

2

The Hospital

T HE THREE MAJOR FEARS of terminally ill patients are fear of death, fear of pain, and fear of the hospital.

Just as entering a nursing home may signify the beginning of the dying process for the aged, becoming a hospital patient represents a loss of control and a threat to human dignity. Leaving behind loved ones at a time when love and compassion are most needed adds to the trauma of hospitalization. Hospital patients discover quite soon that privacy is difficult to achieve unless one can afford a private room. And not many of us can pay for the luxury of a private room, especially if the hospital stay is a lengthy one. All in all, a stay in a hospital does not always offer needed emotional peace and quiet.

Persons who may spend only a short time in a hospital and who have no major health problem to contend with can probably tolerate hospital life and then forget about it when they return to a normal environment. But persons with a chronic or terminal illness, who may spend most of their remaining lifetime in a hospital room, must face the realities of regimented, and often impersonal, health care away from home.

Although the majority of Americans die in hospitals or institutions such as nursing homes, only a small percentage of America's hospitals are equipped to meet the special emotional and practical needs of someone who is dying. Nonmedical support groups staffed by chaplains and medical social workers within hospitals are generally inadequately staffed and cannot possibly help seriously ill patients cope with their problems. Some hospitals do not have a hospital chaplain on their staff. Clergymen from the community share visitation responsibilities.

When I was a hospital patient, following the diagnosis, no social worker, chaplain, or rehabilitation specialist visited me. I had questions to ask, but I did not know where to get answers. I was a novice and did not know where to go for help with financial, emotional, and other problems associated with my illness.

Today, some hospitals make provisions for a patient advocate's office or for an individual who can listen to patients and report problems to the hospital staff and management. At some hospitals, registered nurses who have worked with seriously ill patients are given this responsibility. Also, many hospitals are now offering brochures to patients at the time of registration, informing them of hospital policies, available resources, and answers to the more obvious questions. But much work remains to be done in the area of patient support and the quality of life within hospitals. It seems to me that the majority of hospitals I have visited in America and Canada are operated more for the benefit of the staff than for the patients who come there to be treated. And they should be treated not just as organisms with medical problems, but as human beings.

Some of the problems seem to be magnified because of the lack of qualified health-care persons such as registered nurses. Nurses tell me it takes a special kind of person to work with the terminally ill. Medical staffs working with terminally ill patients have emotional problems of their own to cope with, including depression and a feeling that no matter what they do, a majority of the persons under their care will die. Therefore, some nurses tend to stay away from seriously ill patients, except to care for them from a strictly medical standpoint.

"I used to become emotionally involved with every cancer patient under my care," a nursing supervisor told me. "Now I maintain a distance between me and them. I care, but it isn't easy to watch people suffer and die. Now I find all sorts of excuses to stay away when I think the patients want to talk or when they need someone to hold their hand. I feel guilty, but I just can't take it any more."

Chuck Colombo, Jr., twenty-nine, of Mason City, Iowa, was diagnosed as a Hodgkin's disease patient in 1968, a lymphoma patient in 1975, and in 1976 it was discovered he had cryptoccol menengitis. He has spent over two years in various hospitals since his first diagnosis. He learned what it was like to be lonely, even though there were people all around him in the hospital.

"It seemed to me that people, including the hospital nurses, were avoiding me when my condition worsened," Chuck told me. "They performed necessary routine tasks, such as taking my blood pressure and temperature, and they asked me questions pertaining to my illness. But no one ever really took the time to sit down and talk with me and find out how I was *really* feeling.

"No chaplain or social worker or anyone like that visited me the last time I was at the hospital. I spent about two weeks there. It was like, well, I existed, but only that. I know I wasn't very handsome. I was bald because of the chemotherapy. My skin was sort of a clammy white in appearance and I had lost considerable weight. But I was still a human being and I had feelings. But no one wanted to reach out to me. I realized I had lost my dignity, and my pride. I wanted to talk. No one would listen. I was always told men shouldn't cry. But I did. My emotional problems caused me more worry than the medical problems."

What did Chuck expect from nurses? And could a visit from a chaplain or social worker have helped him?

"If the nurses, for example, had come up to me while I was in the recovery room, perhaps held my hand for just a moment, and asked me how I felt, I would feel much better about it in retrospect. And if those nurses who did visit me said, 'We'll be back to see you later,' had actually returned, I would feel better about it. But they didn't come back. Since I was lonely, I looked forward to their return. I was very disappointed. I guess they forgot, or they didn't really plan to return.

"I was angry, too, because they couldn't give me just a few minutes of their time. I don't understand why nurses can't spend more time with patients. I just wanted to know someone cared—I wasn't looking for an emotional involvement.

"I think I should point out that my family was 250 miles away at this time."

While I was in the hospital, I felt I was rapidly losing control of my life. My world changed suddenly when I became a patient with a chronic illness. I had always valued

37

my privacy, but I found myself lying in a bed, clothed in a ridiculous hospital gown, which exposed parts of my body, while hospital staff members, employees, and visitors often glanced at me as they walked by the room. (I was in one hospital where patients' rooms had one door that served both the room and the toilet.) My dignity was slowly taken away at a time when I needed it. As a patient, I felt helpless, with no part to play in my own destiny.

One of the initial examinations was a berium dye test which helped the doctors determine the progress of the cancer. To obtain accurate results, the patient must be prepared by means of an enema (or rather a series of enemas). In my case, I was aroused from sleep one day before dawn and a nurse inserted a seemingly endless section of rubber tubing into my bowels, through my rectum, while I was still half asleep. Then I ran (and I mean that literally!) to the toilet at the end of the corridor to relieve myself. The nurse came into the toilet to make sure I wasn't cheating. (It's awfully hard to cheat.) Then she repeated the procedure several times while I continued leaping out of bed and galloping to the bathroom. Finally, I was cleansed. I assure you that it is very difficult to maintain a sense of dignity during this process, just as it is quite impossible to use a bedpan in a dignified manner.

I understood the necessity for the tests, but I only wish the nurse might have said or done something to make me feel a little better about it all. As it was, I felt so . . . well . . . *dirty* about it all. I felt rather guilty about having cancer in the first place. Perhaps the nurse might have said something like this:

"This test bothers most people. It isn't really painful, just uncomfortable, but it's the thought of having it done that bothers people. I want you to know I do understand this and I'm sure I would probably feel the same way, but let's make it through the whole thing as best we can and then it will be over."

I'm certain those words, or words like them, would have helped.

Incidentally, the nurse wasn't cruel in any way—just indifferent. I really don't know how she felt about it all.

The story of a young dying patient, as told by Dr. Robert Veatch, a senior associate at the Institute of Society, Ethics and Life Sciences, illustrates only too well what I am talking about when I discuss a loss of dignity in hospitals:*

Susan was 21. Her case history came from the files of the psychiatrist at the hospital where she was a patient: "I interviewed the patient," the psychiatrist stated, "and she left the hospital soon afterwards, to return on New Year's Eve of the same year. At that time she was not expected to live through the night.

"When I went to visit the parents outside the intensive treatment unit, the father was in so much agony and pain that he was unable to relate and could not enter into the conversation between the patient's mother and me.

"The mother related the following anecdotes: She said the moment there was some publicity about her child's illness, the tenants in the apartment house they owned stopped paying rent, claiming that she must have a lot of money as a result of the publicity.

"And, the mother went on, that day when the

*Reprinted with permission of the Euthanasia Educational Council, 250 West 57th St., New York, NY 10019.

emergency call came from the hospital, she and her husband wanted to use their car, only to find that the battery had been stolen out of it.

"I looked at the mother, and wondered why she related these two strange incidents to me while her child was dying. But when I listened to my own emotional reaction to them, it suddenly occurred to me that both incidents represented people as insensitive, imperceptive and cruel.

"I asked her if something cruel and insensitive was happening right now to her child.

"At this point, the father lifted up his head and started to cry, and the mother pointed with her hand in the direction of her daughter's room.

"When I visited the patient, I realized what the parents had tried to relate. She lay there, half naked, on her bed, hooked up to infusion tubes, on a respirator, staring desperately around the room.

"My first impulse was to cover her with a bed sheet, but a nurse approached me and said, 'Don't bother, she'll only push it off again in a minute.'

"I approached the patient and she held my hand and pointed up to the ceiling.

"I asked her if the light was bothering her. She grabbed my hands and kissed them, thus communicating that my impression was correct.

"When I asked for the light to be switched off, the nurse came in again and reminded me of the rules and regulations of the intensive care unit.

"Then I asked for a chair for the mother to sit with her child. I was told they could not give her a chair any more, because the mother stayed more than five minutes during the previous visit.

"This girl died eight hours after the physicians

had informed her parents of her imminent death. She died with the light in her eyes, the tubes in her mouth and veins, and her parents sitting outside in the waiting room."

Father Michael Lynch, a Catholic chaplain at Wausau Hospitals, Inc., a community hospital with 325 beds, located in Wausau, Wisconsin, has worked with seriously ill patients for four years.

"The major restriction in keeping me from doing my job more effectively is a lack of other chaplains to help and a lack of time. A Protestant chaplain and myself serve five institutions, which include two hospitals, two nursing homes, and a mental health care center. There is no way we can spend sufficient time with even the terminally ill patients who need our help. There are patients we never see, including seriously ill ones. I do know there are too many patients who die alone.

"From a more personal standpoint, just the energy it takes to work with terminally ill persons, from a significant point of view, causes a chaplain to 'burn out' very quickly. There is also a feeling of guilt because I *know* there are patients I should see, or return to see, but I just don't have the time, nor the energy.

"I find that, based on my own experiences, it is often difficult to get help from the patient's own pastor. I feel this is because clergymen, too, have little time for personal contacts of this type. Too, this sort of relationship would probably require the clergyman to become involved on a long-term and emotionally draining crisis level. Many clergymen feel uncomfortable with this type of relationship, and they think chaplains are obligated to perform these duties."

Father Lynch has found that often patients are not referred to him until members of the health-care team can no longer cope with the situation and decide that as a last resort the patient may need some spiritual help. Actually, he feels, patients would often benefit from earlier intervention.

"As soon as a person has a health problem, I feel he should be treated using the 'team concept' under which the whole patient is treated, not just the disease," Chaplain Lynch summarized. "I feel at the initial stage the patient should be interviewed by not just a doctor, but by a medical social worker, nurse psychologist, and clergyman, and the family should be involved from the beginning, both as a source of information about the cause of the problem and as a means of support for the remedy."

I agree with Chaplain Lynch, and I believe that the patient should become a part of the health-care team from the beginning if he or she is willing to become involved. If a physician or members of a family make a decision not to tell a patient the truth if the diagnosis is cancer, for example, hoping to protect him from the reality of a tragedy, there is no way to involve the most potentially important member of the health-care team—the patient himself.

Knowing that nurses must cope with their own problems, and that there are different reasons why patients find themselves isolated when seriously ill, I talked with members of the nursing profession to get their side of the story.

Mary Ann Dykes is a registered nurse who has worked in an intensive-care unit of a hospital for over ten years.

"I often feel a sense of unfinished business when we are involved in a crisis situation with a person who is dying," she commented. "I feel that in some ways I have failed to meet the complete needs of the patient . . . and the family. As a nurse, I am involved in doing everything I can to keep the patient alive, which means I am busy with tasks not related to personal interaction with the patient or family.

42

"A conscious effort has to be made on the nurse's part to remind her she is dealing with a whole person . . . a human being . . . not just organs or systems."

Nurses often try to protect themselves from a feeling of loss each time a patient in their unit dies.

"I think that the nursing staff needs an opportunity to identify their own feelings and to be able to talk about their emotional needs," Mary Ann continued.

"Remember, too, that we must deal with family members during a time of crisis and help them from a practical standpoint. As an example, just a few days ago a male patient in our unit died of cardiac arrest. He had a history of heart disease, but his wife did not expect him to die so soon because he seemed to be doing well. She brought him a newspaper to read on the day he died, placed his glasses by his bed, and left. When she returned, he was dead.

"Sometimes we must deal with family members who faint or become hysterical. We might have to give them a mild sedation. We recognize the need for this type of assistance, but we must also offer verbal and emotional support."

I asked Mary Ann: "What about the patient's feelings that he is no longer important because he is left alone so much when seriously ill or dying? What if a nurse visits the patient and then promises to return later, but doesn't come back?"

She answered, "She may not return for a variety of reasons, of course, such as an involvement in an emergency situation. But she also may not return because she feels uncomfortable with a patient who is dying. Nurses can always find things to keep them busy if they want to do so."

I asked Mary Ann what might be done to bring nurses and seriously ill patients closer together.

"I guess it all comes back to the question of whether the nurse is sensitive to the emotional needs of these patients in the first place. Some nurses are working at their jobs because they want to supplement a husband's income or make a living. But there are many nurses who do care about more than the salary and try to reach out to the patients. I think, too, that nursing schools could devote more time to teaching student nurses how to respond to the needs of the seriously ill patient. Perhaps the students could be exposed to situations in hospitals as part of their training ... working in special units, with the seriously ill, or in units where there are patients with illnesses such as cancer.

"I do think that a lot depends, too, on how the nurse regards her *own* mortality," Mary Ann concluded.

In other words, it is difficult for a nurse who has not yet accepted the fact that we are *all* terminal and that she will die, too, someday, to feel comfortable when in the presence of dying patients. And because we are individuals with different thoughts and feelings, there will always be some nurses who are compassionate and some who are not. We can only hope to be as selective as possible when assigning nurses to special units for seriously ill persons, expand curriculums in nursing schools to include more courses relating to the care of seriously ill persons, and offer special hospital in-service training programs to nursing staffs to promote better patient care.

Other nurses I talked with about the problems associated with care of seriously ill persons told me about some of the barriers they had encountered as they treated these patients:

- It is difficult to feel at ease with patients unless you know what information they have received about their illness from their physicians. As a nurse, you know you aren't supposed to respond honestly to the patients' questions if the doctor has decided not to inform the patient of the basic diagnostic results.

- Not all patients react the same way to nursing care. Some persons become angry because of their illness and it is difficult for even caring, compassionate nurses to ignore the tirades and the constant complaining. Just as there are good and bad nurses, so are there good and bad patients. And patients have a responsibility to let their needs be known.

- When a nurse is first assigned to a unit, she may want to do everything she can to make patients comfortable and to meet their emotional needs, but she quickly loses her enthusiasm in the face of hospital rules and regulations and the attitudes of co-workers who have been in the unit longer than she has. She soon learns to "join the crowd." One nurse told me she wanted to brighten up the rooms in her unit and even went so far as to bring flowers to the patients and recommend changing the white sheets to various other colors. She was soon branded as a "troublemaker." One doctor asked her if she had become involved with the "death and dying fad."

- It is impossible to become emotionally involved with patients, to listen to them, to hold their hands, without losing a part of yourself. Some people live a lifetime and lose fewer friends than a nurse may lose in a month if she becomes friends with every patient. A nurse would quickly reach a "burn-out" stage if she responded to the emotional needs of every patient.

- When the nursing department is understaffed and overworked, nurses cannot meet the emotional

45

needs of the patients because they are kept busy monitoring equipment, maintaining records, and performing necessary, but nonpersonal, tasks.

I talked with a nurse who told me of her first experience with a patient:

"As a first-year nursing student, I was assigned a patient who was dying of cancer. All we could do for him was change his bedding, bring him orange juice, or just 'be there.'

"I felt very helpless and even useless to him until I decided the best thing I could do was hold his hand, talk to him quietly, and convey to him that there was someone with him who cared.

"Suddenly, the head nurse burst into the room, took his pulse, saw I was holding the patient's hand, and said sharply to the other nurses, 'Get her out of here!'

"Before I could leave, a group of doctors entered the room. The patient roused himself sufficiently to ask, 'Am I a goner?'

"No one answered.

"He repeated, 'Am I a goner?'

"Finally, I found enough courage to speak up and repeat his question to one of the doctors. He, in turn, turned to the next doctor, and so on, like a row of dominoes.

"Then one of the doctors muttered, 'We're doing the best we can,' and they marched out. I was also sent out.

"The patient died two hours later. No one held his hand again."

How do nursing instructors feel about the problem of not meeting the psychological needs of seriously ill patients? I talked with Katherine Rhoades, R.N., B.S.N., who teaches nursing students:

"From an educational point of view, I find a sad division between education and practice," Ms. Rhoades said. "In their first semester, students attend lectures and small group discussions designed to investigate the emotional needs and feelings of patients. After their didactic experiences, they enter the 'real world' of the patient, where they focus their attention and activities on the emotional needs of the patient."

What occurs during this period to cause the young nurses to begin ignoring the patients' emotional needs?

"Invariably, during these early experiences," Ms. Rhoades continued, "students will report incidences to me such as, 'The head nurse told me I shouldn't be holding the man's hand,' 'The nurse told me not to bother with Mr. C.—he's a hopeless case,' or 'You'll learn sooner or later that you don't have time for that sort of stuff.'

"This type of derision continues throughout their nursing experiences and becomes, perhaps, an even greater problem when they take their beautiful ideals into the work situation and are forced either directly or indirectly to compromise on their efforts toward tender, loving care."

How can nurses continue their careers and still feel they are not violating their principles?

Nurses who have entered nursing because they wanted to help and care for the emotional needs of others should assert themselves, Ms. Rhoades feels, and they should maintain dignified and tender care of patients.

Are nurses so overworked they have no time for meaningful patient contact?

"Certainly the majority of nursing staffs are short of help and overworked," a professor of nursing at a university told me, "but it's a cop-out for nurses to claim they have no time to spend with the patients."

A director of nursing at a large hospital confirmed this:

"No doubt part of the problem is that some nurses do withdraw from the pressures of caring for seriously ill patients. One possible solution, I feel is to schedule sessions for the nursing staff so they can freely express their own feelings about dying patients and emotional involvement, and their own thoughts about death. Unless nurses feel comfortable themselves, they cannot relate to dying patients."

Once again, I stress there is more to health care than just treating a person's illness. Showing compassion is just as important as checking pulses, listening to heartbeats, and dispensing pills. Sometimes patients respond more to love and compassion than to the medical treatment.

Hospital management must initiate patient support programs which will affect the quality of life for *all* patients—not just those who can be treated successfully and cured. In other words, the dying process itself must be considered. Some hospitals have established special care units for the terminally ill, and trained professional persons work in these units. The teams treating patients in these special units may consist of physicians, nurses, clergymen, medical social workers, volunteers, and therapists.

Although I am not aware of any programs now under way, I feel all hospital employees should receive some training if they work around patients in these units—housekeeping personnel, nursing students, and nurses' aides, for example. Because nurses were in supervisory positions at the hospital where I was a patient, I spent more time conversing with nonskilled employees than with nurses. And the doctors were in my room only a few minutes each day. I do not feel the persons I refer to should be turned into amateur psychologists or therapists, but they could be trained to be aware of the major "do's" and "dont's" when talking with seriously ill patients. I know of one nurses' aide who told patients of a special quack treatment for cancer, available to them outside the hospital. She was obviously trying to help, but in a very dangerous way.

A physician who became a cancer patient told me how disturbing it was for him to enter a large hospital as a patient, where no one knew him. He just wanted someone, anyone, to talk with him. It was an orderly who initiated a conversation with him, and he never forgot this man. In fact, when he returned to the hospital as a patient some time later, he encountered the same orderly and remembered his name. But he could not remember the names of any of the hospital staff persons.

Somehow this protective barrier constructed by persons caring for seriously ill patients must be removed. Special training for medical, nursing, and seminary students must be initiated at the schools where these persons are educated. This is not being done effectively on a national scale. Many young nurses have been taught to sit on the edge of a patient's bed or hold a patient's hand, but not enough specialized training is offered to health-care persons.

An instructor in advanced medical/surgical nursing told me, "Our students are often very uncomfortable and unsure of themselves when working with patients who have life-threatening illnesses."

I once spoke to a group of junior and senior students at a large medical school in the United States. The young student who arranged for my visit told me, "My professor wasn't very helpful when I asked for some material which would help me to someday work with terminally ill persons. And all we have available in the curriculum are optional courses. About a third of the students here are interested in learning more about the problems of the seriously ill, but the emphasis here is on 'healing' and 'caring.' I became interested because my mother has cancer, and although I am going to be a physician, I don't even know how to help *her* when it comes to emotional needs. And I've never been to a funeral, so I know nothing about dying and the problems associated with the process. How am I going to help someone when I'm confronted with a dying patient in the future?"

Not too many people are willing to speak out about some of the problems that exist today in the area of treating terminally ill persons. But a medical oncology/hematology social worker from a large medical center in California told me: "I work with many individuals and their families, in a hospital setting, and these persons are facing the specter of a neoplasm or malignancy and its frightening implications. All of a sudden these people find themselves singled out to know their death trajectory and, simultaneously, their friends and families withdraw from them in pain and fear. An enormous protection racket is established to avoid coping with the repercussions of a terminal illness."

Unfortunately, the protection racket also exists within the framework of hospitals. Terminally ill patients often find themselves "written off" not only by relatives and friends but by those persons caring for them.

However, patients do have rights—and some hospitals do recognize them. These rights should be a part of the standard operating procedure of every health-care institution in America. Another way of expressing the needs of seriously ill persons is the Dying Person's Bill of Rights. (In Appendix D you will find a Patient's Bill of Rights, recommended to hospitals by the American Hospital Association, and a Dying Person's Bill of Rights.)

I would like to offer some of my own suggestions for improving the care of hospital patients. I realize some of these recommendations may be difficult to implement, and we can always find excuses for not initiating changes to which we are resistant, such as insufficient funding. However, the recommended changes are:

To allow more privacy for married couples. There's more privacy during visiting hours in some prisons than in many hospitals. A husband and wife should be able to hold each other, at least, without someone opening a door or interrupting them to give the patient some pills.

To designate special "family rooms" on each floor, where patients can visit with their children. The rooms should be furnished comfortably in warm colors and easy chairs and couches and not have the sterile appearance of hospital rooms.

To offer briefings by resource agencies during time periods when outpatients return to the hospital for examinations and/or treatments, and to provide a room where family members and/or patients can meet with volunteer representatives from Social Security, Veterans Administration, Visiting Nurses Association, insurance companies, social service agencies, and other support or resource groups. Since patients and family members often wait several hours to be examined and treated, it seems to me this would be a more productive way to spend the time.

To encourage hospitals to investigate the possibility of mobile medical teams qualified to administer chemotherapy treatment for cancer patients in outlying communities. Often, cancer patients find it difficult to travel long distances for a routine chemotherapy treatment. Another alternative would be for hospitals to work with a selected physician in each community, so the physician and his staff could administer chemotherapy drugs to patients. I realize some community physicians treat patients with chemotherapy drugs now, but I feel it should be done in conjunction with oncologists from a hospital offering specialized treatment for cancer.

To assign one nurse to each four or five patients, with that nurse being responsible for their nursing care—just as doctors are responsible for certain patients. There is also a need tb upgrade the nurses' professional standing in the healthcare field. There should be a "nurse-patient" relationship, just as there is a "physician-patient" relationship. Nurses are often with patients twenty-four hours a day during their hospital stay.

To brief patients when they enter the hospital. Briefing should be conducted by a "team," with members of the team, such as medical-social workers and chaplains, meeting separately with patients as soon after their admittance as possible. Patients should be told what to expect before each test is conducted and why it is being performed, unless the patient objects to receiving this information.

If the patient has a life-threatening illness, the hospital should offer counseling for both patient and family. This counseling should be extended to include help in preparing the family to cope with the problems of home care of the seriously ill if the patient returns home and needs special care. The family should be cautioned about decision-making when cancer is diagnosed. Costly and vital decisions can be made which the family may later regret, such as deciding not to tell the patient of the diagnosis if it is a serious illness.

Doctors and nurses (especially ones who treat seriously ill patients) should receive special in-service training and be allowed to attend workshops which help them identify and understand more thoroughly the psychological needs of patients and families. A keener awareness of the emotional problems associated with a serious illness would enable doctors and nurses to offer more complete care for patients without necessarily spending more time with them. In other words, the quality of time spent with patients and family members could be improved with more education for the health-care staff.

More emphasis should be placed on making patients comfortable through better control of intractable pain. Some doctors have become more lenient with their restrictions on drugs that alleviate pain, realizing that from a practical standpoint there is little danger of dying patients becoming addicted to the drugs. From a humane standpoint, relief of pain is extremely important, both for the patient and for family members who must watch the patient suffer.

More provisions should be made for those persons who wish to die at home. Hospital staffs should not "write off" those patients whose prognosis is poor, whose death in the near future is probable; but rather they should offer training programs in the communities to help families learn how to care for a loved one at home. More community-oriented programs, such as the hospice movement, should be encouraged so maximum support is offered to these persons on a broader basis.

I feel that patients must assert themselves by demanding that their basic rights be considered by hospital staffs, and family members of patients must make certain the basic rights of a patient to receive humane medical treatment are not violated.

If we expect medical and nursing schools to graduate doctors and nurses who have not been dehumanized by the teaching process, then we must insist the curriculums be changed and courses be added so graduates will be more qualified to treat not just diseases, but rather whole persons.

They must be trained to consider patients' psychological needs as well as their medical needs.

Physicians list three acceptable methods of treating cancer—chemotherapy, radiation therapy, and surgery. I would like to add one more—T.L.C. (tender, loving care)!

3

Doctor and Patient

MY RELATIONSHIPS with the physicians with whom I have been involved since the diagnosis of my cancer have all been satisfactory. However, I must make allowances for the fact that I have spoken at medical conferences and other events at the hospital where I am treated, and have a unique relationship with some of the physicians, one closer than most patients would have achieved. In fact, some doctors are personal friends of mine. But I have talked with hundreds of patients and family members about their own feelings toward physicians, and I have discussed this subject with many physicians and medical students.

First of all, I have discovered (perhaps obviously) that oncologists, radiologists, and other physicians who specialize in treating cancer patients have a deep understanding of the emotional problems associated with cancer. They are generally willing to become emotionally involved with their patients. However, since 80 percent of all cancer patients in America are treated at community level by physicians not specialized in the care of these patients, there is sometimes a poor physician-patient relationship involved. Some family physicians are reluctant to admit cancer patients to a large hospital for specialized treatment even when problems arise. And patients, feeling intimidated, do not object, even though they feel more effective treatment is available at another location. Some patients do not want to leave the security and familiarity of local surroundings to "become lost" in the computerized network of a large university hospital or treatment center.

Further complicating the problems in this area is the question of a "second opinion." I feel that second opinions are extremely important, especially when nonemergency surgery has been recommended. A House of Representatives subcommittee charged in 1978 that American surgeons performed over 2 million unnecessary operations in 1974, at a cost of $3.9 billion. (These statistics have been challenged by some medical groups.)

One survey in New York City indicated that one out of four Medicare patients got a different opinion from a second doctor regarding the need for surgery.

In my opinion, the medical profession should welcome second opinions as a means of supporting a physician's original diagnosis or showing a need for further examination and testing, thereby improving patient care.

There are many benefits to be obtained from surgery, but there are also risks. No surgery should be considered routine, since all surgeries can be potentially dangerous. Patients and physicians should be concerned about the possibility of nonsurgical procedures which may be just as effective as surgery, but less dangerous.

Suggestions that patients seek a second opinion should come from the physician making the diagnosis or recommendation for surgery, and should involve more than surgery. My family physician in Burlington, who is not associated directly with the treatment of my cancer, told me I should get a second opinion about some medical problems not associated with the cancer. He told me that he often tells his patients to consider seeking a second opinion. His willingness to recommend this gives me more confidence in his abilities as a physician and is good for our doctor-patient relationship.

A mother, whose young daughter was being treated by a physician for cancer, decided she should seek a second opinion because she had heard a medical center in California specialized in the treatment of the same type of cancer. When she mentioned this to the physician who was treating her daughter, he became enraged and shouted that if another doctor was to be consulted, he refused to be involved in the case any longer. The mother burst into tears and fled from the room. At the time she related this story to me, she still had not made arrangements to have another doctor examine the young patient.

"I'm afraid I'll end up with no one to treat her locally," she told me. "We can't afford to take her to California for every treatment, and I don't know of another doctor in this area who specializes in the treatment of childhood cancers." Because she did not want to antagonize the physician, this mother had delayed seeking a second opinion. The daughter was the pawn in a life-and-death game between a timid mother and an arrogant, inconsiderate physician who resented any intrusion into "his" world. Doctors like this need to be reminded that the letters following their names read "M.D.," not "G.O.D."!

When I first became a hospital patient following the diagnosis of my cancer, I was routinely scheduled to undergo a laparotomy (abdominal surgery), but I decided I did not want this type of surgery performed. I felt the potential benefits to be derived from the surgery would not compensate for the risks involved. At the time, I am sure my motives were misinterpreted, but not long after my decision, physicians came to the conclusion that sometimes laparotomies did constitute unnecessary surgery. In any event, I feel I made the right decision under the circumstances. I responded to chemotherapy treatment, and my body was not weakened as a result of the surgery.

When I hear patients say, "They told me I don't have any choice—I *have* to undergo surgery," I remind them that they *do* have a choice—but that they should be aware of both the benefits and the risk. The final choice is one the patient should help to make; it should not just be the physician's decision.

One of the major problems associated with doctor-patient relationships is the lack of communication. To begin with, the average patient visiting a doctor's office spends about 15 minutes with the doctor. Visiting time varies, of course, from an average of 11.9 minutes with a dermatologist to 46.9 minutes with a psychiatrist. Physicians spend very little time with their patients, so this time must be well utilized from both a patient's and a doctor's standpoint. I recommend that cancer patients write their most important questions on a piece of paper so they will not forget them while in the doctor's office or treatment room.

If a physician should refuse to answer routine medical questions asked by a patient, I would recommend considering a change of physicians. But I think that most doctors will try to answer reasonable questions. Sometimes, though, they may not have an answer.

I have talked with patients about their feelings toward physicians, and sometimes they tell me their doctors just don't understand them or their problems. But then I find patients often fail to ask questions or to make their needs known.

One afternoon, in the waiting room of the University of Iowa Specialty Medicine Clinic, while awaiting a chemotherapy treatment, I was talking with another cancer patient.

"I'm having problems with depression and a feeling that I'm losing control of my life," he told me. "I just hate to get out of bed some mornings."

He continued to tell me about the emotional problems he faced as a cancer patient. The oncologist who treated him walked by and asked this man how he was getting along.

"Just fine!" he replied.

I asked the patient why he lied to the doctor, after telling me about his problem.

"Oh, he's too busy to listen to my complaints," the patient replied.

Perhaps it is asking too much of physicians to become emotionally involved with patients, but I have met some who openly display compassion toward patients and family members.

I remember a night when I was speaking to a group of doctors and nurses at a medical conference in Tennessee. A doctor explained to the group *why* he refused to become emotionally involved with patients:

"I know that I would lose some of my efficiency as a doctor if I worried about the welfare of each patient," he stated. "I feel that my obligation to the patient is to treat his disease and get him well, if possible. I am not qualified to help him with his psychological problems."

A chest surgeon in the audience responded to the doctor's statements:

"I disagree with this approach to patients' problems. Most of the people who are brought to me are desperate cases, either because of heart problems or lung cancer. Sometimes I am the last person to be with them before they die. I care about every one of them. This has not affected *my* efficiency as a surgeon."

Doctors are individuals. Some are compassionate; others are not. Most care, but many do not want to become emotionally involved because it is too devastating. Some doctors have entered the medical profession because they are interested in the financial rewards; others become doctors because they want to serve mankind.

If you are not satisfied with the services rendered by your physician, you should contact another one. You can come up with all sorts of excuses that will keep you from doing this, but it is probably because you do not want to antagonize your doctor. You feel intimidated. But remember that your health is the most important factor. If you are seeing a physician who is proficient in treating your illness, but displays little compassion, then you must make a decision: Do you want to be treated by a well-qualified physician who may not be as emotionally responsive as you would like him to be? Perhaps you can locate a physician who possesses all the qualities you are looking for, but to find one who feels committed to his patients, is compassionate, considerate, and well qualified from a medical standpoint is a most difficult accomplishment. So until things change, you will have to continue going to waiting rooms at a designated hour, only to find a roomful of persons who have appointments at the same time you do, and be made to feel so fortunate to be shuttled into an examination room that you do not complain about the two-hour delay. And when you are finally blessed with a visit by the physician, you feel so relieved that you say nothing when you find yourself out in the street again, walking to the nearest pharmacy to have a prescription filled, still not knowing what is really wrong with you, nor what to expect in the way of a prognosis.

Incidentally, nearly half of all visits to doctors' offices result in a drug of some sort being prescribed. And out of nearly 600 million visits to doctors' offices in 1975, no services were provided in 15 million cases. This indicates that we depend on doctors for nearly every sort of ailment, serious or not, without assuming some degree of responsibility for our own health. And doctors apparently resort to drugs for the treatment of millions of medical problems. It seems to me that we treat the symptoms of an illness but fail to look for the underlying cause of the problem. We have become a nation of pill-poppers, believing that there is a curative drug for every ailment.

One of my relatives, who was suffering from a common head cold, called me the other day and said, "I'm going to see my doctor and ask him to give me a shot for this cold."

I bet he received the shot.

As physicians continue to seek help in coping with the problems associated with a serious illness, medical schools are looking at various ways to help prepare future physicians for confrontations with death and dying.

In the past, doctors have learned through experience how to tell (or not tell) patients they have a life-threatening illness. Some learned well; others did not. Now patients and family members are demanding more than a diagnosis, and since the majority of deaths occur in hospitals or nursing homes, doctors are being forced to become involved with the dying process.

Representatives from about half the nation's medical schools attended a conference in Seattle during June 1974 to watch a series of films, film strips, and similar audiovisual material pertaining to death and dying. However, based on my own conversations with medical students, I feel that professors at our nation's medical schools would generally object to courses on death and dying, whether or not audiovisual materials were used as a part of the course.

There is a reluctance on the part of the medical profession to admit that doctors are unable to heal or cure patients in all cases; and, since the emphasis is on successful treatment, a dying patient represents a form of failure. However, I believe courses that would acquaint medical students and doctors with patients' feelings when they are faced with a life-threatening illness would help the health-care professionals cope with not only the emotional problems associated with such illnesses but some of their own feelings about death as well.

Courses on death and dying offered at hospitals, medical schools, nursing schools, and seminaries might include such topics as "Communicating with Dying Patients"; "Should We Tell Patients the Truth About Their Illness?"; "Leaving the Patient and Family With Hope"; "The Importance of Not Abandoning Dying Patients"; and "The Patient's Point of View."

How many medical schools in the United States offer courses on death and dying, which might help doctors cope with related problems? "Probably not over a dozen schools offer these courses, out of one hundred and twenty-two medical schools in the United States," commented Chaplain Don Young of Miami Valley Hospital, Dayton, Ohio, who is also an associate professor, Department of Medicine in Society, Wright State University Medical School, Dayton.

"At Wright State, we have offered such a course for the

past three years, during the first year of training for medical students, and we essentially try to help future doctors become aware of their own understandings of death and dying as it related to patients whom they come in contact with during their life experiences," Young said. "We also try to stress the availability of resources, such as Make Today Count and Hospice, which doctors can use to supplement what they are attempting to do when treating patients.

"In the third year of medical schools, the students actually work with patients facing a life-threatening illness, and their families, so they, the students, can better understand the real problems associated with such illnesses."

How do the medical students react to courses on death and dying?

"The students resist the courses a bit at first," Young admitted. "Later, however, they begin to accept them and they seem glad to have had the experience of working with seriously ill patients and their families.

"What we are doing is no panacea but I think it comes closer to helping future doctors cope with these problems than a medical curriculum that doesn't include clinical courses on death and dying," Young concluded.

I do feel that these courses would make young doctors more sensitive to the needs of dying persons. Some of the students I talked with at a West Coast medical school had never attended funerals. And their professors had not been very helpful except to recommend that they read a book about death and dying or seek information outside the classroom.

At one medical students' conference where I spoke once, there was a great deal of interest in what I had to say, from the patient's point of view. During the question-and-answer period, several senior medical students, working at a large midwestern hospital, asked me the following questions: "How do you tell a lung cancer patient he probably has less than six months to live, without removing all elements of hope? And how do you tell his family the truth, without destroying them as a family? How do you tell the truth, as you see it, and still leave the patient and the family with some quality of life?"

Doctors should not place a time limit on patients' lives, but sometimes they do know approximately how long a patient might live, according to the most recent statistics. It is true that patients respond differently to treatments, and there are always exceptions to any rule, but how can a doctor tell a patient the truth unless he tells it as he sees it?

I suspect, though, that sometimes, because of the growing interest in patients' rights, doctors may tell too much. Perhaps they are telling some patients more than they need or want to know. The issue is always a matter of hope. Once patients lose hope, whether it is for another remission or for a cure, they have very little quality of life left.

Do patients who know the truth about their prognosis live more complete lives than patients with similar medical problems who do not know? Although some surveys indicate there is little difference in life-styles, my experience has been that we must realize we are dealing with individuals with varied responses. Some patients want to know whether or not they can expect to die from their illness; others refuse to listen to the truth, even if they are told.

Another curious thing I have learned is that when groups of seminar participants, consisting of patients, family members, doctors, nurses, and others, are asked if they would want to know the truth from their doctors if they had a terminal illness, the vast majority of them indicate they would. However, if these same people are asked whether they would want a spouse, son, daughter, or relative to know the truth if one of these persons were dying, not nearly as many reply in the affirmative. And not so many would want anyone else to know they were dying.

In other words, we apparently think *we* can cope with the truth about a terminal illness, but we're not so sure about *others* around us.

The real problem in arriving at any conclusions about this information is that we never *really* know how we will react to terminal illness until it actually happens to us or to someone we love.

What should we expect from doctors who are treating a seriously ill patient?

First of all, I think doctors are obligated to tell patients the truth about their diagnosis. If the patient is found to have cancer, he should be told, in language he can understand. And the spouse should be present when the doctor informs the patient of the diagnosis. In some cases, other family members or relatives should be present. Common sense and family structure would dictate who should or should not be present. Telling the patient of the diagnosis with responsible family members present might prevent members of the family from saying, "Doctor, I don't want my husband to know this, since it's cancer." Not to give a patient the truth is to deprive that person of the right to maintain or regain some control of his life, and to play a part in his own destiny. I have found patients generally suspect or actually know the truth anyway, so lying only affects open and honest communications between the patient, the doctor, and the family.

How much should a patient be told about his illness, other than the diagnosis? The doctor must have some basic knowledge about the patient as a person and then wait to find out what sort of questions, if any, the patient asks about his illness. It is wrong for the doctor to advise the patient about his illness, after the diagnosis, if the patient doesn't want to know anything.

I am reminded of a story I once heard about a young student who was asked by his teacher to read a lengthy book about whales and then write a book report. The student wrote only one sentence: "This book told me more about whales than I wanted to know!"

The doctor (or anyone else) should not force too much information upon any patient until some time has gone by, thereby allowing the patient to adjust to what has happened to him. For me, this length of time was about three months; for others, it may not take as long, or it may take much longer. I have talked with family members who tell me of patients who have not accepted what is happening to them even though the diagnosis occurred two or more years ago.

In any event, I feel that patients have a right to make decisions about how they want to live with a serious illness, and I do not think we should force them to talk about it, nor should we feel obligated to give them all the details of their illness, other than the diagnosis.

Doctors must be prepared to make individual decisions about each patient they treat. In order to make correct decisions as often as possible, they must have some knowledge of the emotional problems associated with a serious illness. Earlier in this chapter I stressed the importance of incorporating such training in the curriculums of medical schools. I also think doctors should receive some help from colleagues involved in the field of medical ethics. It is a matter of ethics whether or not a doctor should abandon a terminally ill patient. It is never necessary for a doctor to tell a patient, "There is nothing more we can do." Perhaps no more chemotherapy or radiation therapy can be administered, but the patient can be made as comfortable as possible and assured that he will not be abandoned, nor sent home to die without support.

Sometimes doctors can expect the unexpected from dying patients. I visited a lung cancer patient once who told me he was terrified the night before major surgery was scheduled for him, and when the surgeon visited his room to tell him something about the surgery, the patient asked him to pray with him.

"You mean right now, right here in the room?" the doctor asked incredulously.

The patient assured the doctor he was serious about the request, so the doctor did pray with him, and the patient felt more relaxed.

Certainly not all patients would ask their doctors to pray with them, but when it does happen, I feel it is not an unreasonable request unless the doctor has personal reasons for not doing so. After all, there was a time in the field of medicine when physicians like Ambroise Paré, who practiced during the sixteenth century, in commenting about a patient stated, "I treated him and God healed him." Medicine then was an undeveloped science, and although we have come far since that time, I have not yet met a physician who can explain to me why some persons have spontaneous remission, during which the cancer that should have killed them actually disappears.

I believe we should all realize there is a great difference between preparing a patient to live with a chronic, though terminal, illness and preparing someone for major surgery. It is not wise to depress prospective surgery patients, and there is not really ample time to adjust oneself to possible serious consequences. I don't think doctors should lie to patients prior to surgery, but neither should they burden them with all the gory details.

I think surgeons should explain to patients that all surgical procedures involve an element of risk, but at the same time point out the consequences of not having the surgery performed. Then the doctor should allow the patient sufficient time to make a decision that will affect his life, his future, and the lives and futures of his family.

To view the doctor-patient relationship from both ends of the stethoscope, I talked with David Peters, M.D., of La Jolla, California. David is a physician and a cancer patient. He discovered he had cancer nine months after he started his private practice. Eighteen months later, he attended his first Make Today Count meeting, as an observer. Today, he is our West Coast coordinator for Make Today Count.

David told me about the time one of the MTC chapters invited a psychiatrist to speak to the group. It turned out to be a significant night for David. The psychiatrist was scheduled to speak about problems patients had with their physicians.

"I thought to myself, 'Boy, this guy is going to be eaten up by the audience, because he's going to have to explain all our [doctors'] deficiencies, our faults, all those awful things. I wonder if he will be defensive. How will he handle the situation?' "

The psychiatrist didn't say *anything*. The patients talked during the entire three hours of the meeting. The psychiatrist *listened*. So did David, and what he learned changed some of his own attitudes. He began to really look at some of the problems of the doctor-patient relationship.

"First of all, cancer is a frightening word," David explained. "And the patient often finds himself new to the medical world. Perhaps they have never consulted a physician for a serious illness. Some have never been in a hospital before. Suddenly, a patient is thrust into what I call the 'cancer career,' and it's a world full of oncologists, radiologists, surgeons, liver scans, and all sorts of frightening tests. There are blood tests of every description. It's all new. The patient may even have a new doctor. His family physician has let him go and he may even be temporarily living in a new town.

"In addition, the cancer patient finds his relationships with others have changed. Some members of his family may be cheerful about it all, some of them pray for the patient, some are supportive, and some simply can't talk about the problem. Well-meaning friends send him clippings from newspapers about the latest treatments for cancer and about the grape diet, the wheat grass diet, and about the exotic cures and treatments. But, mostly, people don't talk about the illness and the patient is afraid to burden others with his problems.

"Even the physician's attitude can change," David continued. "A girl once told me that her family physician had greeted her by patting her on the shoulder and then he would remark cheerfully, 'How are you today?' After her diagnosis of cancer was made, the next time he greeted her he shook her hand and just said, 'Good morning.' Things had changed, and the first subtle feelings of isolation began to set in.

"The patient may even be angry at himself or angry at a family member because he didn't seek an earlier diagnosis, when problems first began occurring. He may be angry at his doctor, for not finding the cancer sooner. And there are a lot of questions swirling around in his head. 'Am I going to be ruined financially?' 'Is my health insurance adequate?' 'Can I continue to work?' 'What about my disability—do I have any coverage?' 'Should I tell the kids?' 'How old should they be before they can understand?' 'How will my family live, if and when this thing gets me?' 'What do I tell my friends?' If the patient is single, should he get married?

If they are married, should they have another child? What if they lose all their hair, or one or both breasts? How will their husbands react to them then?

"So here is a patient, walking into a doctor's office, and it may be the first time. This patient is saying, 'You may have hundreds of cancer patients, but this is my first time. I have never encountered it before. Help me. I want to live. Help me regain control of my life.'"

I asked David to comment about some of the problems faced by doctors, in the doctor-patient relationship:

"Of course, the doctor has problems, too," David explained, "and especially doctors who deal with cancer patients to any great extent. The physician knows the cards are stacked against him from the beginning, as far as success is concerned. He knows, by statistics, that two out of every three persons who enter his office will die of cancer. For a doctor whose long education has focused on the healing, curing, and preserving of life, this makes him very aware of his fallibility and his limitations. Maybe in a person's lifetime, he will lose from two to a half-dozen people who are very close to him. But I remember talking to an oncologist who had lost ten patients in thirty days. And he had to grieve over every one of them, because they were nice people. They were people he was trying to cure. He lost them. This can take its toll on the physician, and it's no wonder the doctor hesitates to get too close to his patients, for there is the risk the losses will in the end destroy him by spilling over into his family life, his professional judgment, and perhaps the very thing that holds him together as a rational person. The patient deals with from one to four physicians per month. The physician deals with perhaps a hundred patients each month. There is a difference.

"Then there are other problems to consider," David went on. "Some patients want to know about the cancer—some don't. Some are scared, and the physician must size up the patient in twenty or thirty minutes during their first contact . . . not only what he should do medically, which is the primary problem, but about the patient's needs and his reactions. Above all, the physician must keep up on the latest medical research and knowledge. He must sharpen his skills. All the warmth and the greatest bedside manner in the world can be useless if the doctor lacks medical skill and expertise. The doctor must project authority without being arrogant and he must show empathy without displaying pity."

I asked David to comment about the importance of a doctor-patient relationship, which can never be perfect, and at best is a difficult one. How, for instance, can this relationship be improved and what should the doctor avoid?

"For the doctors, there are several things to avoid. First of all, there is something I call the 'parking meter syndrome,' or 'you have only six months to live.' I realize some physicians are often cornered by an anxious patient or relative who asks them, 'Hey, Doc, how much longer can I expect to live? Give me something solid I can hang my hat on.' And often a physician *then* will throw out a 'ball park' figure. You may have six months. You may have one year. But this kind of prognosis is filled with potential disaster. It's a sort of 'heads I win, tails you lose' mentality. This may cause the patient and family to lose hope and simply wait for their time to come. It's a losing game for everyone. Now, I don't mean to imply we should deny how serious cancer is, nor should we ignore telling the patient the truth as we see it. But what about something like this: 'John, you have a serious cancer. You may live only a short time. It's possible. I want you to know it is that serious. On the other hand, you may have one or two years, or ten years, or you may live a full life. Some people do survive this type of cancer. It could

71

be you. And the treatments are improving every year. I can look up the statistics for you, since they're printed on paper. But you are not a statistic. You are *you* ... and never forget that.'

"Now John can make his arrangements ... get things in order. But he can also prepare to live.

"So I think physicians should avoid predictions. They serve little purpose.

"Then there is something I call the 'second story game.' This is when you get two stories—one for the patient and one for the family. Usually this game is played to protect 'poor old Uncle Herbert.' It goes like this: The patient is in bed and the doctor comes in. It has been a couple of days since the surgery. The doctor discusses the cancer with the patient and is encouraging and positive. The relatives are in the room during this conversation. Then the doctor leaves and the relatives follow him down the corridor, away from the room. 'Give it to us straight, Doctor ... is he going to die?' Now, if the patient finds out the physician has lied to him and his relatives have conspired to withhold the truth from him, he will probably be very angry. He may no longer trust the physician or the family.

"I know one oncologist who refuses to engage in 'corridor conferences.' He tells the relatives, 'If you have any questions, ask me in front of the patient. Then we can all hear it. I don't have two sets of facts.'

"In the life of a cancer patient," David continued, "there is a time when the patient feels he has no control over his life. Before the cancer, we have goals. There are vacations to look forward to. When they purchase radial tires, the 40,000-mile guarantee means something, because they think they are going to be around for another five years.

"But suddenly, there are directives coming at you from the medical people. 'Be at the clinic at 8:45. You are sched-

72

uled for thirty radiation treatments.' This feeling about a loss of control is a very important thing to consider. So I think the patient should be involved in some of the decision-making. It is his body. I think the patient should be presented with alternatives. One patient told her doctor, 'I simply can't go through with the chemotherapy treatments. I've had it. I'm sorry. I feel like I'm letting you down.' The physician replied, 'You're a big girl now. You can make your own decisions. I'm here to help you. I won't desert you. So what do *you* want to do? Let's start out with a plan of some sort.' There is no sermonizing, no threats, no guilt involved.

"Finally, I think the physician should never give up hope. The 'I can do nothing more for you' pronouncement is a deadly one. I think the physician should say something like this, 'I will never give up the hope of a full and happy life for you. I promise that whether you have six or sixty years of life, I will try to make it more meaningful for you. There will always be some way I can help. I will not abandon you.'

What can *patients* do to improve the doctor-patient relationship? I asked David how he felt patients could contribute to this relationship:

"There are some things a patient can do to improve communications between him and his physician. First of all, realize that most physicians *are* working in a time frame. There are schedules to follow. Realize this, but don't be intimidated by this time frame, either. I hear a lot of patients say, 'Oh, he doesn't have time for me.' That is nonsense. You have an appointment and if there is a need, it should be met. I think the 'busy doctor' thing is often a cop-out by the patient who is really afraid to ask the questions. And you're dreaming if you expect physicians to say to you, 'Are there any problems aside from the medical ones you would like to talk about? Is there anything bothering you?' But if you have a specific problem, whether it is medical or emotional, I think you should bring it up. It's difficult for the physician to read your mind. He can't. If you don't mention it, he's probably not going to ask you, and then you will probably accuse him of not understanding your problems.

"I've learned something, as a patient. I write down my questions on a piece of paper. Try this. When you go into the room, get out the list and say, 'I've got some questions to ask and I didn't want to forget them, so I wrote them down.' There are few doctors who can avoid that. There might be some who would say, 'Put it away and forget about it.' But if this happens, you had better look for a new doctor.

"There is another thing you can try—call ahead and tell the nurse or receptionist you need some extra time for questions. Ask her if she will relay this to the physician. I must reemphasize that the patient has a responsibility to ask these questions. If you don't ask them, I doubt you will ever get answers, because doctors are just not going to go through a list of a hundred questions to try to find out what is bothering you. But I think the majority of doctors will respond to intelligent and concerned questions. I have heard many patients complain about their doctors' nonsensitivity to their problems and needs. Then I ask the patient, 'Did you talk to him about these problems?' And most of the time, he did not. So I think you should give your doctor a chance, and if he doesn't respond, then it is time to move on to another doctor."

I feel we can assume correctly that most doctors *do* care about their patients. Some have difficulty expressing their concerns and others do not allow themselves to become emotionally involved to any extent. And most patients want to be known as individual human beings, still retaining some control over their lives. We must realize that there is no substitute for the truth, in medicine or anywhere else. Doctors should remember that nature will eventually have its own way, no matter what they do from a medical standpoint. Death is an act of nature. But patients are not "lost" when they die if the doctor does his best to maintain a quality of life for the patient and does not abandon him.

Patients must let their needs be known. If they want the "truth," they must not complain when they hear something they never planned to hear. All news is not good news.

The doctor must remember that it isn't *what* he tells the patient, it is generally *how* it is told that matters. And nothing is more intimate or sensitive than telling someone he has an illness that will probably cause his death at some time in the future.

Hippocrates' charter of conduct or oath for physicians, written over two thousand years ago, but still used during the ceremony of graduation at many universities and schools of medicine, contains the following statement: "The regimen I adopt shall be for the benefit of my patients according to my ability and judgment. . . ."

If the physicians who treat cancer will always remember that there is more to medicine than just treating the symptoms or the disease, and heed the portion of the oath quoted above, knowing that it is truly the *quality* of life that is important, not the *quantity*, then patients will not complain. And if doctors will allow patients to be a part of their treatment by being candid and honest, but sensitive, too, then they will be happy that they were able to play a part in their own destiny.

4

Picking Up the Pieces

WHAT HAS MY LIFE BEEN LIKE since that day in June 1973 when my life was turned around by the diagnosis of cancer? How did I begin to live again?

I remember Thanksgiving Day of 1973. It was a sad holiday season for my family and me; I thought it would be my last one and my family felt the same way.

I had undergone several chemotherapy treatments by the time Thanksgiving came around. But I was having trouble readjusting to a different life-style at home. I had a certain feeling of security at the University of Iowa Hospital, despite all my emotional and medical problems. In the confines of my hospital room, I was sheltered from most of the problems I would encounter when I returned home again.

I feel it is important to tell you about some of the incidents that occurred prior to my permanent release from the hospital so you can better understand how my life and the lives of my loved ones were affected later by embarrassing situations, misconceptions, and the emotional problems caused by the stigmas attached to cancer.

I returned home many weekends during the time I was a patient at the hospital. Sometimes, Wanda would drive to Iowa City and pick me up on Saturday morning; at other times I would ride a bus home.

I discovered quickly that I was coming home to a different world from the one I had left. I was entering the world of a cancer patient. I was not prepared for the uncontrollable changes taking place in my life. I had first sensed what was happening when visitors came to my room at the hospital. I noticed it was difficult for some of them to look directly at me. And many of them were uncomfortable because they didn't know what to say to me. Some even conversed with each other, leaving me out. Even though the doctors had not completed their exhaustive tests, just the word "cancer" indicated to my friends and relatives that I was a "marked man."

Some persons who knew me found it easier to contact me by telephone. "If you ever need anything, just let me know," some said. I needed *them.* I needed a friend who would listen to me without running away when I became angry or depressed.

It was obvious that some persons did not want to confront me. Once, during a weekend at home, an old family friend came to visit us. Wanda and I met her in the front hallway.

"How's he doing?" the friend asked Wanda, pointing at me.

I wondered why she didn't ask *me* how I felt. *Now* I know

why. She didn't want to confront me, and perhaps she didn't want to know how I was *really* feeling, because I didn't look very well then.

Another friend visited us and greeted me by exclaiming, "I've just been *dying* to see you again!" Then she realized she had used "that word" and she apologized. She was embarrassed, and I was uncomfortable. I can cope with this sort of incident now, but it was difficult in 1973.

How would I have wanted a friend to treat me? I would have appreciated an honest approach. Perhaps they might have said something like this: "I don't know what to say to you, because I don't really know what is happening to you. I might even say the wrong thing, without meaning to. But I am here because I care."

Someone told me later that one of my aunts had remarked, "I just can't visit Orville because I know I will start crying and I don't want to depress him." But I didn't know why she was staying away. I would rather have had the tears than to feel ignored without knowing the reason behind it.

Wanda was very depressed during the weeks following my discovery that I had cancer. But she was trying to protect me by not letting me see her tears. I sensed she was troubled, but I was too wrapped up in my own chaotic world to help her. She had many fears and doubts about our future together. We had never talked about the possibility of death separating us unexpectedly. She was wondering how she could raise four children after my death, since we were already having financial problems because of high medical bills and my inability to work. I had no life insurance.

The children were coping with our new problems in different ways. Our oldest son, Mark, refused to even consider the probability of my death from cancer. When Wanda tried to talk to him about it, he would interrupt her, exclaiming, "Nothing is going to happen to my dad!"

Tammy, my oldest daughter, kept her feelings to herself, but refused to study anymore at school. She started skipping classes. When Wanda talked with her about school problems and failing grades, she would say, "No one at school understands me!" The teachers and principal, who had no knowledge of the varied family problems associated with a serious illness, labeled her a "disciplinary problem."

Lori, too, kept her feelings to herself. In her own quiet way, she worked hard at school to earn higher-than-average grades, and at home to please Wanda and me. Her teachers told us she spent more time than most students attempting to complete her lessons as perfectly as possible. Her handwriting looked like something from a penmanship book. But she cared, and sometimes she would cry.

Britton (or "Britty" as we all call him) was a delightful part of my life. He was three years old when the diagnosis of my disease was made. I remember so many nights when he climbed into my bed and hugged me when I was ill from the chemotherapy drugs. Everyone likes Britty. He has no enemies. There is always a smile on his face.

As I look back, I realize it was always Wanda who held things together. When I first married Wanda I felt I should protect her because she was so vulnerable. She seemed so innocent. I have never heard her say anything derogatory about anyone. I never thought she could cope with all our problems, but after an initial period of depression, when she nearly suffered a nervous breakdown, she found a vast resource of inner strength to draw from, and a deep faith in God to help her through the darkest days.

Because of my increasing respect for Wanda's ability to cope with the practical and emotional problems associated with my illness and a desire to "get it all out in the open," I began to tell her about my fears and anger. I told her I was afraid to die and the worst fear of all was the prospect of having to leave her and the children. I also confided to Wanda my dread at the prospect of having to endure pain caused by the cancer. In turn, she leveled with me, telling me how she had spent so many nights alone in the den, crying. After the tears, she would compose herself and somehow begin smiling again before she faced me. By admitting our fears to each other, and sharing them, we were brought closer together than ever before. We no longer had to hide our problems from each other. In trying to protect each other in the past, we hid our problems but created a chasm between us. Renewing communications with each other didn't necessarily make all these problems go away, but they were easier to cope with together. And the concern about letting one another find out about our fears and frustrations was no longer a major problem.

I stepped into an arena filled with enemies named depression, fear, frustration, anger, and self-pity when I returned home from my last hospitalization period.

I had learned something about decision-making under stress prior to my diagnosis, during the time I was ill, but was still unaware of what was happening to me. Because I could no longer work as a newspaper editor and provide for my family, I became depressed and angry. I wanted to flee from my problems. I thought my family and I could find a new life, far from my home in the Midwest. I wanted to go somewhere in the West, where the sun shined even in the wintertime. So we sold all our possessions except for one car, a small camper, and some personal belongings. We drove to Fort Collins, Colorado, and the children were enrolled in school there. However, I was just as ill and unhappy in Colorado as I had been in the Midwest. Our small bank account was soon depleted. It couldn't be replenished because I couldn't work. One day we loaded our belongings in the camper once again and returned home. We had to rent a small three-room apartment, because we could not afford to live in a house.

It was all a big mistake.

I was tempted to "live it up" after I returned home from the hospital, but I could not forget the cost of that ill-fated trip to Colorado. But no matter how hard I tried to return to a normal life once again, the shadows of cancer and death always haunted me. I felt I was a burden to my family. Most of my friends had quit coming to our house. I asked Wanda to pull the covers of my bed back, and I waited to die. I could think of nothing that interested me. If I watched television, sooner or later something on the screen would remind me of death or cancer. I couldn't believe the number of actors and actresses who played the role of a dying cancer patient.

I decided it would be easier to commit suicide and get it over with quickly than to endure the suffering that lay ahead. I wanted to spend one more Christmas with my family, however, sad as it might be, so I never attempted suicide. I'm not sure how really serious I was about it. I was not thinking coherently.

As I wrestled with my problems, it occurred to me that I could never live a normal life again.

Fact 1: There was no cure rate for my type of cancer.

Fact 2: There are no known survivors of my type of cancer.

Fact 3: My cancer was never going to go away permanently.

Fact 4: Unless something else killed me sooner, I would probably die of cancer, barring a miracle.

Therefore, *I had to try living a normal life under abnormal circumstances.* I had to learn to live with the limitations placed upon me because of my illness. Perhaps I could no longer work full-time as a newspaper editor, but I could still *write*. So I unlocked the door to my small office, adjacent to my bedroom and wrote a story about my battle with cancer. It was later published in the local newspaper.

I discovered that I could expect both good and bad days in my life. Sometimes it was difficult for me to even get out of bed in the morning; at other times I felt better than I had in several years.

I learned to delay important decisions as long as possible, and to seek help from others in making them. Should we purchase a better car and assume a new debt which we really couldn't afford to do, or should we try to keep the old one running, despite its 97,000 miles of service? A minor decision? Not for a family facing financial problems because of the high cost of cancer treatment and lack of income.

I found it was best to "lay the cards on the table" when I needed to borrow money. I realize not all bank installment loan offices are willing to take a chance on a seriously ill cancer patient, but some will if you level with them and they know the facts. You will never know whether you can get assistance unless you ask for it.

There were other decisions to make, too. Should we include the children in our discussions? (We did include them.) Should we tell them all the bad news as well as the good news? (I decided it was better to tell the truth about everything rather than try to remember what I had lied about.) Should we try to solve our own financial problems (generally an impossible task), or should we swallow our pride and seek help?

At first, Wanda worked as a laborer at a factory while I did part-time work when I could. Tammy and Mark helped me mow yards and later shovel snow from walks, but I couldn't stay healthy enough to work much that first winter. We had to seek help from Social Security disability funds and I convinced myself I had earned the right to draw a pension. I also discovered that there is a Veterans Administration pension available to qualified veterans who meet all the prerequisites. (You will find detailed information about many of these resources available to qualified persons in Appendix B.)

One of the major problems I encountered was that I felt as if I were the only person to face the obstacles placed in my path. It took me a long time to realize I was not alone, nor was the world going to change because I had cancer. It was *me* who had to change. I began to realize this when, because of my illness and treatments, I became so tired each afternoon that I had to lie down for several hours in my bedroom. At first, I was angry because I couldn't do all the things I had once done in the past. For instance, I could not work eight hours each day. When a task required energy and concentration, I had to accomplish it during the morning hours. I couldn't make plans for long trips at the beginning of my illness. I couldn't leave my family and return to Paris for a final look at the city that held so many memories for me, but I could create a bit of Paris right in my home, during a candlelight dinner with Wanda. I could not return to Germany, where I spent three memorable years, but I could take my children to the woods near my home on a day in September when the trees were on fire with the flames of autumn.

In other words, I could start smelling the roses again, and include the dandelions, too.

There were days, though, when I was so depressed I could *feel* it close in around me like the fog in California in the early morning hours. I found that writing was my own personal therapy for depression. Giving my thoughts a shape and form on paper helped me to cope. Just the other day, I was looking at something I had written during some of my darkest hours:

> *I count the days that give me*
> *life in their passing;*
> *drops of rain against a window-glass*
> *and a leaf that falls from a lonely tree.*
> *Dear God, the torment in my mind*
> *is worse than the depths of Hell.*
> *I am waiting for the end of time.*
> *Will the lilacs bloom for someone else*
> *as once they did for me?*

I would recommend writing as a therapy and an interesting hobby for any seriously ill patient. If a patient cannot sit up to type or write, I often ask them if they have access to an inexpensive cassette tape recorder. They can record their thoughts on tapes and perhaps later they can transfer the words to paper.

Many patients and families of patients have sent me poetry and articles they have written, mostly about their experiences in living with a serious illness, or how it feels to watch someone you love die of an illness. Through these poems and articles, I learned that from the deepest tragedies can come a new and greater awareness of life, and a determination to help others. It soon became apparent that people from all over the world were having to adjust to their own new worlds after the diagnosis of a life-threatening illness. Some faced it bravely; others were terrified. I couldn't find any common thread linking responses to a terminal illness, but it was apparent we all must choose our own life-style. We could consider each passing twenty-four hours as another day closer to death, or as another day of life. A too-simple, Pollyanna-type approach to death? I think not, for we are all terminal; we all have but one lifetime to live.

I wanted my own life, no matter how short, not to be a wasted one. I knew that a person could live for seventy years and waste much of the time, or live only twenty years, with a full life involved.

No matter how you decide to spend the rest of your life, time keeps moving along. For those of you who feel cheated because of an unexpected illness or tragedy, I suggest you quit asking "Why me?" and discover how important life is. If you have recently been diagnosed as having a life-threatening illness, you might find it difficult, if not impossible, to believe that some of your most memorable days might be ahead of you. But my files are full of letters from patients who have told me this is true. And it certainly has been true for me.

I cannot forget the story of Marjorie Wood from Dayton, Ohio. Marjorie, her husband, Jim, and her son, who recently graduated from West Point, all knew she had a short time to live because the cancer in her body had spread and could only be treated, not eliminated. Marjorie decided she wanted to start a Make Today Count chapter in Dayton. She spent the last three months of her life speaking with people who she thought could help her with the organization of the chapter, and sharing precious moments with her family.

When I spoke with Jim recently, we talked of the mark she had left on this world and of the memories she left behind for her loved ones to share.

Marjorie had a choice to make, and it was her decision to not waste the time she had left. Her family, while suffering the grief of her death, realizes, in retrospect, the wisdom of sharing her thoughts and feelings about death.

I have learned that no one can predict the limits of human endurance. Just when we think we can no longer sustain another tragedy, we rally and bounce back again. There is some unknown strength inside all of us that allows us to withstand even the worst of disasters.

Every day we read about people who suffer terrible tragedies and we say to ourselves, "I could *never* live through such things." But we *can* and we *do*. Few people anticipate having cancer. Most of us have never really considered our own mortality, nor do we know how we would react to the diagnosis of a terminal illness.

Each year, for the past five years, nearly 400,000 people in the United States have died of cancer.* Few of them *wanted* to die. But death is an inevitable act of nature. Until death occurs, though, spend your days as wisely as you spend your money. Time is the most valuable possession you have. It's literally priceless; it can't be purchased. But if you have been given time, don't waste it.

What can you do to make each day count if you are a bed patient, for example, and suffering from great pain?

Once I was asked to visit a lady who had been a hospital patient for over three months. Pain was causing her extreme discomfort. She probably would not leave the hospital alive.

I wondered what I might say to this lady to brighten her day. Frankly, I was disturbed that I had agreed to visit her, because my mission seemed hopeless.

When I entered her room, she turned to me and said, "How kind of you to share part of your day with me! And

---

*Recent cancer death rates in the United States are: 1974—360,472; 1975—365,693; 1976—377,312. Estimates for the past two years are: 1977—383,000; 1978—389,000. Source: American Cancer Society, New York, New York

isn't is a beautiful day? The sun is touching the tops of the mountains there, in the distance. How fortunate I am to have a room with such a magnificent view. I never grow tired of watching a new day being born, nor a sunset in the evening. I was a schoolteacher once, and I taught English to thousands of boys and girls. Now I am teaching myself how to appreciate these final days before I die. God has given me some time."

Her beauty and her philosophy were an inspiration to me. *She* cheered *me* and I will never forget the sparkle in her eyes, despite the pain.

Another person who saw beauty despite her suffering caused by cancer was Charlotte "Tiki" Galt. She died of Hodgkin's disease at age twenty, but remained objective about her illness, never asking, "Why me?"

Tiki was a fine horseback rider and loved to ride in the forest, through the sand dunes and along the shore, near her home in Atlantic Beach, Florida. She had long hair and went barefoot most of the time, loving every breath of wind in her hair and every grain of sand under her feet.

She kept a diary, and onto its pages she transferred her thoughts and feelings:

> *Go feel,*
> *live, love.*
> *Don't be afraid.*
> *No one knows.*
> *And if they do,*
> *Why care?*
> *For you are you.*

Sometimes, when I am depressed, I read the lines on one page of Tiki's diary, written by her at a time when she knew she was dying, when she realized that "life for me isn't going to be perfect and lovely, and have a prince charming ride up and take me away into a land of castle green and loveliness."

But Tiki still found beauty. On the last page of her diary are these haunting words:

> *I can feel life,*
> *can you?*
> *I feel it in the wind as it brushes*
> *lightly over me.*
> *I feel it in the darkness as it captures*
> *me in its blackness.*
> *I feel it in the light as it takes hold*
> *of me and sings, "Here is life!"*

Perhaps not all of us can find as much beauty in life as Tiki did, after the diagnosis of her terminal illness. But since we all have one lifetime left to live, regardless of the time involved, I believe we should place more emphasis on the quality rather than the quantity of the days remaining. In order to do this, we must first of all accept the reality of what has happened. The cancer, if it has metastasized, will not go away. We should accept the fact that we must learn to live within our new limitations. Tiki admitted to herself that her life was not going to be normal, after the diagnosis of cancer, compared with the lives of healthy people around her, but she was able to find happiness in ocean waves, love, the wind and the hot sun on a summer day. She accepted her own mortality. When we are faced with tragedy, we can give up and spend our remaining time waiting to die, or we can make each day count by recognizing that we at least have *this* day to live. We are not dead yet. How we spend our time living today is up to each of us.

PART II
Living Despite The Cancer

5

The Patient: Problems of Readjustment

THANKSGIVING HAS COME AND GONE. I am back home in Burlington.

There is talk now among members of the Kelly family about the proper time to decorate our Christmas tree. I am in agreement with the children; it should be done immediately. Wanda did want to wait until the first week of December, but I think she is weakening in the face of overwhelming opinion to the contrary. Perhaps tonight, while it is still snowing, will be the right time for this special holiday occasion.

Several weeks have gone by since the discovery of an enlarged lymph node beneath my arm, but I haven't really reached a stage of depression (which I anticipated happening), nor has fear engulfed me as of old.

I suppose it is true that I still have hope—that I am still

bargaining for more time. I am just not ready to say, "good-bye" yet. Life is still too full of exciting events for me to prematurely celebrate my own funeral. Much of the joy in many matters may be in the anticipation, but not for me—not when the subject is my own death. I am prepared to discuss this future occurrence if there is a reason to do so, but I am not willing to dwell on it, nor become obsessed with the thought of it. I am content to live my life as I have been doing, as completely and joyfully as I know how, still maintaining dignity and control. I recently read an article about my work with patients and families, and one paragraph quoted a psychiatrist as saying that I am still in the "bargaining" stage. I suppose he is right. I don't really know what stage of life (or dying) I am in, but I'm not too concerned about it; I'm too busy just living.

The psychiatrist was referring to one of the five stages of dying, as described by Dr. Elisabeth Kubler-Ross in her book *On Death and Dying*. The first stage described by Elisabeth is "denial and isolation." Next, is the "anger" stage. The third stage is "bargaining," followed by "depression," and finally, the fifth stage, "acceptance."

Sometimes I think I pass through all these stages in one day. Elisabeth is quick to point out that these stages are recommended only as guidelines for persons who work with the terminally ill.

Some cancer patients do not have sufficient time before death occurs to pass through the various stages of dying, nor do they have to become concerned about the problems of readjustment. But since the true prognosis of any patient whose cancer has metastasized is from Day One, onward, many cancer patients live for months or years, even though the disease may not be cured. A member of our Make Today Count chapter in Burlington lived with Hodgkin's disease for nine years before he died of his illness. This is not uncommon. I have met people who have had a serious recurrence of cancer several years after treatment and an apparent remission (stabilization of the disease) had occurred. Thousands of persons are living with cancer at the present time, and each must readjust to a new way of life. (Over one million persons will be treated for cancer this year, and nearly 700,000 new cases will be diagnosed, based on present incidence rates.)

In addition to the problem faced in seeking ways to improve the quality of life for these one million patients (two thirds of whom will eventually die of cancer) there is the challenge of assisting family members, relatives, and friends to cope with the unexpected problems caused by the diagnosis of cancer.

One question confronting many cancer patients who may be considered "cured" is whether the cancer will ever return. (There are over 1.5 million persons in America who are pronounced "cured" of cancer.) We consider persons "cured" if they have no evidence of the disease for at least five years after diagnosis and treatment. But we should keep in mind that the five-year survival mark does not necessarily mean a person will *never* have a recurrence. And some persons are considered cured after much less time has passed, after the diagnosis and treatment.

Persons with cancers of the mouth, colon, skin, and rectum run a greatly increased risk of having a second cancer in the same organ. Patients with cancers of the breast, ovary, and perhaps in the lung have an increased chance of developing cancer in the paired organ. Such combinations of cancer as colon and breast, uterine, cervix, and rectum, and malignant sites in the female reproductive organs, digestive tract, and respiratory system often occur together.

Another problem faced by persons living with cancer is

93

their chance of survival. The prognosis for all patients depends on many things. Two of the most important are the degree to which the disease has spread when the treatment is started and the location of the tumor in the body. Patients whose cancer is localized or restricted to a small area usually have the best chance for survival. At the present time, eleven out of the one hundred or more types of cancer are controllable to the point of being curable in a significant number of cases, and eleven more types of cancer have shown marked improvement in survival. This statement could not have been made eight to ten years ago. We must keep in mind that the time needed for new cancer control approaches to become part of general medical practice is counted in years. It can take up to fifteen years from the time of a preliminary determination that a new treatment is better than a standard treatment until it can have measurable effect on national survival rates, according to the National Cancer Institute.

Although no one except God knows when we are going to die, there are statistics and medical facts that might indicate an approximate time frame if we really want to know the truth. But we must ask ourselves if we actually want to possess this information. Would a patient with a particular type of lung cancer want to know that the general prognosis indicates less than five months of life? Would family members want to know this much about the prognosis? These are the questions everyone must ask of themselves when seeking the "truth" from their physicians.

I chose to know as much as possible about the type of cancer that I have and the survival rates. Even when confronted with "facts," you must realize that all statistics, for instance, are not up to date, based on latest responses to newer combination treatments for cancer. Physicians are now considering a few types of cancer curable even in advanced cases, as opposed to the probability of most patients dying from these same types several years ago.

As patients and family members begin the readjustment to living with a life-threatening illness, the prospect of death is always in their minds. Since patients hear so much about what they *can't* do, and not enough about the things they can still do despite their illness, it is impossible for them to remain objective while wondering how soon they are going to die and how much pain they will be forced to endure. Under these stressful conditions, it is difficult for patients to consider such practical issues as going back to their old jobs or seeking new employment. Personnel managers representing industry's viewpoints about cancer often aren't reassuring, and some patients are placed on disability lists or retired early. I must emphasize that some companies aren't reluctant to hire or rehire cancer patients, providing they can perform the work they are employed to do.

Possible job discrimination against recovered cancer patients has been the subject of relatively few systematic studies, according to a report prepared for the National Cancer Institute.* Evidence of its existence has been mostly anecdotal, with some reports of individual discrimination appearing in newspapers and magazine articles. The question is: Are these incidents truly isolated accounts, or do they indicate a more pervasive national attitude?

The Metropolitan Life Insurance Company and the American Telephone and Telegraph Company conducted studies of their employees with a history of cancer to see how well they did on the job after treatment for their disease.

The Metropolitan Life study examined the work experiences of seventy-four persons with known cancer histories

*Coping With Cancer: A Sourcebook for the Health Professional, 1978, National Cancer Institute, NIH (National Institutes of Health)

who were employed during a period of twelve years. The company's policy was to hire recovered cancer patients who had been disease-free for five years, and to consider those treated more recently who showed no additional evidence of disease since treatment. Over half of the employees in the study had been hired within five years of treatment.

Approximately one year after the study had ended, fifty-five percent of the seventy-four employees were still working, most of them with one to five years of service; three percent were on disability and forty-two percent were "discontinued." The discontinued group consisted of people who left their jobs voluntarily, usually within one year of hiring. Metropolitan felt that this indicated job dissatisfaction, and concluded that the turnover rate for employees with a history of cancer was comparable to that of non-cancer employees.

Working performance ratings for thirty-nine members of the seventy-four-person study population were satisfactory for the majority. Absentee records for the same group compared favorably with non-cancer employees. The study concluded that "the selective hiring of persons who have been treated for cancer, in positions for which they are physically qualified, is a sound industrial practice."

Although exact hiring criteria for recovered cancer patients were not explained, Metropolitan's experience "indicates that forty-seven percent of cancer history applicants can be medically accepted for employment," and "acceptance rates are increasing as we get more experience with these cases and as cancer (survival) rates improve."

The American Telephone and Telegraph Company studied 1,346 employees with a history of cancer in the Bell System Operating Telephone companies, according to the same National Cancer Institute report. Most of the cases of cancer had occurred in employees forty years of age and older. Overall, seventy-seven percent of the patients returned to work after absences lasting an average of 106 days. Thus, the Bell System enjoyed the return to work of many "valued older employees." It should be noted, however, that the 1,346 persons in the study population were already employed by AT&T when they became ill. The study did not address the question of hiring a cancer patient, but rather the work performance potential of a recovered patient.

If the attitudes of these two companies are predictive of industry practices in general, the employment outlook for the cancer patient is promising. Certainly the findings of both studies indicate satisfactory work performance with low absenteeism for those with a history of cancer and, in the case of Metropolitan Life, an enlightened attitude toward hiring cancer patients.

But what about individuals attempting to find work with companies other than Metropolitan Life and AT&T? To investigate possible job discrimination against cancer patients, the Ad Hoc Committee on Employability Problems of the Recovered Cancer Patient was formed by the California Division of the American Cancer Society. A report was prepared by this group on the job discrimination experienced by fifty-six cancer patients, as expressed by their letters of complaint to the California Division of the American Cancer Society.

Based on the evidence contained in that report, it was decided to study the recovered cancer patient population at large. In 1976, the California Division of the American Cancer Society conducted a study examining the work experiences of 130 persons treated for cancer. The sample consisted of the "most employable" recovered cancer patients in the California work force; that is, "persons 25-30 years old who were working at the time of cancer diagnosis who had at least a high school education and worked in one of six occupational groups calling for some special education or on-the-job training." Additionally, cancer treatment had been undertaken during the past five years. If these "most employable" people suffered discrimination, it could be inferred that those with lesser difficulties would have the same or greater difficulties.

Twenty-two percent of the study sample reported that at least one job application had been rejected because of previous cancer experience. This included recovered cancer patients currently working for their pre-cancer employers, but seeking other jobs at the same time.

California's Fair Employment Practices Act was amended in 1975 to eliminate discrimination because of a "medical condition," defined as "any health impairment related to or associated with a diagnosis of cancer, for which a person has been rehabilitated or cured based in competent medical evidence." Thus, the study's finding of illegal job discrimination in California has strong implications for states without such legislation.

Other, more subtle work-related problems were reported by the patients in the California study, including hostility expressed by fellow workers, or changes in work location apparently designed to force the recovered cancer patient to resign. Others reported lack of salary advances, reduction in health benefits, or ineligibility for newly-available group life insurance.

On the positive side, over seventy-five percent of the group reported salary increases and health and insurance benefits equal to those of other employees. Nearly half the study population never experienced work problems because of cancer.

Having identified the need for further research, the National Cancer Institute contracted with five organizations to develop and demonstrate "positive programs to modify employer attitudes in an effort to improve the employment and/or re-employment potential for cancer patients." The first stage of the project was an assessment of employer attitudes with a history of cancer. As of this writing, two reports have been published: those of University Research Corporation and the Mayo Clinic.

University Research Corporation's principal finding was "that the charge that there is widespread discrimination by employers against work-able cancer patients does not seem accurate." This conclusion was reached after interviewing 219 employers and 140 patients in three major cities: New York, St. Louis, and Houston. The only possible area of discrimination observed was in health insurance. Recovered cancer patients could be temporarily or permanently ineligible for health insurance in at least one-third of the companies surveyed.

An interesting trend emerged from patient responses to the survey. Those who felt there were problems in returning to work (and they were in the minority) cited mental attitude as the greatest problem. The report pointed out that the stories being circulated about discrimination might contribute to a negative mental attitude. The report concluded that cancer patients may have employment problems because they have been told they will, not because a large number of employers discriminate.

The Mayo Clinic study paralleled these findings: "The refusal to hire persons with a history of cancer or the termination of their employment following treatment is not a widespread occurrence."

Only three percent of the 473 respondents to the Mayo Clinic survey claimed their employment was terminated because of cancer, and only eleven percent of the 97 recovered cancer patients who sought employment were refused a job. The study further found that "favorable opportunities for employment exist for patients following treatment for cancer," based on those who could have or did obtain employment following treatment.

Although the other three reports in the National Cancer Institute series have not been published yet, "informal communication among the organizations indicates that all arrived at the same conclusions—that is, most employers do not discriminate against work-able cancer patients."

For the cancer patient who suffers a handicap as a result of treatment, employability has another fact—vocational rehabilitation. The Vocational Rehabilitation Act of 1973 provides vocational rehabilitation services to severely handicapped individuals. A severely handicapped individual is one who "has one or more physical or mental disabilities resulting from amputation, arthritis, blindness, cancer ... or another disability or combination of disabilities determined on the basis of an evaluation of rehabilitation potential to cause comparable substantial functional limitation." This legislation, then, focuses on the most severely handicapped individuals and requires the states to guarantee that they receive rehabilitation services first.

The Vocational Rehabilitation Act also prohibits discrimination against qualified handicapped individuals by institutions having more than fifty employees and having a contract to provide goods or services to the federal government in excess of $50,000. Complaints are filed with the Department of Labor, and if they are upheld after review, the Secretary of Labor may cancel the federal contract in question. Employers are also required to judge handicapped applicants against the job to be performed, not against a general standard. If the applicant cannot perform the required duties, the employer must try to make a "reasonable accommodation," involving altering the work setting, changing access to the work site, etc. The applicant can be denied the job only if a reasonable accommodation is impossible.

Thus, the 1973 Vocational Rehabilitation Act is a potent piece of legislation toward ensuring the rehabilitation and subsequent employability of the handicapped cancer patient.

A portion of the Mayo Clinic's study of discrimination toward cancer patients addressed cancer patients' accessibility to and use of state vocational rehabilitation agencies. Information was sought on the services used by cancer patients and what programs had been implemented or proposed in accordance with the 1973 Act.

Three findings emerged from the study:

Cancer patients are not being made aware that they might be eligible for vocational rehabilitation services. Only a minority of the cancer patients surveyed (fifteen percent) were aware of their eligibility for such services.

The Vocational Rehabilitation Act of 1973 has not had a substantial impact on the rehabilitation of cancer patients. As of this writing, special programs for cancer patients are conducted by only five states: Delaware, Florida, Michigan, New York, and Texas.

Some medical criteria used in the evaluation of cancer patients' eligibility for vocational rehabilitation services appear unreasonable. Of the medical eligibility criteria provided by some agencies for the study, two states (Maryland and New Jersey) used standards felt to be "unreasonable." Maryland, for example, considered chemotherapy and radical cancer surgery forms of "unusual medical treatment." Among the cancers considered by New Jersey to carry very poor prognoses were cancers in young people (under thirty years of age) and cancer of the blood and lymphatic system—cancers which generally carry good prognoses.

101

Progress is being made in the employment and re-employment prospects for cancer patients, but misconceptions and lack of knowledge on the part of the employers, patients, and some government agencies still exist. Inconclusive, fragmented, and scarce data make the picture difficult to evaluate, according to the National Cancer Institute report.

Most of my mail on the subject of cancer patients' employment problems comes from people who have had bad experiences when seeking employment or in attempting to return to their old jobs.

Those patients who make decisions to keep working are often faced with obstacles such as the ones encountered by Chuck Colombo, from Mason City, Iowa, whom I mentioned in Chapter 2. Chuck was fired from his job with a worldwide retail corporation because he had cancer. He was told when he was fired that the company where he worked had a corporate policy against retaining employees who have malignant diseases. Upon the recommendation of a Make Today Count member, Chuck contacted the Iowa Civil Rights Commission and he was eventually reinstated in his former job, with back pay. He also understood that the company had changed its worldwide policy calling for the firing of persons with malignancies. Local store officials at Chuck's place of employment said the firing was a mistake and that the corporate position had been changed some time ago, but through an error the Mason City store did not receive the corrected policy change. Corporate officials said no such policy was ever in existence in the first place. But the fact remains that Chuck was fired. He had to contact outside help in order to get his job back, and it took him several months and many telephone calls to do it.

When our Make Today Count chapter in Des Moines, Iowa sponsored a seminar entitled "Employment Problems of the Cancer Patient," one speaker told about the job problems he had encountered as a patient. Following treatment for his disease, this young, highly qualified account executive tried to return to his job, but discovered the employer did not want to rehire him. He applied at over one hundred other firms and was once offered a job as a truck driver. Finally, a firm where he had worked earlier in his career gave him a job commensurate with his skills. This man found out what it is like to be successfully treated for cancer, though perhaps not cured, but unable to return to work because an employer was concerned about all sorts of potential problems in the future.

If a patient is aware of the possible obstacles he may encounter in returning to work or seeking a new job, he should find ways to cope with them. Chuck Colombo turned to a state civil liberties bureau. The young account executive refused to give up, as evidenced by the number of job interviews he scheduled.

The alternatives to returning to work or seeking new employment are resorting to incomes from pensions, applying for Social Security disability funds, supplemental security assistance, or such programs as veterans' pensions. (For more detailed information about resources available to disabled persons, see Chapter 11, "The Cost of Cancer," and Appendix A.)

As a cancer patient, you will encounter a variety of reactions toward your illness by members of your family, relatives and friends. One young lady told me that her husband wanted her to go to Mexico for laetrile treatment for her cancer, while a friend advised her to seek medical help from a specialist in the Bahamas. Still another acquaintance told her she should ignore everyone else and locate a competent specialist.

After being bombarded with all sorts of suggestions about how she should be treated for the cancer, this young lady decided to contact a physician in her city. Later she received chemotherapy and radiation therapy. She lived for several years after the treatment. Some of her friends and relatives probably still feel she chose the wrong type of treatment.

Most cancer patients will encounter what I call the "positive thinkers." I believe in taking a positive approach to illness and other problems, but I am talking about those persons who say something like this to dying patients: "Now, just don't worry about it. Everything is going to be all right. You'll probably outlive me!"

I encountered someone who used this approach to a terminal illness while I was visiting patients in a hospital here in Iowa. A young man was bending over to talk with a dying lung cancer patient, who probably couldn't hear a word the visitor was saying to him.

"Uncle John," the young man shouted, "you're going to be home in a couple of days and before you know it, you will be working in your garden again!"

This patient had already faced the fact he would not return home. He knew he was dying. He never said a word to his nephew. He was beyond the point of being able to respond to things the young man was saying.

While in Virginia I was asked by a relative to visit a man in his early forties who was dying of stomach cancer. The relative, a sister of the critically ill patient, told me tearfully that her brother refused to talk with any members of his family. He had given no reason other than his desire to be alone.

When I entered the man's room, he was suffering from pain in his abdomen and pleading with a nurse to bring his pain medication. It wasn't time for it yet. I felt as if I might be prying into his private world at a time when he certainly did not need any more problems. But I had promised his sister I would talk with him.

Instead of becoming angry because of my presence, he eagerly began discussing with me *his* problems. He told me that whenever he tried to talk with his family about dying, they made him feel guilty because he had accepted what was happening. His wife would exclaim, "Please! Don't talk like that! You're going to be home with us for Christmas!" This patient had fought a long battle with cancer, but he knew he was dying. *He* could accept death, but his family could not. Because of their attitude, he refused to talk with them any longer. He needed support from them which they apparently could not offer.

When I explained why he refused to talk any longer with his family, the sister went into her brother's room. She stayed for over half an hour. When she exited from the room she was crying, but she told me they had finally been able to hold each other and they cried together for the first time.

"I am so glad I'm finally able to be honest with him—and with myself," she told me.

When a patient returns home from the hospital, knowing the truth about the diagnosis, the children may not yet have been told what is wrong. During the intermission of a lecture I gave in Illinois, a young mother approached me and asked for help. She was being treated for a brain tumor. Both she and her husband were able to discuss her medical and their emotional problems. They had not yet told their two children, ages ten and thirteen, that their mother didn't look ill but that she could die at any time, with little or no warning.

"My husband and I have always shared everything, except this problem, with our children," the young woman told me. "The question in our minds is whether or not telling them the truth would disrupt their lives and cause all sorts of problems, at a time when I need their love. I want to make them as happy as possible and yet there are so many occasions when I am tempted to tell them the truth. They do know that I don't feel very well and I have to go to the doctor a lot, but they have no idea what is wrong or how serious things really are for me."

"Have you ever thought about what might happen after your death?" I asked her. "Do you think your children might someday resent the fact you withheld the truth about your illness from them? And are you trying to protect them, or yourself?"

I told her that the decision of whether or not to tell her children about her illness should be made by herself and her husband. I wanted her to know what could happen if she *didn't* tell the truth to the children. I related the story told to me by a man whose wife had died of leukemia. At the time of her death, the three children in the family were all under twelve years of age. Neither the mother nor the father had ever told the children of the seriousness of their mother's illness. When death occurred, the children were not told. Information about the funeral was withheld from them. The father told the children that their mother was visiting relatives. When they learned the truth, they reacted by becoming disciplinary problems both at home and at school. Based on my own experiences, I feel children (depending on their age and ability to comprehend) can cope with death and dying as well as adults can. Children will grieve over the loss of a loved one, just as adults do, but hiding the truth from them causes unresolved grief later. Also it deprives them of a chance to share time with someone they love, prior to death.

Several weeks later, I received a letter from this young

woman, informing me that she and her husband had decided to talk with their children about the existence of a brain tumor and the probability of death at some time in the future.

"I do want to tell you that my two children did not fall apart emotionally. They cried. My husband and I cried. But we all cried together. I asked for their help, and the important thing is that I feel so much better now because I am not hiding anything from them. I feel as if a weight has been lifted from my shoulders."

The reactions of children in the family may surprise you, if only you will be honest with them.

One of the most serious, yet least discussed, problems to confront many seriously ill patients and their spouses is sexual adjustment. To begin with, the patient probably feels terrible from both a physical and a mental standpoint, while the spouse is still healthy and has the same sexual drives as before. To complicate matters, the patient may have undergone disfiguring surgery, or may suffer from uterine or testicular cancer. A colostomy or similary operation may have been performed. The chemotherapy drugs being used may decrease the sexual drive of the patient.

Once I received a call from the son of a seriously ill woman who was suffering from cancer and heart disease. The son asked me if I would visit his mother and his father. I agreed, so he drove me to his parents' home, located in a nearby town. En route, he told me his father had discussed with him the problem of adjusting to the sexual dilemma caused by the illness.

"My father wants to know how his children would feel if he found a girl friend, for sexual purposes, even though he still loves Mother," the son explained. "We have mixed feelings about this, but how do *you* feel?"

I wasn't prepared to comment about the problem.

When I spoke with the patient, she told me that she secretly desired a divorce so she could die in peace. She said her husband couldn't understand her problems and her children thought she was just feeling sorry for herself part of the time.

"They want me to keep smiling and try to regain a normal life, but I am tired and I hurt all over," the lady explained. "I want to go to a nursing home so I can rest and not be bothered."

When I spoke with her husband, he seemed to be an understanding person, but he did tell me that he was having trouble living with a wife who "complains all the time."

"I want her to go to Hawaii with me next month," he said. "We can afford to go, but she just wants to stay home."

"I understand you are considering seeking some feminine companionship other than that of your wife," I said. "What does she think about this possibility?"

"She *wants* me to find someone else," he replied. "I know it sounds like I'm not very compassionate, but I've been living with these problems for the past four years, and I've got a life to consider, too."

"Do you love her?" I asked.

"Yes, I love her," he said after pondering the question for a moment. "However, it's more like she's my sister instead of my wife."

By this time, I was beginning to wish I had never become involved with this family. Both the husband and his wife seemed like nice persons. They lived in a comfortable, well-furnished home and on the surface appeared to be a normal, middle-class family. But their lives had been disrupted by an illness. I felt maybe something had been missing from their marriage prior to the illness, though, and now it was coming to the surface because of what had happened to the wife. The problems had probably always been there.

I do not have a happy ending for this story. The patient died, putting an end to all the problems associated with her illness. I am not sure that I could have done anything to alleviate the problems that existed. I could not have caused all the frustrations to disappear, nor could I have eased the pain and suffering of the patient, thereby perhaps solving some of the sexual problems. I did talk with both persons about the importance of love and compassion. I told them how other married couples had solved similar problems because their love for each other had been deep enough to tolerate the sexual maladjustments caused by a serious illness.

I have been contacted many times by persons who have had problems with sexuality, associated with cancer or other diseases. I recall the case of a man, in his thirties, who became intimate with his secretary during a time when his wife was hospitalized because of a double mastectomy. Later, he confessed the infidelity to his wife. She became hysterical. I talked with both of them during a seminar and the wife was still not willing to forgive her husband.

"Here I was, lying in a hospital bed while you were sleeping with your secretary! I couldn't have hurt you the way you did me. How can you ever expect me to forget what happened? At a time when I really needed you, but believed you were working overtime to help pay our bills, you were with another woman!"

Making it even more difficult for this lady to accept what had happened was the fact that one of her sons had helped his father hide the romance and had even been present at times when the girlfriend had been brought to the house.

When I heard this story, from both the husband and wife,

the question in my mind was whether the marriage could be salvaged. The sin had already been committed. The husband had told his wife what had happened. I could sympathize with the wife and feel angry toward the husband. But they had come to me for help.

"Do you still love your husband?" I asked the lady.

"Yes . . . that's the trouble. I do still love him. But I can't bear thinking any more about what he did to me."

"How about you, do you love your wife?" I asked the husband.

"Yes, I love her, but I can't change what occurred. I wish I could turn the clock back and change everything."

"Both of you must decide if you want to make an attempt to hold your marriage together," I told them. "If you are going to try making your marriage work, I have some advice for you. If not, then you should seek help other than what I can offer you."

They looked at each other. The thought entered my mind that perhaps neither person had ever consulted anyone else about their problems.

"Incidentally, have you discussed this with anyone else?" I asked them.

"No, we don't want anyone to know," the wife told me.

Once again I was reminded that the sexual problems associated with a serious illness are generally hidden somewhere beneath everything else that is happening. Even doctors, nurses, and clergymen hesitate discussing this problem.

"First of all, both of you must realize that it is true you cannot change the fact that one of you was unfaithful to the other," I told them. "You, as the wife, must make up your mind you are going to pick up the pieces and go on with the business of living, under the circumstances, if you do want to remain together. I want you to know what happened should never have occurred, but it is not the first time I have heard a story similar to your own. Other patients and spouses have had to cope with this problem. Sometimes there is a divorce. Other couples somehow manage to 'weather the storm' and the marriage survives. Both of you must try to put the past behind you. Just as I have learned to live despite my illness, perhaps you can learn to live despite what has occurred in your own lives."

I have talked with married couples who have managed to live, and love, despite the presence of cancer and the resultant side effects of chemotherapy and radiation therapy.

"My wife has had several operations, one of which could be called a 'disfiguring-type,' since the diagnosis of her cancer," a man once told me. "Most of the time, she is very tired and our sexual activities have nearly stopped altogether, if we were to compare them to most people's versions of sex. But when she is lying in my arms at night, snuggled next to me, I realize how much she needs me. I love her very much and because of our mutual love, we experiment with different ways to satisfy our sexual desires other than making love. Why would I leave her at a time when she needs me more than ever? She may be living an abnormal life in some ways, but inside, she is still the same person I married and still love."

I feel married couples can survive a serious illness without the healthy spouse resorting to extramarital sex. First of all, though, both persons in the marriage partnership must face the problems they encounter in an open and honest way. They must communicate with each other. Once the problems have been identified, they can seek ways to cope with them.

A young woman told me that she was terminating her chemotherapy treatments because her hair had fallen out from the side effects of the drugs and her husband didn't like her appearance. I immediately became angry toward her husband. I asked if she would arrange a meeting between him and me. She agreed.

When we met, over coffee, I soon learned that he *didn't* dislike his wife's appearance at all. He seemed honest enough, so I had no reason to doubt his integrity.

"I am having a hard time convincing my wife that I love *her*, all of her, and not just her hair, which, incidentally, will return someday when the chemotherapy treatments are stopped by the doctor. I want to be natural about my love, without forcing myself to constantly pay attention to my wife."

"I think she needs some extra attention during this period of time," I told him. "She needs reassurance that you love her."

Most of the time, I find that problems associated with sex and love, apparently stemming from a diagnosis of cancer, have their roots in the past, before the discovery of the cancer. If a husband was unfaithful *before* the diagnosis, he will probably continue his extramarital activities. If two people love each other, the diagnosis of a serious illness and the subsequent medical and emotional problems can bring them even closer together through their sharing of these problems.

Loneliness and depression rank among the major emotional problems faced by cancer patients, and no one is more aware of these problems than the solitary cancer patient. Living alone with cancer is something I have never experienced, but I have talked and communicated with many single cancer patients. In some cases, a cancer patient's spouse cannot cope with a mate's cancer and subsequently leaves home. Divorces and separations are frequent. No matter what the prior circumstances, cancer patients who live alone need special support and understanding.

112

I remember talking with a 62-year-old cancer patient who taught school in Ohio. A widow, she returned home from work each night to the isolation of a three-room apartment. I will never forget seeing her take a single hamburger patty from the refrigerator and cook it for her evening meal. There was no one to share her thoughts and feelings with during mealtime, so she usually propped a magazine on the table in front of her to read while she was eating.

"The worst time of all is at two or three o'clock in the morning," she told me. "I generally wake up then and I start thinking about the past and my disease. I get very lonely."

A cancer patient from Oklahoma, whose wife and children no longer lived with him (his wife decided she couldn't cope any longer), told me, too, that nights were worst for him.

"Sometimes I get so lonely I dial information operators in various parts of the United States and ask for names of people I make up because I just want to hear the operator's voice. I don't go out because radiation therapy has damaged one side of my face."

"Please be my friend," an elderly widow from Wisconsin pleaded, in a letter to me. "I have cancer, but worst of all is the loneliness. My friends don't come around any more but I still need friends."

A lady from Illinois calls me at least once each month because she needs someone to listen to her problems. I don't say much to her; I just listen. When she is through talking, she always tells me she feels so much better. I have discovered that you can help someone who is lonely by just being their friend and letting them talk about their problems. On the other hand, many people ask me what they can do to help a lonely cancer patient besides just being their friend.

113

They find it hard to believe that being a friend is often enough.

"But I want to *do* something for them," they reply.

I explain the importance of listening and not staying away because we feel so helpless when someone has an illness such as cancer. Listening and caring is just as important as medical treatments in many cases. If the patient doesn't want to get well, all the medicine in the world may not help.

Early one morning, my telephone rang in my bedroom. I answered it and heard a lady's voice on the other end of the line telling me that she was going to commit suicide.

"I'm calling you because my minister once gave me your name and I just wanted to talk with someone first," she said.

I never assume someone is bluffing when they threaten suicide.

"Do you have a family?" I asked.

"No. My husband is dead and my son lives far away from me. I hardly ever hear from him. He's too busy now and besides, he has a family of his own. I want you to know I'm not feeling sorry for myself. I just have nothing to live for. I'm tired of being lonely. I have cancer, but my doctor tells me I could live several years with it. But why should I? I'm tired of living."

I asked her if she was interested in traveling, or had a hobby of any kind. But apparently nothing interested her.

Finally, though, I discovered she liked to write.

"Surely there are some incidents which occurred during your past life that are interesting enough to write about," I told her.

"Well, yes, I suppose there are some," she replied.

She became more interested in the prospect of writing down on paper her thoughts and feelings as we conversed.

114

Finally, she promised she would do it.

"Remember, you *do* have a friend now," I reminded her. *"I'm* your friend."

Some of our Make Today Count members live alone but they have found that helping others eases loneliness. There is no better therapy.

A lady from Chicago asked me if I would convince her aunt that Make Today Count meetings would help her cope with cancer. The aunt lived alone and even though she could walk and drive her car, she stayed home most of the time.

I approached this lady with the suggestion that she give one of our meetings a try. She seemed to think it was worth trying and I forgot about her for a couple of months until one day my telephone rang and her niece was on the other end of the line.

"Do you remember me asking you to talk my aunt into attending one of your Make Today Count meetings?"

"Yes, I remember."

"Well, I know this may sound strange, but I wonder if you could talk to her again and convince her she shouldn't go to so many Make Today Count meetings? She goes to a different meeting every night and we can never catch her at home, even for a visit! When she is home, she's on the telephone most of the time talking with other cancer patients. I wanted her to get involved, but now she's *too* busy!"

Certainly not all of our Make Today Count members are this enthusiastic, but our meetings do provide a way for single cancer patients to find friends. Doctors sometimes become friends with factory workers and teenagers become friends with the aged. We share common problems and goals.

Compassionate visiting nurses and homemakers provide conversation and friendship to lonely persons. One single lady I know, who is not well enough to leave her small apartment, eagerly anticipates the weekly visit of a homemaker who cleans the apartment each week. They have become close friends and sometimes they visit on other than the regular visiting day.

I have talked with people who answer the telephones at some of the various cancer centers offering a "hot line" telephone service for cancer patients. Some of them have told me that many of the patients who call just want to talk with someone because they are lonely.

I feel the Make Today Count visitation program would be beneficial for all patients, but especially for those persons who live alone. Some of our chapters have visitation programs, such as our San Diego units, and the visitors undergo a training program conducted by nurses, social workers, and other professional persons who teach them the dos and don'ts of visiting patients. For example, *do* listen, offer to perform tasks such as mailing letters, and offer to return if the patient seems to enjoy the visit. *Don't* force the conversation into areas *you*, as the visitor, wish to discuss, don't overstay your visit, and don't offer "miraculous cures" for the patient.

If you are a cancer patient, living alone, you should realize that there are other persons who *do* understand and share your problems. Seek the companionship of self-help groups such as Make Today Count. Get involved in helping others with *their* problems. You do not have to sit at home, thinking about your problems and worrying about the future. If your old friends have quit visiting you or calling you, because *they* cannot cope with *your* illness, seek new friends. Don't wait for people to come to you.

Some people are afraid of the transmission of cancer, and that brings up another problem sometimes faced by cancer patients. I have encountered some people who feel that "cancer just *might* be contagious"! Because of a tremendous fear of cancer, and the mystery surrounding it, plus the fact that we often hear the word "virus" associated with this disease, some people don't want to take a chance by being close to a cancer patient.

Quite a number of people have asked me if they could "catch" cancer by having sexual relations with a wife or husband who has the disease. I explain to them that the cancer is not considered contagious. As a matter of fact, there is no higher incidence rate of cancer among doctors and nurses who are closely involved with patients.

I know of several families with cancer in their midst where the patient's eating utensils, bedding, and clothing are washed and laundered separately.

Some husbands and wives refuse to kiss their mates who have cancer.

I believe there is only one solution for alleviating these needless fears: knowledge. We must somehow educate the public about cancer. Since two out of three families will be or have been touched by cancer, it is a national problem of major proportions.

As a cancer patient, I am aware of the sexual problems associated with cancer. I know about some of them first-hand. I became impotent because of the chemotherapy treatment and some of the medicine used for the treatment of my hypertension. The impotence lasted for a period of approximately two and one-half years, and even today I have occasional problems. I quit taking the chemotherapy drugs over a year ago, but I still take drugs for hypertension. One of my doctors changed the medicine he was using to treat the hypertension and this helped my problem. As of now, I do not know how much of my problem with impotence is caused by the medicine as compared to psychological factors. I do know Wanda and I found ways to live with

117

the problem. I would like to share our own experiences with you, with the hope that it may help you cope with any problems *you* might have.

First of all, I discovered that there is no magical solution to the problem of living with impotence. There is no *complete* substitute for sex in a marriage. But I found that just being able to talk about my problems with my wife helped me learn to live with them. At first, just as I was reluctant to talk about my emotional problems associated with the cancer, I tried to cover up my sexual problems. This caused Wanda to wonder what was *really* wrong with me. At a time when I was wondering how Wanda could still love me, *she* was wondering if I still loved her as much as before. When she discovered what was wrong with me, she would lie in my arms at night and we would hold each other and just talk. Touching was one substitute for sex in my own life. Knowing that Wanda still loved me helped me cope with my doubts and frustrations. And it helped *me* very much to realize Wanda needed *me*, too.

I believe that my busy life has helped me, too. Once again, I realize that there is no way to substitute a busy life for a sexual life, but it helps to become involved in helping people with their *own* problems.

I have learned that reactions from friends and relatives toward my cancer often mask their true feelings. They just do not know what to do or say, so they act differently and say foolish things. It is up to *me* to put *them* at ease, if I do not want to accept their attitudes.

I know that some people are afraid they might "catch" cancer from me. I am willing to explain the fact that cancer isn't considered contagious. Some listen and believe me. Others do not. If they do not believe me, it is *their* problem, not mine.

Each patient confronted with a serious illness is an individual, as different from you and I as one snowflake is from another. But we can help each other by sharing our problems and finding ways to cope with them together.

6

The
Spouse

THE RINGING OF MY TELEPHONE awakened me. I looked at the clock on the table beside my bed. Two thirty A.M. I picked up the receiver.

"Hello."

"This is Tom, from Los Angeles. Is this Orville?"

"Hello, Tom. It's me."

Tom's wife, Kathy was a cancer patient. I had met both of them during a speaking tour through California. Nice couple. Young. Two children.

Kathy had taught school before becoming too ill to work. Tom worked as a chemist in Los Angeles. I remembered that they were very much in love.

"Kathy died two hours ago."

Silence. I could hear Tom sobbing. I am at a loss for words. What *can* someone say at a time like this? The important thing was to let Tom know that I cared and that I was willing to remain his friend, that I would never desert him.

"Tom, I don't know what it's like to lose someone you love, but I want you to know that I care. I care very much about what has happened."

After the conversation, I could not get back to sleep. I thought of Wanda and her own problems in coping with my illness. I wondered if someone would be able to comfort her when I die. Not a pleasant thought, but I have learned something about reality through my work with the terminally ill and their families: People die. Loved ones grieve. Life goes on.

I remembered how the diagnosis of my cancer affected Wanda. (At least I thought I could remember.) However, Wanda can recall clearly how she viewed what was happening to our lives:

"It was a spring day and certainly not one that seemed any different than most others. When the alarm clock rang that morning, I got up, dressed, and went downstairs to make breakfast for Orville and our four children.

"I set the table, put the coffeepot on to perk, and made some oatmeal. The sun was coming up by this time, but I was too busy trying to figure out a math problem for Mark, my thirteen-year-old son, to notice how beautiful it was, as it came up over the Mississippi River and the far hills of Illinois beyond.

"Orville sat down at the kitchen table and said, 'Honey, I found something under my arm while I was shaving. There's a lump there.'

"Normally I wouldn't have paid much attention to a remark such as the one Orville made, but he had been complaining for months about being tired, and he had pneumonia twice the previous winter. I just couldn't imagine anything being seriously wrong with him. After all, he had recently undergone several physical examinations and nothing was discovered. Orville was a healthy man, who fished, hunted, and lifted weights in the evening after work. At least I wanted to think he was healthy, but it wasn't like him to complain about being tired, so I was haunted by a nagging fear that something just *might* be wrong.

" 'If the lump doesn't go away in a few days, you should have it checked,' I cautioned him.

"The lump didn't go away. As a matter of fact, he discovered two more lumps later, one more beneath his arm and one in his groin. Orville went to a doctor and told him about the lumps and how he had been bothered by a feeling of fatigue most of the time recently. The doctor, who was a surgeon, said he wanted to remove one of the lumps beneath his arm. The doctor told Orville he suspected it could be lymphoma, but he hoped he would be proven wrong when the biopsy was performed.

"On the day the surgery was to take place, I was afraid. My mother, Mark, Orville, and I got into the car and I drove to the hospital. I didn't say anything to the other children about their father's problem."

While Wanda, my mother-in-law, and Mark waited in the hospital lobby, I lay on an operating table as the surgeon removed one of the tumors beneath my left arm. I don't remember how long the operation lasted, but I do recall the doctor saying that the results of the biopsy were back and the tumor was malignant. I knew I had cancer.

"Do you want to tell your wife, or should I do it?" the doctor asked.

I realized I couldn't look into Wanda's eyes without losing control. I didn't want to upset her any more than necessary.

"Would you please do it?" I asked.

A nurse went to the waiting room and escorted Wanda to the lobby outside the operating room. Out of the corner of my eye, I could see the doctor talking with Wanda. The nurse placed my left arm in a sling and I remained sitting on the edge of the operating table.

"Your husband has lymphoma," the doctor said to Wanda.

"Is that cancer?" Wanda stammered.

"Yes, it is a form of cancer," the doctor replied. He explained to Wanda that this type of cancer could be treated with chemotherapy and radiation therapy. She heard little of what he said after the word cancer was mentioned.

Wanda stumbled from the lobby back to the waiting room. She fought to hold back the tears because she didn't want to start crying in front of everyone. It just didn't seem to be the right thing to do. "Not here in the hospital," she told herself. "I've got to wait until I'm by myself."

She remembered that some hospital papers had to be signed before she picked me up for the return trip home. Somehow, she managed to complete everything and then she stopped in the lobby to get her mother and Mark. Together, they walked toward the car in the hospital parking lot.

"Mom, I'm going to lose him!" she sobbed. "How could this ever happen to us? We were all so happy together. It seems like a nightmare. Can it really be happening?"

After a few minutes, Wanda pulled herself together and drove to the hospital entrance where I was waiting. I could tell she had been crying, but all I could say was, "Honey, don't worry about it. Everything will be all right." I didn't feel that way, but I just didn't want to worry Wanda.

Wanda dropped all of us off at our home, so she could take the baby-sitter to her own home. I wasn't feeling well, so I lay down on a sofa in the den.

After Wanda dropped the baby-sitter off, she started back home again. On the way, she passed a church.

"I decided to stop in the sanctuary and pray," Wanda recalled. "I was really glad no one else was present, because I was sobbing. I threw myself in front of the altar. I asked God for a miracle. I wanted Orville to be healed. I don't remember how long I stayed there, but I felt better afterward.

"When I got home, Orville was lying on a davenport, staring at the ceiling. He didn't even look at me. I said something about fixing supper and went into the kitchen. Orville ate in silence. Not once did he say a word about what had happened at the hospital. I wanted to hold him close and comfort him and tell him how scared I was, but I felt it would be the wrong thing to do.

"From then on, Orville and I didn't talk with each other very much. A tension began to build up in our home and the children sensed it, too. We were no longer a happy family. We quit going places together. No more picnics, even though summer had come to Iowa. No more evening ice-cream cones. All of our lives were affected by the cancer."

I was sleeping alone during this time. I knew that if I went to bed with Wanda, we would be forced to talk to each other. I had a feeling that neither of us wanted to do this. I wanted everything to be normal again. I just couldn't bear to upset her.

When I finally decided to talk openly about my feelings and fears, I didn't know how Wanda and the children would react. I discovered that Wanda had been praying for a long time that I would be honest with her about all my problems. I thought she wouldn't be able to cope with everything, nor be able to meet my needs when I expressed my fears and frustrations. But she was much stronger emotionally than I had imagined. I thought I would have to help her, but *she* was the person I turned to when I became depressed.

"When Orville told me he wanted to talk with me about his problems, I felt as if part of a great burden had been lifted from my shoulders, and I felt alive again," Wanda remembers.

"At the beginning, I felt so guilty when I thought about my own problems in comparison to what Orville was going through. I just thought I shouldn't bother anyone with my own suffering. I have since learned that the family members often need more psychological support than the patient."

Since Wanda and I have been living with the problems associated with my illness for over five years now, I asked her recently if she had any suggestions for other spouses who might be faced with the same things we had encountered.

"The first suggestion I have is that husbands and wives learn to share their problems," Wanda said. "And it is important to include the children. Also, for me, a strong faith in God was important.

"Talking with other family members in our Make Today Count chapters helped me to realize I was not the only wife in the world whose husband had cancer.

"It was important to me to be involved in what was happening. If you were going to try living despite your cancer, then I wanted to do my part. So I would recommend to other spouses that they face up to the fact that they cannot change what has already occurred, but they can make decisions and take action which will change the course of their lives.

"One of the most difficult things for me to accept was that I had to learn to sometimes depend on others for help. It is easier for most of us to give help than to receive it. But if you want assistance, you must let your needs be known."

Most difficult of all for the husband or wife of a cancer patient to accept is the fact that someone they love may die of cancer. When do we leave hope behind and move on to acceptance of death? When is the right time to start talking to a loved one about dying?

I will discuss death and dying in more detail later on in the book but now I do want to stress the importance of having as close a relationship with the doctor as possible. He will be able to tell you, as a spouse, when things look bad from a health standpoint. It is so important to always have hope, if not for life then for close contact with someone you love before death ends your relationship. I meet so many survivors who tell me how they failed to communicate with a loved one when that person was dying.

After I spoke once to a group of patients and family members in Pennsylvania, a man came to me with tears in his eyes and told me the following story:

"My wife died of cancer last year, but we were never able to talk about it. I didn't want her to know the truth about her disease and I guess she was trying to protect me. I found out later that she knew she was dying. During the final weeks I tried to be as optimistic as possible, but inside I was falling apart. I wanted to tell my wife how much I loved her. I wanted to hold her in my arms and tell her how much I would miss her. But I didn't do any of these things, because I knew I would start crying if I did and that would upset her. Now I wish I could talk with her for just five minutes, to tell her how much I really loved her."

I meet married couples who have planned for years for retirement and the time when the children are grown, so they can travel and do all the things they wanted to do for so long. Then cancer or another illness strikes one of them and their dreams of the future are destroyed. Accepting what has happened and adjusting to the changes in their lives are very difficult for them. When I spoke at a hospital in Tennessee once, I talked with a man who had retired from his job and then discovered a month later he had cancer. He was still in the hospital at the time I met him, confined to a wheelchair and hospital bed. His wife was at his side.

"We bought a travel trailer a year before my husband retired, because we were going to go wherever the weather was nice, all year long," the woman said. "We've never driven it any farther than a campground near our home. I suppose we should offer it for sale now."

"The doctors told me I won't be able to do very much now," the patient said. Then he added wistfully, "I even bought some golf clubs when I retired. I was going to learn to play."

The lesson to be learned from all this, perhaps, is to not wait until the "right time" to enjoy yourselves. Do some of the things now. Work is important, but there are weekends and vacations. For many of us, the "right time" for going on our dream vacations never comes.

Another goal is learning how to live with the limitations placed upon you by an illness. Spouses must adjust to a new life-style or live in a fantasy world. The cancer is not going to go away, unless it can be successfully treated in the early stage. Nearly two out of three cancer patients die of the disease. An amputated limb will not reappear. It is not realistic to pretend a heart attack never occurred.

Make new plans, if you are a patient or are married to a

patient with a chronic illness. Become aware of the limitations. Find out what you *can* do, as well as what you can't do. As a spouse, you should learn from physicians about limitations for your husband or wife on work and recreational activities, so you can offer encouragement when necessary.

I visited a cancer patient in his home one time and he told me how discouraged he was because he could no longer go fishing. Since he was ambulatory, even to the point of driving his car to the hospital, seventy miles from his home, for treatments, I wondered why he had to give up fishing.

"Why can't you go fishing anymore?" I asked.

"My wife thinks it would be too dangerous for me to be out in the woods alone, because something might happen to me and I couldn't get to a doctor."

This excuse seemed to me a rather flimsy one because something could happen to him just as easily during the drive to and from the hospital.

"What does you wife think might happen to you in the woods?" I asked him.

"Well, one of our neighbors told her about a cancer patient with the same kind of cancer as me, who died of a ruptured spleen before they could get him to a hospital."

"Have you still got a spleen?" I asked him.

"No, the doctors removed it when I was in the hospital. But my wife thinks something similar might happen."

I had never heard of many cancer patients worrying about a ruptured spleen, even if they had one, but I *was* very aware of numerous cases involving patients and spouses who needlessly worried about things that would probably never occur.

"Why don't you ask your doctor if you can go fishing again and make certain your wife is with you at the time?" I recommended.

Several weeks later, this patient brought me some catfish he had caught. I accepted them with gratitude.

Thousands of letters have been sent to me from persons whose loved ones have died, most of them because of cancer. Each letter told me of various ways individuals had coped with the trauma of death. Many of the letter-writers complained about not having someone to share their grief with, since even close friends and relatives stayed away from them.

A widow from Missouri, Jeanetta New, whose husband, Fred, died of malignant melanoma, visited Wanda and me in Burlington. While staying with us, she explained how she had difficulties adjusting to the new life of a widow:

"After Fred's death, I attended a meeting for young farm wives and one person said she didn't expect me out so soon. Actually, it was two months after my husband's death. I guess I was expected to remain wrapped in a cocoon of grief. But I was lonely. I needed to talk with people . . . adults . . . not just my children.

"One girl invited me to visit her some afternoon, and then she added that her husband was always gone in the afternoons. The thought came to my mind that my husband was gone forever and that I needed some company in the morning and evening, too.

"All my friends are afraid to talk about Fred's cancer. Talking about his disease and death seems to hurt others more than me. No one realizes that I have a great need to talk about it. I need to speak about the nightmares in order to forget them. Even members of my family refuse to discuss his illness with me. One relative said, 'Don't try to talk about it. Forget everything that has happened. Try to imagine he died a normal, peaceful death.'

"I can't pretend Fred had an easy death. He died of cancer. It is a horrible, frightening disease. Everyone else can play their games, but I can't."

Jeanetta also remembered that one of the most painful parts of her husband's illness was the fact that people would not visit him during the time he was suffering from cancer.

"I remember that a young farmer who was injured in a tractor accident was on the floor above Fred's and mutual acquaintances came to visit the injured man, but they didn't come to see Fred. When I met them in the corridor they would say, 'I'm sure Fred needs his rest,' or 'Fred is probably asleep and I don't want to wake him,' or 'I just stopped in to see someone for a minute and I've really got to run.' It seems like everyone is running when you have cancer in the family."

I would like to comment about some of the things that happened to Jeanetta and Fred. First of all, why did their friends ignore them at a time when they most needed friendship?

Perhaps it is true that we really don't find out who our friends are until we really need them. However, I have talked with many "friends" who asked me, "What can I say to someone who is dying of cancer? I want to help, but I don't know how."

I stress to these people the importance of not waiting until the funeral to send flowers. Visit ill friends *now*. Spend time with loved ones in a family touched by a serious illness or death. Listen and let the family members know you care.

Sometimes husbands or wives of cancer patients aren't aware that they haven't really let their needs be known to friends and relatives. So these persons also have obligations. People can't respond to their needs until they know whether or not they can openly discuss the illness, or how far they can go in offering support and friendship during such an emotional period.

There are support groups for widows, such as Theos in Pittsburgh, founded by my late, dear friend, Bea Decker. (Theos has many chapters in the United States and Canada, so check with the main office at 10521 Lindberg Avenue, Pittsburgh PA 15235; telephone [412] 243-4299).

Phyllis Silverman, Ph.D., who lives near Boston, has edited a book about her research into the problems of widows entitled *Helping Each Other in Widowhood*. It is available from Health Sciences, New York, New York, or can be ordered through a local bookstore. When I talked with Phyllis recently, she told me there was no central number for widows to call when they are seeking support. However, she pointed out, there are many programs for the support of widows in the United States.

There are other groups available in many cities. I recommend you check in you local telephone directory. If you can't find an organization offering support for widows and widowers, why not organize one yourself? You might want to become affiliated with an existing group, or you can start your own nonprofit organization. It is better to become part of another organization for various reasons, including legal responsibilities and publicity purposes as you try to reach prospective members.

After death occurs, survivors must live with grief and sometimes with guilt. There is no way to define the limits of grief. Some persons suffer longer than others. But grief can sometimes reach an abnormal stage, such as in the case of the lady in Illinois who told me about her husband's death and how she kept his memory alive in her home.

"I have never destroyed or given away his belongings," she said. "Everything is there, just as he left it the day he died of a heart attack. His pipe is still on the stand beside the chair. His suit is hanging in his closet, ready to wear. His fishing equipment is just where it always was, in the garage."

"How long has he been dead?" I asked.

"Seven years, three months, and fourteen days," she replied, after a pause.

I consider this an example of abnormal grief. It is one thing to keep alive the memory of someone you love, but to go to the extreme I have just outlined is wrong.

Whether we like it or not, grief is a part of living. One half of all married couples in the world today will eventually become widows or widowers, unless both are killed in an accident or similar circumstance. Yet, we are never prepared, even when we know death will eventually occur because of a fatal illness.

How can we prepare for such a terrible thing as grief over the death of someone we love? By living and loving and sharing now. We can prepare for grief by not leaving anything unsaid or undone while the person we love is still alive. If we love someone, we should tell him or her today. I find different attitudes toward the death of a loved one from survivors who were unable to communicate with the patient, as compared to those who shared their love during a tragedy.

"We both knew what the verdict would be," a lady told me, in referring to the death of her husband from cancer. "Prior to his death, we grew close in our shared beauty of each day of life together. We talked long into the nights. Time didn't count anymore. The morning hours of insomnia and pain became beacons of shared feelings, hopes, dreams, remembrances, and affirmations. We loved more deeply and less physically. Even though the body is dying, the mind can remain alive and alert.

"I thank God for the enriched seven months we shared

together. We lived and loved more in that span of time than we did in thirty-five years of previous life together."

I talked recently with Lois Neubrand of New Port Richey, Florida, the lady whose story I just related to you, and asked her if any of her feelings had changed since she first wrote to me about the final months of her husband's life.

"Oh, no!" she exclaimed. "I'm so grateful God gave us the chance to share those last seven months together. Otherwise, there would be so many unresolved things. I have no feelings of guilt at all, nor did I ever at any time feel guilty."

Some of the more tragic letters I receive come from survivors whose loved ones refused to communicate with them even when dying, or from persons who realize, after the death of a loved one has occurred, that they might have done things differently.

A man from New York, whose wife had died of cancer at age thirty-three, had second thoughts about the way he approached this tragedy.

"We never talked about the possibility of Beth dying," he told me. "I just kept telling her everything would be all right. I kept saying the doctors might find a new miracle drug for cancer or she might live for years. We never told our two boys their mom had cancer. In fact, they didn't find out about her death until much later. I told them their mother was visiting some relatives and would return home someday."

"How did they react when you told them the truth?" I asked.

"That's why I have contacted you," he replied. "I've had a lot of trouble with them. Both are having trouble in school. I am aware I did the wrong thing, so I hope I can help someone else before they make the same mistake. I was just trying to protect them, but my wrong decisions only made

133

matters worse. I'm suffering, too. I lay awake at nights, thinking of all the things I wanted to say to Beth, but didn't. Now it's too late. I don't even know how she felt about dying. I wonder now if she ever did accept what was happening to her?"

A girl from California told me she had nightmares from which she awoke, screaming. "I dream about killing my father," she said. "My life is falling apart because I actually *did* wish he was dead, many times, when he had cancer. He died and I feel responsible. Oh, I know I didn't really kill him, but I just can't seem to cope with my guilt because of the way I felt when he was alive, when I couldn't bring friends to our home because Dad was sick all the time. And because I wanted him dead when I became angry over all the things we could no longer do together as a family. I used to wonder why it had to be *my* dad who had cancer."

What common thread runs through these stories, binding them together? *Guilt!* We feel guilty after death occurs because of the thoughtless things we said and did while the person we loved was still alive. We blame ourselves for not being more compassionate, more understanding. But we must realize that what happened is not our fault and, in fact, such things happen more often than we might think.

Instead of joining the ranks of people who live with guilt, I suggest you do and say the important things now, whether you are living with someone who is seriously ill or not.

These words from Ecclesiastes seem most appropriate as we continue to ponder life and death, and search for a reason why unpleasant things happen in our lives:

To every thing there is a season, and a time to every purpose under the heaven . . . A time to weep, and a time to laugh; a time to mourn, and a time to dance . . .

7

Relatives and Friends

"MISFORTUNE shows those who are not really friends."

These words were written by Aristotle, over three hundred years before the birth of Jesus Christ. Yet, his message is timely today, for it is true we often discover who our real friends are during times of adversity.

"Friends of today are not of love," wrote an unknown author of ancient Egypt, in the year 2000 B.C. He may have lived nearly four thousand years ago, but he was referring to a problem that confronts most of us at various times during our lives.

Curse them as we sometimes may, without friends life would not be worth living for most of us. But what frequently happens when a misfortune or a serious illness befalls us?

135

I am constantly told by patients that their friends stop visiting at a time when they are most needed. Relatives, too, often stay away. Earlier in this book, I discussed some of the reasons why friends and relatives find it difficult to visit seriously ill patients. In this chapter, I will treat the problem in greater detail.

Lack of communication is one of the most common obstacles to friendship when someone is seriously ill. Friends sometimes want desperately to visit patients, but since they don't know what to say to them, they stay away. They are also afraid they might say the wrong thing if they do visit, and upset the patient and family.

"Are the results of your autopsy back yet?" a friend once asked a patient who was awaiting the results of a biopsy.

It is not just our friends who have problems in coping with the side effects of a serious illness. It is also the patient who isolates himself from everyone around him, unable to cope with both his illness and unrestricted conversation.

Friends who want to support seriously ill patients through continued friendship may find obstacles confronting them when they try to visit these patients.

Two social workers from Omaha, Nebraska—Penny Bainbridge and Jeanette Lynch—reminded me that friends are often noticeably excluded from the process of dying in many ways. They spoke to me as friends who had visited patients themselves.

"Some families do not share the information about the diagnosis," Penny commented. "Of course, sometimes the results of the tests are not shared with the patient either, so the family doesn't want to trust the friend with the information.

"When hospitalization occurs, the friend is again often left out," Jeanette added. "When friends go to visit a patient, they are asked if they are close relatives. To make the visit a legitimate one, friends often resort to bringing something for the patient. Or they are asked if they can run errands for the family or their friend, to further justify the visit. They are asked to excuse themselves when the doctor comes into the room, even though the family members are allowed to stay, and they are told they cannot be given any information when they inquire about the patient's condition."

As we discuss the problems encountered by friends of sick persons, we should remember that sometimes friends are much closer to the patient than relatives. And for persons who live alone, this is especially true.

For example, a patient who belonged to one of our Make Today Count chapters died of cancer. He had no family and lived alone in a small hotel room. Three cousins, who all lived far away from him, were listed as his closest relatives. He had several friends who were members of our MTC chapter. But while he was dying, it was the relatives who were allowed in the room, not his friends.

"Hospitals usually provide a family room," Penny said. "This is a room where family members and relatives can find privacy and a place to rest. It is also a room where these persons can give in to their emotions and cry if they want to do so. Meanwhile, friends sit among strangers in the hospital lobby or cafeteria, attempting to conceal their distress."

I have experienced some of the things mentioned by Penny and Jeanette. It is frustrating to go to a hospital for the purpose of visiting a close friend, only to find you cannot enter the room. A dear friend of mine had asked me to call him in the event he had another heart attack and was hospitalized. When this occurred and I did try to call him, I was asked by the nurse, "Are you a relative?"

"No, but I'm a close friend," I replied.

"I'm sorry, but Mr. Henderson can receive calls only from family members and relatives." I think all hospitalized persons should give staff members and their doctors the names of close friends authorized to have the same visiting and telephone privileges as relatives.

Another problem I have encountered is that of family members who go to extremes to protect the patient. I can understand why patients should not be disturbed needlessly or bombarded with telephone calls, but certainly provisions should be made for close friends to call or visit, if visiting is allowed on a limited basis.

I asked Penny and Jeanette if they had any suggestions for helping friends of seriously ill persons cope with their own unique problems.

"I believe friends should be encouraged to ventilate their own feelings," Penny replied. "They should be allowed to talk about their own worries and fears. Why can't families invite friends into 'grieving rooms' with them if they are close to the family? And I think friends should be made to feel welcome at the hospital, without them having to feel uncomfortable."

Both of these social workers feel, as I do, that the medical staff should be informed so close friends can be given all the visiting privileges that are normally available to the family.

"Some friends would like to help take care of patients while they are at home," Penny said. "If friends do want to help, why not let them cook meals and take care of the children?"

If death occurs, friends can help. Both Penny and Jeanette stress the importance of asking friends to do things, such as writing "thank you" notes, attending the funeral with the family, and maintaining contact with the family after the funeral.

The most important thing of all is for friends, patients, and family members to maintain communications with each other. As I continue my work, I talk with friends and relatives who want to help with patients who need the support that could come from this source, but so often there is a lack of communications between the two factions.

"What if I say the wrong thing?" friends ask me.

"What can anyone say that I haven't already thought of many times?" patients say.

"Where is everyone, now that the funeral is over?" survivors ask.

"Why doesn't my friend call me anymore?" a friend wonders.

When people fail, for one reason or another, to express their needs, no one can be aware of those needs. Open communications seem to be the best way to alleviate many problems.

"I am so angry with someone who *used* to be my closest friend," a widow told me. "She hasn't even been over for coffee since my husband's funeral. She has hurt me very much with her attitude at a time when I really needed her friendship. I'll never forgive her!"

I was acquainted with this lady's friend, so I asked if she would object to me talking with this person about the problem.

"Okay, but don't you dare tell her I am concerned."

Without seeming to pry into a private matter *too* much, I visited with the friend.

"Have you seen Helen lately?" I asked.

"No, I haven't. As a matter of fact, she has been ignoring me since her husband's funeral. At first, I thought perhaps I had offended her in some way, but I can't think of anything I might have done to displease her. But if that's the way she wants to treat me after all the years of

139

our friendship, then I'm going to stay away from her."
There was obviously a lack of communication involved
with this friendship. The solution wasn't so apparent to me.
Bringing the two friends together wouldn't be easy. But I
did manage to arrange it. They talked and discussed what
had happened. They felt very foolish about it when the truth
was known to both of them. Now they are friends again. I
wonder how many friendships have ended the way this one
nearly did?

At a Make Today Count seminar on Children and Cancer, I asked twelve mothers of children who had died of
cancer what their major problem was, aside from the death
of a child, in coping with the worst tragedy that can occur in
a family. All of them shared a common complaint: There
was no one available for them to talk with during times
when they needed someone just to listen to them.

"Everyone kept telling me to forget about it," one
mother said. "I needed to talk about what had happened.
I couldn't forget it. But my friends and relatives didn't
want to listen. It was too depressing, I guess. But aren't
friends supposed to help each other during both good *and*
bad times?"

Another mother spoke bitterly about the lack of support
from her friends.

"I live in a small town, where I was born and attended
school. I know almost everyone in the community. Shortly
after the death of my daughter, I was walking downtown
when I saw two of my friends, who were former high school
classmates, approaching me. So help me, they walked across
the street in the middle of the block so they wouldn't have to
confront me!"

It is a fact that not *all* friends want to become involved
with us at a time of tragedy. Some cannot accept the
emotional challenges. The fact that a friend is dying, or is

140

seriously ill, reminds many of us of our *own* mortality, which is something we don't like to think about.

"I want to remember my friend the way he was before his illness," someone might say. This is a frequent excuse for not visiting someone who is seriously ill. But it is a poor excuse for staying away from the bedside of a friend. I assure you that you will feel much better later if you will go anyway. Maybe you will be sad. Perhaps you will cry. You will probably be reminded of the final act of life, which is death. But let me tell you about something I have learned during the past six years: Terminally ill people have a way of inspiring the healthy people around them. I have watched this happen frequently. A sixteen-year-old girl dying of cancer in San Diego inspired persons of all ages, in our Make Today Count group there. A dying woman in a Florida hospital touched the lives of the nurses who took care of her. One of our MTC chapter members in the Chicago area, Anita Siegel, stricken with lung cancer, did so much for so many people in her community that she was named "Citizen of the Month." She works full-time as an accountant and still finds time during the day to visit other patients. Even her doctor was impressed with Anita's determination to help others cope with cancer through her work with Make Today Count.

Isolating yourself from the specter of death is to deprive yourself of sharing one of the two most unique experiences of humankind with someone you care about. (The other experience is the miracle of birth.)

I would like to tell you about some of my own friends, and how they helped me. One was Steve Sloan, a young man from San Diego. I visited him several times during his illness and even as he approached the end of his life, he was cheerful. His mother, Ruth, said, "Steve complained less about cancer and dying than most of us do about a cold."

Steve graduated from San Diego State University with a degree in clownology. He wanted to make other people happy. He was also a talented artist. His mother gave me one of his drawings and it is one of my most prized possessions.

I first met Steve at the home of a Make Today Count member in San Diego. He was helping to design the brochures and name cards for a forthcoming seminar. Even then his body was beginning to show the ravages of cancer. But his spirit was alive. He radiated hope and good humor. He was able to see life all around him. Once he wrote these words as he lay in a hospital bed: "I urge all of you to open your eyes and look around you. See what you have never seen before. I know that cancer has made me more aware of life. I now see the beauty of humanity and have a new awareness of God. I am now able to love people as never before."

I wondered if Steve had always been so optimistic and able to confront his own mortality. I asked mother this question.

"At first he worried about dying," she said. "Then he finally decided 'Why worry?' So he began living one day at a time. Actually, he taught *me* how to live."

Steve's life had not been an easy one. His father and mother had polio at the same time. When Steve was born, in 1949, his mother was undergoing treatment. His father died. So when Steve was diagnosed as a cancer patient, tragedy was not an uncommon occurrence in his life.

The last time I saw Steve, he was lying in a hospital bed in San Diego. His features were distorted by pain. His frail body was feverish. But he still managed a smile when he saw me.

"How is Wanda?" he whispered. "Are your children all right?"

142

"Everyone is fine, " I managed to answer, fighting back the tears.

Steve helped me, because he reminded me that my battle with cancer was not just my own fight. He loved life and didn't want to die, but when he realized there was no choice, he refused to surrender his dignity. He set an example for me and all who knew him to follow in the future.

My friend, David Peters, a medical doctor and cancer patient whose remarks you read earlier in this book, is another person who has touched my life. We have shared many memorable moments together. Although we are victims of two different types of cancer, we were diagnosed at nearly the same time—Dave in May 1973, and I in June of that same year. I can identify with Dave's problems, because I face the same ones.

Dave shares my appreciation of laughter, so we have managed to find humor in some of the incidents that have occurred during the past five years of our lives.

One night we were talking in Dave's apartment, both of us feeling a little depressed about things I don't recall.

"Dave, do you think it's true that W. C. Fields asked that the words 'Rather Here Than Philadelphia' be inscribed on his tombstone?" I asked.

"Gosh, I don't know!" Dave replied.

"Well, whether it's true or not, it reminds me of something. Don't you think you should consider yourself fortunate to be a cancer patient living near the ocean in California, compared to one who has to live in Philadelphia?"

I don't know why we laughed so hard over this remark, because it really isn't humorous. But we did. Then one night, a few months later, while on a speaking tour of the East Coast, I called Dave at home.

"I'm really depressed tonight," I told him. "I guess I've been pushing too hard."

"Where are you?" Dave asked.

"I'm in a motel room, in Philadelphia," I said innocently.

There was a pause, followed by laughter from the other end of the telephone. Then it occurred to me why Dave was laughing, so I joined in with him. I felt better afterward. Laughter really *is* good medicine!

Not all of my friends are cancer patients. I mentioned Jeannie and Tom Kuster in the introduction of his book. Jeannie has been my secretary for about five years, almost from the beginning of the Make Today Count organization. I have relied on Jeannie to help me with many things other than secretarial duties, such as some of the tasks that must be performed at seminars in Burlington and errands that I can't find the time to run. She doesn't really consider her work a "job." Tom has driven me to speaking engagements when I was too tired to drive myself, as well as helping to barbecue ribs at our annual Make Today Count picnics.

The most important thing to me, though, is that Jeannie and Tom are my friends. I feel comfortable with them and enjoy our conversation. I think it is remarkable that we have never had an argument (although Jeannie *does* push me extra hard when I have deadlines, such as these book chapters, to meet!).

So I am reminded once again of the importance of friendship, as I write these words. These last five years would not have been as rewarding as they have been if I had had no friends.

I also mentioned Dr. Norman Vincent Peale in the introduction of this book. I told how he has provided financial assistance to our Make Today Count program, through the Outreach Ministry Program, *Guidepost* magazine. Dr. Peale and his wife, Ruth, are coeditors of that publication.

Aside from the financial support Dr. Peale has provided to my organization, he has been a faithful friend. His notes of encouragement have given inspiration to me during times of need. Whenever I visit him in New York, I come away impressed once again by his down-to-earth optimism and compassion. I've never told him this, but in many ways he represents the father I always wanted but never had.

I want to remind *you* of the importance of letters. Everyone appreciates letters, just as I always appreciate hearing from Dr. Peale. If you have a friend who is ill (or healthy, for that matter), drop him a line and reaffirm your friendship.

I carry friendship cards with me as I travel and I ask people in the audience to sign them, after telling them whom I plan to give them to. Then I send or give them to seriously ill patients, who appreciate them so much.

(I do wish there was a larger variety of friendship cards, reading simply, "I Care," or "We Care," or "I Am Your Friend." There are too many "get well" cards for people who probably won't ever get well.)

Even after getting over 100,000 letters from people around the world, I still appreciate receiving cards and letters. I remember a postcard I received one day. There was no signature. The message read, "Thank you." I have never forgotten the card. And just the other day I received another card from Janet Heller, a friend of mine who lives on a farm near Wisner, Nebraska. Janet's five-year-old son, Jeff, died of leukemia, and I will relate her story to you in the next chapter, when I talk about children and cancer. Janet's cards and letters have brightened many dark days for me during the past five years.

I have been helped so much by my friends. But there have been instances when I was *not* helped, such as the time a neighbor lady, who was not a close friend but an acquaintance, told me about her uncle who had cancer.

"I think he had the same kind you've got," she told me. The fact that she spoke of him in the past tense escaped me.

"What did the doctors do for his cancer?" I asked, since I was awaiting my first chemotherapy treatment with much apprehension.

"They gave him some of those drugs like you're going to get," she replied.

Innocently, I blundered on with my inquiries. "How's he getting along?" I asked.

"Oh, he died," she said. Then she continued raking the leaves in her yard. I just stood there, letting the impact of her last statement settle in my mind.

Too many friends of cancer patients want to do something practical, such as offering suggestions for alternative methods of cancer treatment. I have already discussed cancer quackery, but I should add that without the help of friends and relatives of patients, cancer quacks would not be nearly so successful in promoting their "cures."

I urge friends and relatives to spend time just "listening" to patients. It is difficult to find good listeners. They are as scarce as green grass in Iowa during December. Most of the people who visited me during the early stages of my illness wanted to inspire me or cure me. Few wanted to just hold my hand and listen to me. Fewer still were willing to tolerate my fits of anger and depression and accept me as I was.

During question-and-answer periods, when I speak at seminars, I am often asked questions like this one: "How can I get Uncle John to talk about his illness?"

I answer questions like this by explaining that perhaps Uncle John doesn't want to talk about his illness. I think people have a right to make personal decisions about how they want to cope with their illness. Maybe denial is Uncle

John's only defense against the emotional problems confronting him. But you can tell Uncle John that you are willing to talk to him anytime, and that you are always available to listen to him. Just say something like this: "If you ever need to talk with anyone about anything, I'm available." But don't try to force patients to change their attitudes.

I learned to not directly contact cancer patients without their knowledge shortly after I started the Make Today Count organization. I received several letters from relatives of cancer patients, asking me to send the patients a copy of my newsletter. I did so without hesitation. Not long afterward, I was threatened with two lawsuits by two separate families who did not want their loved ones to receive a newsletter about cancer.

I do not know what the basis for the lawsuits might have been, since I heard no more from either family after my apologies and an explanation of why I sent the newsletters in the first place, but I learned a lesson. The lesson was to never contact anyone unless I heard from them first. I have even had a few difficulties when I have sent Make Today Count material to patients who requested it.

"How dare you send my wife all that garbage about cancer!" shouted an angry man, who had telephoned me at my home. I told him his wife had requested the information. He slammed the telephone receiver down and I never heard from him again.

Another lady, from Georgia, called me from a neighbor's house. "I want to order your book," she told me, "but I want you to send it to my friend because my husband would be upset if he knew I was reading a book about cancer."

Several times people ordered my book, but asked that it be sent to them in a plain wrapper with no words pertaining to cancer visible.

These attitudes sound ridiculous, don't they? But these examples give you a hint of how careful you must be in approaching some patients who are being "protected" by their families, or who allow themselves to be intimidated by others.

Be aware that you are entering a sensitive area when you approach a seriously ill patient (and family) to offer your friendship and support. Just be yourself and listen. You will soon find out what the patient wants to talk about.

Once a newspaper reporter accompanied me as I visited terminally ill patients in my city. (I first obtained the patients' permission for him to come with me.) The first patient we visited asked me if I would move his hospital bed so he could see the sunshine outside his window.

"Last night, I dreamed about my army service in Japan," the patient told me. "I spent two years there, not long after the war."

"I was there, too," I reminded him.

For the next thirty minutes we talked about military duty in Japan. After the reporter and I left the house and were driving away, she asked me if I thought it a little strange that a dying man would talk about the Army.

"No, not at all," I answered. "I think it's important for someone to listen to terminally ill patients, no matter what they talk about."

"But I thought he would want to talk about dying, and how he felt about it," she said.

"Maybe he will, the next time I visit him," I replied, "but I never try to force people to talk about dying, or anything else. I visit them because I care about them. If they want to scream or cry or complain, it's okay with me."

While I was speaking in Lincoln, Nebraska, a friend of mine who is a nun asked me if I would visit a dying cancer patient in the hospital where she worked as a nurse.

"He's being guarded by someone from the state penitentiary, because he was a prisoner there before he came to us. They couldn't give him proper treatment at the prison hospital, so the warden authorized his transfer to our facility."

"Does he *want* me to visit him?" I asked.

"Well, we gave him some Make Today Count literature," she replied hesitantly. "He didn't read it, though," she added. "He doesn't respond to much anyone says to him now."

I wasn't encouraged. I was tired and I thought perhaps I might excuse myself from making the visit because of fatigue, but I didn't.

When we entered Jim's room (this was not his real name, but I see no reason to identify him), he was sitting up in bed, ignoring the luncheon tray on the table beside him.

"Orville is the founder of Make Today Count, a group for cancer patients and their families," the nun told him, while introducing me. But Jim didn't seem impressed.

"Are we interrupting your luncheon?" I asked. After all, sometimes I'm at a loss for words, too, and I could think of nothing to say to him. Since he didn't answer my question, I assumed we weren't keeping him from eating. But I felt obligated to say something. I felt foolish just sitting there, while Jim stared at me.

"Have you got cancer, too?" he finally asked.

"Yes," I said. Something told me I shouldn't spend time telling him all about my own life and battle with cancer. "Look," I continued, "I came here because I care about you. I am not trying to enlist you as a member of my organization. I have no miracles to offer you. I'm not going to tell you everything will be all right, because we both know better. But I care. Now, if you want me to leave, I'll go."

"Well, you might as well stay since you're already

here," Jim retorted. "Anyway, I've got something I'd like to tell you because you might understand. You see, I've made my peace with God and I'm ready to die. I'll pay for my sins, I know that. But I'm ready. I committed the crime I'm serving time for. I just want them to let me die in peace."

For the next hour, Jim talked while I listened. At times, he lashed out at the people around him, and at other times he talked about his feelings about death. Then it was time for me to go to another speaking engagement.

I got up from the chair and walked over to say good-bye. Jim stood up beside his bed and shook my hand. I saw a tear falling down his cheek.

"Well, thanks a lot for stopping by," he said.

"Give me your address and I'll write to you," I said.

I did write to Jim, when I returned home, but the nun told me he never got the letter. He died before it could be delivered. "But he asked if your letter had come before he died," she added.

The two essential aspects of my visit with Jim are the importance of listening and the need most people have to know someone cares about them. I have visited many dying patients, but not once have any of them turned away from me when I held their hands and told them I cared about them.

A lack of communication is also responsible for many of the problems existing in the relationships between patients and relatives. Sometimes relatives of the patient and members of the patient's immediate family are divided over the best way for the cancer to be treated. The patient is caught in the middle of these controversies.

Sometimes husbands and wives are too zealous in trying

to "do what's right" for the patients, to the extent of not telling relatives what is happening to the patient.

"For some reason, my nephew's wife refuses to let us know when Bob is in the hospital," a lady complained to me. "We resent finding this out accidentally, because we have always been close to him."

Spouses may shield patients from the overtures of friends and relatives during a serious illness because they want the husband-wife relationship to be as intimate as possible. They consider other relationships with the patient as an interference with their own.

Unless there are special circumstances, patients should not be denied the right to spend time with friends and relatives. Special circumstances might include such factors as insufficient rest or the patient's decision to not see some visitors for various reasons.

Family discussions about visitation and relationships with friends and relatives should be held frequently, with the patient included in these talks. Spouses should be aware of the emotional strain placed upon them during an illness and recognize the fact that they might make hasty decisions they will later regret. Sometimes a frank talk with a social worker or clergyman will help the spouse cope with some of the unexpected problems arising from the illness of a loved one. But bottling all the emotions up will not solve these problems. Identify them. When you need help, admit it. It is not a sign of weakness. Friends and relatives can be very helpful if you give them a chance. And they have their needs, too. Their own feelings of grief should not be denied. They should not be deprived of an opportunity to spend time with someone they care about, unless they are doing and saying things detrimental to the patient.

Speaking now as a patient, to my family, friends, and

relatives, I choose the words of Albius Tibullus, a Roman poet who lived in the first century B.C. and had no yearning for immortality, but an awareness of the importance of love and friendship:

> *May I look on you when my last hour comes:*
> *may I hold you, as I sink,*
> > *with my failing hand.*

8

Children
and Cancer

"SUFFER THE LITTLE CHILDREN to come unto
me, and forbid them not. . . ."
These words from the Gospel according to St.
Mark (10:14) always remind me, when I read them, of my
concern and compassion for children. This is a difficult
chapter for me to write, for no matter how optimistic or
positive I might try to be, I am going to be reminded of
many young victims of childhood cancer I have known, and
the parents who loved them.

I know doctors are now successfully treating thousands of
children who would not have responded to the therapies of a
few years ago. I know of the advances that have been made in
the treatment of childhood cancers, such as acute childhood
leukemia, and I am grateful for these strides, but I hear from
the parents of children who aren't going to survive.

I have already mentioned Janet Heller, a Nebraska farm wife who frequently sends cards and letters to brighten my days, but now I would like to tell you how we met.

I opened a lengthy letter I had received in the mail one morning from the mother of a five-year-old boy who had died of leukemia, and read it. The letter touched me. The woman's name was Janet Heller. She and her husband, LaVerne, earn their living from five hundred acres of Nebraska farmland, plus four hundred acres they rent. Being the parents of four children, and accustomed to childhood illnesses, they weren't too concerned when young Jeff contracted chicken pox. His sister had already been through the ordeal of the disease and his two younger brothers had them, too. Everyone but Jeff bounced back to normal from the disease. Jeff didn't recuperate as quickly. He seemed to be tired all the time, complained of headaches, and was running a low-grade temperature.

The family physician became concerned about Jeff's continuing medical problems. A series of blood tests were conducted. Further testing at a large hospital in Omaha was recommended. All at once things seemed to be getting out of control.

One April morning, before sunrise, Janet, LaVerne, and Jeff started on the trip to Omaha. They tried to be optimistic during the journey, but deep inside they anticipated the worst.

The tests took three days to complete. Jeff never cried, even when numerous needles were poked into his body. Meanwhile, LaVerne returned to the farm, but Janet stayed with Jeff. Then, one morning a physician and a nurse escorted Janet into a room at the hospital and asked her to sit down. She was frightened. Finally, the doctor looked at her and spoke.

"I'm sorry to have to tell you this, but your son has leukemia."

Janet doesn't remember what else the doctor told her.

She tried not to lose control of her emotions. She managed to maintain a relatively calm exterior, but inside her there was a pain she would never forget. She told Jeff later that something was wrong with his blood and he would have to stay in the hospital so they could make him better. He accepted his mother's explanation without comment.

LaVerne came back to Omaha. "How can I ever explain to anyone about the depth of our pain during those first few moments we spent together, as we cried and held each other, seeking strength from our love?" Janet said. "But then we had to pull ourselves together. There are always things to do, even during times of tragedy. We had to tell those people whom we wanted to know about Jeff's illness. We didn't want them to hear it from someone else."

There is a time, just after the news of a diagnosis, when so many families make decisions they may later regret. Janet and LaVerne decided that other persons who were related to them, or knew them, should know the truth about Jeff after they had accepted it themselves. And they told their daughter, who was nine years old. They also found strength in their love for each other.

(Some surveys have indicated, however, that there is a high rate of divorce among families affected by childhood cancer. One survey, conducted in California, showed a divorce rate of 80 percent among these families. But psychologists are careful to point out that many emotional problems that existed *prior* to the diagnosis of cancer rise to the surface after the diagnosis, intensified by the tragedy.)

The Hellers turned to their pastor and his wife for spiritual help. "I remember looking into the eyes of the pastor's wife and seeing hurt there, and tears, too," Janet recalls. "The pastor was filled with such warmth and understanding. He said something the first time we met after the diagnosis was known, which I will never forget. He told us we would have to accept the responsibility of preparing Jeff for his eventual death. I couldn't help but wonder, though, how you prepare a five-year-old child for death, if you don't understand it or accept it yourself."

(Some pastors respond with warmth and understanding to the needs of parents whose children are facing a life-threatening illness; others are unwilling to meet the emotional requirements associated with such relationships. Sometimes clergymen do not know *how* to respond, especially if parents ask for help but do not define their needs. This is why special training should be required for seminary students, on a much broader basis than is now evident, so graduates can better cope with these sensitive problems.)

One of the most difficult things to face, when a child has been diagnosed with cancer, is reality itself. Should parents tell children the truth about the diagnosis? At what age can children comprehend the meaning of death?

"When we visited Jeff in his hospital room, we all pretended to be enjoying it," Janet remembers. "But he looked so small and helpless, lying there in that hospital bed, and we were so sad."

"It is so difficult to watch someone so young, whom you love very much, having to endure pain, IVs, needles, and swallowing so many pills." Once, during his hospitalization, Jeff was allowed to return home with his family. But he soon begged to be taken back to the hospital because of pain. "God will give me the goodest medicine to make me better back at the hospital," he told his mother.

Jeff's condition worsened and Janet was at his bedside

most of the time. Once he had a seizure. It was then Janet decided she could no longer watch her son suffer without help from somewhere.

"I realized then how much I needed God for strength," she said. "I went to the hospital chapel and for the first time since the day of the diagnosis, I cried. And I found peace once again."

"As Jeff grew worse, there was one horrible incident after another," she continued. "The doctors had to do a spinal test. Jeff was scared and hurting and screaming."

One night while Janet was in the room with him, Jeff prayed. "Jesus, if I can't get better, it's all right for You to take me to Heaven, where I won't hurt anymore," he said.

Jeff was transferred to an isolation room because he was so vulnerable to infections. Janet remembers the nurses in the ward.

"The new room where Jeff lay had a big window, facing the hospital corridor, and the nurses, as they walked by, would knock on the window and smile at Jeff. He always smiled back."

How important it is for doctors and nurses to openly display compassion, to not be afraid of allowing their emotions to show a little bit! Patients and families remember these things, and, as I have said so many times, compassion and caring are just as important as medical therapies.

By this time, the physicians had told Jeff's parents the treatment being used for the leukemia was no longer effective. And they had tried everything available to them.

"It was then that I asked myself when and how I could say good-bye to my son," Janet said. "When and how do you *ever* say good-bye to someone you love so much?

My heart was filled with sorrow as I looked down at Jeff and saw his bloodstained pajamas."

Jeff looked up at his mother. "Mommy, don't let them hurt me anymore," he pleaded.

"I wanted so much to protect him," Janet explained, "but I felt so helpless. I think this is when I finally did say good-bye to Jeff. I said, 'God, he is Your child now. Do whatever is best for my little boy. You know I love him so very much. Treat him well, God, for he has suffered long enough.

"That night we kissed him before we left his room. He looked up at us and said, 'Mommy and Daddy, I love you very much.' Those were the last words I ever heard my son speak."

This isn't a story with a happy ending, but it is true. These are actual people, with real names. The Heller family still lives on their farm near Wisner. But I related this story to you for a reason, and you haven't read the end of it yet.

"My son was dead, his suffering had ended, but my grief was overwhelming," Janet said. "But I must tell you something. I will always be grateful for the support we received from our pastor. And we met other parents whose children had died. There is one other person I would not have met if it had not been for Jeff's death, because I paid little attention to death before he died. This person has helped me learn to live. That person is you, Orville. I have learned that the seriously ill learn quickly what life is all about. They make each day count."

(She was talking about me, but I must tell you, as is usually the case, it was Janet who had helped *me*, because she made me realize once again that my work is important.)

"Jeff's life *was* worthwhile," Janet continued. "He helped

158

me so much. I want to help others, because I have suffered. I wrote a poem for my son, after his death, which helps to explain how I feel:

> *"In death*
> *you gave so much to me,*
> *my son.*
> *You taught me to feel the beauty*
> *of a starry October night,*
> *and because of you*
> *I now see the colors of a flower*
> *and a smile.*
> *Your death was not defeat,*
> *my son,*
> *for in your dying,*
> *   you taught me how to live."*

Janet has spent many hours since her son's death talking with parents of children who have cancer and with patients themselves. Through her own suffering, her faith was the sustaining force that supported her. Unfortunately, this is not true for some people. But persons of all faiths soon find out how strong their religious convictions really are during times of adversity. I have discovered there are many "middle-of-the-road" Christians, whose faiths are strongest when the sun is shining and there are no major problems to plague them.

I talked with a young minister's wife whose child had died of cancer. "There is no God!" she angrily exclaimed. "God wouldn't take my little girl away from me!"

The feeling that death is "God's fault" is so often intensified through remarks made by friends and relatives, such, as, "It's God's will that it happened."

I have already explained that I feel cancer is God's

enemy, too. Why should we blame God for all our disasters? Life and death occurrences could be part of a master plan, but I believe it is wrong to tell a mother and father that the death of their child was God's will. I attended the funeral of a young girl and heard a priest say during the services, "I cannot tell any of you *why* this happened, but to blame God is not the answer. It did happen, though, and we all want the family to know *we care.*" I believe he said the right thing. It was right, certainly, for this family.

It is vital to let parents of a child with cancer know you are available, whether a friend or a relative, if either parent ever needs a good listener.

The great Athenian statesman Pericles once said, "Wait for that wisest of all counselors, Time." The wound caused by the death of a child never heals completely, but time takes away some of the hurt and makes the wound bearable.

Earlier in this chapter I posed the questions: "Should parents tell children the truth about the diagnosis of a serious illness, and at what age can children comprehend the meaning of death?"

I receive quite a few letters from teenagers who have cancer or whose parents have cancer. I would like to quote from a recent letter to emphasize that children often seek ways to cope with serious illness, while parents find it difficult to move beyond the denial stage.

"I am fourteen years old and I have leukemia. My parents and my doctor told me about it, but they never talk to me about my problems. They keep saying I should concentrate on getting well, but I'm sick a lot of the time. I can't talk to the kids at school and there is no counselor there, since it is a small school. I'm lonely. I wish I could talk with someone who understands. I think I would feel better."

I am convinced that although the young girl who wrote

me this letter was in need of help, her desperate parents probably refused to admit it. It is so difficult to offer support and understanding to young persons without offending or angering their parents. Because of the protective wall constructed around the young patients by some parents, I cannot respond to many of the letters I receive. Young persons with cancer have fewer rights as human beings than anyone else I know. Many must cope with their anger and fears alone, since they're not even supposed to know about the diagnosis.

I recommend that doctors, patients, and clergymen be frank with youngsters who are ill. First of all, the doctor-patient relationship is very important, so why jeopardize it by resorting to dishonesty? It should be a relationship of trust. Many pediatric oncologists feel that youngsters should be told as much as they can understand about their diseases. However, the element of hope should not be eliminated. For instance, if it is true, doctors can explain that sometimes children die from the type of cancer the child has, but that some children are cured.

Not only does honesty make it easier for the child and his parents to cope with the disease, but the hospital staff can do their job better because they feel more at ease around the patient and the family.

Both children and adults generally find it more difficult to cope with fear than reality. Once the truth is known, the emotional problems can be identified and the family can seek ways to cope with them.

Ten or fifteen years ago, many health professionals treating childhood cancers felt that children should not be told they were dying. But during the past few years, there has been a growing trend at some hospitals toward more candor in this sensitive area. Actually, it is nearly impossible to hide such things as the side effects of chemother-

161

apy drugs and radiation therapy from older children.

"The parents of a fourteen-year-old girl with leukemia asked me not to tell their daughter she had cancer," a radiologist told me, "but I informed these parents that I would not be responsible for her treatment unless I told her the truth about her illness, if she asked me.

"After all, how could these parents expect me to hide a waiting room full of cancer patients from a teenage girl?" he continued. "This girl had a right to know the basic truth about the diagnosis, if she *wanted* to know."

I would guess the girl might have already known the truth.

Once you realize that cancer is the major killer of schoolchildren among all diseases, you can imagine the potential emotional problems that exist in the area of treating childhood cancers. Each year, thousands of parents must cope with the suffering caused by watching a child live with what we consider to be the most horrible of all diseases—cancer. And many of them feel helpless as they watch their children die. What we seek now are ways we can support the children and the parents, such as offering them love and friendship, in addition to any practical help they may need.

There is much that parents of a child with cancer can learn from the way the Diamond family—Arlen, Darrie, and Tony—coped with the disease.

Tony was approaching his third birthday when his parents began to notice unusual occurrences which seemed unimportant at the time. For instance, even though he was left-handed he started eating with his right hand. He didn't like walking up and down stairs—he would crawl instead. His little-boy smile became a sneer. Darrie tried to get Tony to hold toys in his left hand, but he wouldn't do it. Both parents became more concerned. They arranged for a pediatrician to see Tony. The Diamonds lived in Iowa City,

Iowa, at that time, and the pediatrician examined Tony and made an appointment for him to see a pediatric neurologist at the University of Iowa Hospital. Darrie kept asking the doctor if Tony might just have a virus, but nothing serious. On Sunday they went to church and their friends reassured them, saying that everything would probably turn out all right. When Tony grabbed the minister's hand with *his* left hand, his parents were hopeful.

The next day at the hospital, Darrie became so frightened that she was ill. What was happening to Tony was so unreal for her.

With the return of each test result, the situation became grimmer. Then a tumor was discovered in the right frontal area of Tony's brain. The doctors were amazed at its size. It was as big as a man's fist!

"What kept us going during that time was the support from our friends," Darrie said. "I would awaken in the morning, crying, then to the hospital where I would do my best to make it through a long day, and then I would do it again the following day."

The doctors realized Tony's condition was deteriorating rapidly. Surgery was planned. Arlen and Darrie had already talked at great length about the possibility of Tony coming out of the operation a "human vegetable." They decided he should not have to exist this way. Darrie asked the surgeons if they could let Tony die on the operating table if his brain was affected by the surgery to the extent that he would no longer be able to function as a human being. But the surgeons explained to her they couldn't let Tony die if there was a chance to save him.

"I remember signing the consent papers for the surgery and trying to express my feelings about letting Tony die on the operating table if his brain was extensively damaged," Arlen said, "but the surgeon and I were not communicating

163

on the same wavelengths. He wasn't answering me, but rather was telling me he felt there was hope and that there was a chance Tony would still be able to use his arms and legs and that his brain would not be damaged."

The waiting period for Arlen and Darrie during the surgery was a three-hour nightmare. They asked God to do what was best for Tony and them. They felt that God was guiding their lives. Tony's fate was in His hands. They had faith in the medical team and in the chief neurosurgeon. But the agony of waiting would later be impossible for them to describe. During those hours, images of Tony as a baby, scenes at Christmastime, and carefree summer days when Tony played in the yard cascaded through their minds. Meanwhile, the little boy hovered between life and death in the operating room.

Then the neurosurgeon came into the waiting room and told them it had been a good operation. They were also told they could see their son immediately. Tony's whole head was covered with bandages. But he could talk! He looked up at Arlen and said, "Daddy, I want a drink and I want my toys!"

Darrie said a prayer. "Thank you, God, for my son."

The battle wasn't over, though, and radiation therapy was started. It continued for five weeks. There were complications. But Tony survived them.

One crisp October day a year after the surgery, Darrie, Arlen, and Tony visited me while I was staying at a cabin on the Mississippi River, near Burlington. I talked with Arlen and Darrie while Tony chased a butterfly nearby.

"We know the prognosis for Tony indicates he has a ten to fifteen percent chance for long-term survival," Arlen admitted, "but I have learned a lot of things since Tony's diagnosis of cancer. I have had an opportunity to set my values in line. And I now have inner peace. Until you're faced with something like this, so many trivial things in your life seem important. For instance, one of Darrie's friends, the mother of a three-year-old boy, is very concerned whether or not she should enroll her son in swimming lessons at the YMCA. *My* concern is whether or not Tony will live long enough to take swimming lessons."

"We're closer now as a family than ever before," Darrie added. "This has been the most difficult part of our lives, but I have never felt more loved by friends, relatives, and by mankind."

It was easier for friends and relatives to approach Arlen and Darrie than it would be in the case of many other mothers and fathers in similar circumstances, because both parents have been completely open about Tony's illness, with themselves and with others.

"We don't view Tony's problem as his alone," Darrie continued, "because it is our problem, too. We think Tony has the right to a normal life, as much as possible. We spank him when he is bad. We treat him as a normal child because for the moment, he *is* a normal child. He goes to preschool twice a week. He plays on his swing. Once this summer, he climbed a tree."

"We don't brood about what might happen tomorrow," Arlen said thoughtfully, as he gazed to the far side of the river. He paused and then added, "It's hard to avoid becoming depressed, but we still have hope."

What has helped Arlen and Darrie cope with Tony's life-threatening illness?

"We're doing our best to live with this situation," Darrie explains, "But we couldn't do it without our faith in God and the help we receive from other people. And for today, we still have Tony. Arlen and I still love each other.

"Oh, I still get upset with things around me," she continued. "The hardest thing for me to accept is that there is no instant cure for anything! In our society, we are programmed into believing in instant relief or cures. Got a stomachache? Take Alka-Seltzer. Got a headache? Take aspirin. Got an infection? Take antibiotics. Got bad breath? Use mouthwash. Have a bad marriage? Get a divorce. We expect instant relief. In Tony's case, nothing is instant. Instead, it will be months, or years, of waiting and wondering. We are learning to be patient. We try to make today count, taking each day at a time. It's hard. Sometimes I look at my little boy and think that maybe he won't be here six months from now, and I want to hold him and *never* let go. But I know that for Tony's sake, this would not be the best thing to do. We have always been warm and loving with each other, but we do not smother him because someday we may have to let go. Every parent has to let go, in some way, at some point. That, too, is part of the natural order of things.

"I really do feel there is a spiritual force guiding our lives," Darrie said. "I used to think everything was a coincidence. I don't anymore. Too many things have happened to us, so many it just can't be a matter of coincidence. Is it just a coincidence we ended up in Iowa City, not knowing when we first arrived there that at the University Hospital there is one of the best neurosurgery departments in the United States? Is it a coincidence that, after ten years of avoiding church, we joined one here at Iowa City before Tony's illness? Is it a coincidence that the head of the neurosurgery department himself volunteered to do Tony's surgery? This surgeon has a son of his own, a year older than Tony, and he has sort of taken our son under his wing. We trust and believe in this doctor.

"I think we have helped Tony adapt to his hospital surroundings when he has to be there by not saying, 'Oh, my, you have to go to the hospital again!'" We try to make the hospital seem to be his 'home away from home,' and now Tony calls it 'his hospital.' We don't talk about home until it is time to return there. We don't act sad because he has to be in the hospital. Sometimes he is apprehensive, but he views the 'people in white' as his friends, not as people who want to hurt him.

"Tony knows he was operated on for a brain tumor, and his hand works again, but I'm sure it's difficult for him to connect the two facts. We talk about his radiation and how his hair fell out and about his stitches and how the surgeons cut his scalp and skull and sewed it up again. We show him his stitches in the mirror. If the other children are curious, we tell them about it. We accept it and don't hide it and this has made it easier for Tony.

"It's hard to talk about death to a three-and-a-half-year-old boy," Darrie explains. "Tony does ask about dying, and we don't want him to be fearful of it. Our dog died last January of cancer and he links cancer with death, so we haven't told him he has cancer. He sometimes asks, 'Will I die?' or 'Will you and Daddy die?' and we answer, 'Yes, everyone dies.' Some die old, we tell him, and some die young, but none of us knows when it will happen. Tony is not preoccupied with death, but seems to have the usual pre-school-age curiosity about it. We have found that it is best to treat death openly and honestly and to talk of it as a part of the natural order of things."

The day was beginning to end, and tinges of gray shadows of dusk touched the world around us. It was apparent that Tony was becoming weary.

"We are very active in the Make Today Count chapter in Iowa City, because we feel that people should help other people," Darrie pointed out. "We feel it is important for *all* of us to make today count, every day. Personally, we now, more than ever, realize that life is a gift, not something

167

owed to us. We greet each new day with a special sense of joy, thankful that God has given Tony and us another day. We are sad about Tony's illness, but happy in our new growth and our increased awareness of life. And most of all, no matter what the future holds for us, we are so thankful that *we* were chosen to be the parents of this wonderful, warm, little human being."

If Arlen and Darrie had decided not to discuss Tony's illness with anyone else, it would have been difficult for friends and relatives to respond to their needs. I know that not all families react to the diagnosis of cancer in the same way, nor do parents always have time to accept what has happened. Each case is an individual one. But there is a common bond—the need to know there are people willing to listen to us when we want to talk about our tragedies. I hope more and more parents in the future will refuse to try sweeping their troubles under the rug. I feel the best approach is to not dwell upon the details of the tragedy, but to also not deny what has happened. I hope parents of youngsters afflicted with childhood cancer will give their friends and relatives a chance to respond to their needs.

I hope, too, that parents of seriously ill youngsters will not forget the other children in the family. Don't exclude them from conversations about the illness. Give *them* a chance to accept what has happened, too.

Sometimes mothers feel guilty because they spend so much time with a child who has a serious illness and not enough time with the other children in the family. If the child has a chronic illness and remains hospitalized for long periods, major family problems can develop. Refusing to acknowledge these problems won't make them disappear. Include the entire family from the beginning in the discussions and explain *why* some changes must be made in the life-styles of family members because of illness. I would recommend that mothers and fathers take advantage of the time they *do* spend with their children who are not ill to let these youngsters know how much they, too, are loved.

I have talked with many brothers and sisters of seriously ill children and found there is a considerable amount of anger (and later, guilt) among these siblings.

"I don't see why my brother gets his own way all the time, just because he's sick," a young boy complained. "Sometimes I wish he would just die and get it over with."

"Mom spends all her time with my sister," another boy said. "Sometimes I wish it was me who was sick, so I could miss school and have all those privileges."

Some family problems can be solved by including these children in family conversations, starting at the time of diagnosis. I do not mean to imply that *all* problems can be solved through communications, but it helps to be able to talk openly about them. Give all family members an opportunity to ventilate their feelings.

Many young children with cancer can attend school because of the improved treatment methods for some childhood cancers and the subsequent extension of their lives.

Leslie Loper, a fifteen-year-old student who lives in Burlington not far from my home, knows what it is like to live with an inoperable brain tumor and still try to maintain a normal life-style under abnormal conditions. Students called her Kojak in the halls of the junior high school she attended, because her hair was falling out due to the chemotherapy treatments she was receiving weekly. She also was given thirty-five doses of radiation therapy.

After tolerating the teasing for a while, Leslie told the students in her speech class that she was losing her hair because she had a brain tumor and was suffering from the side effects of the drugs being used to treat it. The students were astonished. After Leslie spoke, the word spread among the students and the teasing stopped.

Her decision to make a speech about the tumor came after the heckling and her teacher's request for students to give a speech on the best or worst thing that had ever happened to the students.

"It's just that I wanted them to know what happened to me, and get it through their minds that I did not want to be teased," Leslie said.

She broke down and cried during her speech, but she went on. Leslie's remarks helped the students in the speech class to better understand what was happening to her.

I have been so impressed with the magnitude of the problems encountered at schools by both children with cancer and children of parents who have cancer that I have proposed a plan to establish a model program in an Iowa school district to assist teachers, principals, counselors, social workers, school psychologists, and school nurses in identifying and coping with the emotional problems associated with cancer that affects students.

My program, to be initiated in selected school districts in the State of Iowa, would assist teachers, principals, counselors, school psychologists, and school nurses to help students who have a serious illness, such as cancer, cope with the psychological problems associated with their illness. My experiences have shown a great need for this type of support for school staffs because, although everyone may recognize that these students have special needs, they do not know what help to offer.

Part of my plan would be to establish a program in the same school districts to offer special guidance and training to the teachers, principals, counselors, school psychologists, and school nurses so they can better understand and assist students whose parent or parents have a life-threatening illness. I have encountered numerous instances where students receive no help in coping with the emotional problems they encounter when a parent has a serious illness. Many of these young persons become "problem students," and some of them become school dropouts.

The program will be a year-long endeavor to establish an effective model within the selected school districts, which can then be offered to other school districts throughout the United States.

In my own family, I experienced the trauma of watching two of my children make the transition from students with passing grades, through a period of emotional instability, to becoming high school dropouts. We received little help from teachers, counselors, or psychologists. Most of these persons expressed an opinion that the problems stemmed from my diagnosis of cancer, but no one had any suggested remedies or proposed solutions.

I have discussed some of the school problems with Dick Rosenkrans, supervisor of school social work, Area Education Agency 12, Sioux City, Iowa, who will assist me with my project.

"I intend to discuss this project with one of our smaller school district superintendents and one of his principals and teachers. Two weeks ago they referred a ten-year-old boy and his nine-year-old sister to me. They desperately wanted me to work with the two children and their grandparents and the small farm community where they live. They also desperately wanted me to help them to cope with their own emotions and decisions on how to help the children. The children were new to the school and community, having just moved there from another state. Several days before their move while living at their previous home, the children came home after school and discovered the bodies of their mother and father who had been brutally tortured and shotgunned to death. The children still cannot cope with the sudden and tragic loss of their parents; the school feels helpless and incompetent to do the right thing for the children; the grandparents are stunned by their own loss and grief and their need to suddenly support two small children; and the small farm community is horrified, afraid to reach out to the family and neutralized by an attitude of 'what should we do?' How ill prepared we are, how incapacitated we are by our own emotions! How numb we become when we don't have the confidence and self-assurance to be humane when life demands it of us! How useless we can be to each other when we need each other most!

"Please try to understand that we as professionals aren't much better equipped to deal with the subjects of serious illness, deteriorating health, impending death, or the realities of death itself than the school administrators and faculty we are supposed to help," Dick said. "Schools are oriented toward growth, maturation, increasing skills, knowledge, and abilities, increasing health and psychomotor maturation, budding talents, and increasing athletic prowess. They are preoccupied with growth, development, healthiness and increasing opportunities, liveliness and prosperity. Sickness, death, grief, deterioration, and decreasing abilities and opportunities are the antithesis of the school's very existence and reason for being.

"Unfortunately, too many educators feel that if a problem exists the solutions are to try new or modified educational techniques, have a doctor prescribe tranquilizing medication so the student won't have a 'problem,' or remove the problem (student) to a different location so the school faculty won't have to deal with it. Fortunately, an increasing number of school principals and teachers want to know how to appropriately cope with and help these students and parents, and how to deal with their own attitudes, values, opinions, fears, and inadequacies in these areas. There are few people, with or without professional degrees, who are knowledgeable and skilled in this area. Our hope for the future seems to lie in educating and building attitudinal and emotional skills in our children."

Can children cope with terminal illness if given an opportunity? Some can. Others can't. Children are individuals. But I have found that young persons, on the average, can accept illness as well as adults.

Sometimes it takes a third person to help initiate communications within the family. It is not enough to simply state that the child of a person with cancer "has problems." Some of these problems can be solved if it is possible to discuss them with someone else.

Once I was in Chicago, speaking to a group of cancer patients, family members, and health-care professionals, and after the meeting, a man, woman, and young girl were waiting for me in the hallway outside the conference room. It was the lady who did the talking. She introduced me to her husband and then told me she was a cancer patient. As she spoke, I noticed tears were beginning to form in her eyes.

"It's bad enough to have cancer, Mr. Kelly, but when your own daughter hates you and won't talk to you, the situation becomes almost unbearable. Julie won't even eat at the same table with me; she takes her food to her room and eats her meals there."

I asked Julie, who by this time was moving slowly toward the exit, if it was true that she really did hate her mother.

"Yes, I guess so," she replied.

I was tired and also felt like an intruder, so I was tempted to bring the conversation to an abrupt end. But because of the look of hopelessness in the mother's eyes and a feeling inside of me that this family had not really been expressing their feelings openly, I decided to try talking with the young girl.

"I really don't want to talk to you," she said, when I asked her for just a few minutes of her time.

"All right, give me just five minutes," I pleaded.

"If it will make all of you happy, I'll talk to you for a minute," she replied.

Back inside the room, away from her parents, I asked Julie if she really did hate her mother.

"You know what is happening at home now, and I can't help you unless I know the truth," I explained to her.

Julie looked down at the floor and hesitated before replying. "No, I don't hate her . . . but don't you know how hard it is for me to watch her die? By the way, do you enjoy watching people cry?"

By now the tears were flowing down Julie's cheek. She covered her face with her hands.

"Julie, what would happen if I called your mother into this room and you told her how you really feel about her?"

"I guess I would cry harder than I am now!"

"What bothers me is that your mother doesn't know how you *really* feel about her or why you have rejected her. But ignoring her now will only make it more difficult for you when she does die. And she isn't dead yet. It's not too late to do something about what has happened."

"All right, call her in."

When Julie's mother entered the room, Julie put her arms around her neck and sobbed, "Oh, Mom, I *do* love you. But I don't want you to die!"

"Honey, we've got some time left. After all, I'm in a

remission and we don't know how much time is left for us. But you don't know how wonderful it makes me feel to hear you tell me you love me!"

Julie's mother told me the following morning that for the first time in many months, her daughter had come into her bedroom before going to school, leaned over and kissed her on the forehead, and said, "Good-bye, Mom. I love you."

My solution to this specific family problem sounds so simple. It isn't always this easy to help someone and to reestablish communications, but I feel it is always worth my time to try.

Sometimes cancer patients decide to fight for whatever happiness can be found during the time that might be left to them, regardless of the length. Their will to live and their open attitudes can affect the lives of the people who love them.

Diane Dolphin is a fifteen-year-old student who lives with her father, Donald, and three brothers, in Lincoln, Rhode Island. I received a letter from Diane one week after her mother, Janet, died of cancer. The letter from her was unique, because she told me it was not her mother's *death* that she now reflected upon, but her *life* and two-year battle with cancer, which ended in a victory.

Death, a victory? In order to understand Diane's feelings, you would have to hear the story of her mother's struggle to seek life as cancer continued to destroy her physical body.

"My mother had always been a strong, dynamic woman," Diane explained. "She believed in speaking her mind and standing up for her rights. We believe these characteristics helped to extend her life. She kept fighting."

From the day Janet learned she had cancer, she began living life with more vitality than ever before. On the same day a call about the diagnosis came from the physician who had examined Janet, she played eighteen holes of golf with her husband and daughter. As she swung her gold club with determination, she announced to Don and Diane, "I'm not going to give up without a fight!"

Janet kept nothing from her husband and children. They heard the good and the bad news. When she went into remission, which meant the cancer was temporarily stabilized, the family rejoiced. When a relapse occurred and the cancer began spreading again, the family cried together.

Don and Janet had earlier planned to take a trip to Bermuda, allowing Don a chance to relax away from his duties as vice-president of a bank. They took the trip, despite the presence of cancer.

Janet had decided, prior to the diagnosis of cancer, that she wanted to earn a B.A. degree in psychology. She continued taking her courses. Then, that winter, she became bedridden because of complications from the newly begun chemotherapy treatment. But every day when their children came home from school, they talked with their mother, played games with her, and they all watched television together. As the days passed, the Dolphin family discovered that the cancer was bringing them closer together.

The snows of winter disappeared and spring came to Rhode Island. Diane and her mother started taking strolls together, each day walking a longer distance from their home. Eventually, Janet regained enough strength to play golf again, and she rejoined the women's golf league. Each Sunday, Don and Janet would go on long automobile rides, stopping to browse in antique shops or dine at some exotic restaurant they had never visited before. They found time to attend a few social functions, because Janet loved people. Everyone remarked how well she looked.

"But you must remember I am *not* well," she would remind her family. "I've got cancer and I get tired and I have pain."

To hear her mother talk like this sometimes shocked Diane, because she had started to dare think her mother might just get well. But her mother kept her in touch with reality and this helped remind her daughter, and her family, never to take life, love, or anything for granted.

Janet decided to teach her daughter how to cook, and she talked to her about boys, school, love, life—and sometimes about death.

"I tried not to think about her dying," Diane recalls. "But now I'm grateful for those talks and her insight, for it has helped us all a great deal."

One day, during a hospital visit, new evidence of cancer was discovered in Janet's body. The medication was changed. Her physician, her friends, and everyone around her reminded her she should begin to take it easy, to slow down. She was continuing to work toward her college degree, but some of her friends urged her to just take one or two courses. But Janet was stubborn. She had made up her mind to pursue life 100 percent, within her limitations.

"She had read about Orville Kelly," Diane said, "and this inspired her to obtain her degree and to try to start a self-help group for cancer patients."

Janet became a full-time college student, taking four courses the first semester and five courses the second semester, while undergoing chemotherapy treatment. She even found time to continue playing golf.

She never failed to give full attention to her four children and her husband, and in turn, they supported her and shared in her dreams.

When she studied, she would sometimes get very tired and sleep an entire day. Often, after class, she would return home and lie down for long periods of time. There were many depressing days for her. Sometimes she would feel like giving up when things would overwhelm her.

177

When the depression began closing in on her, she would refuse to let self-pity dominate her life. She reminded herself how precious life really is and how badly she wanted to live.

That same spring, in May, Janet graduated with distinction from the University of Rhode Island. She had to be helped up the steps and onto the stage to receive her diploma, but with head held high and her family watching with pride, she walked alone across the stage and down the steps to rejoin her family.

Her family was so proud of her accomplishment that they held a graduation party at their home and displayed the diploma on a table in the living room. Many friends came and Janet, though exhausted, stayed up until everyone had left.

"I consider it a triumph to have lived so completely," she remarked to her family.

Janet heard a local hospital wanted to start a therapy group for cancer patients, so Don helped her organize the group. They named it CHAOS (Cancer Hope Advocates Offer Support).

One night, at home with her family, she commented, "I've done everything I wanted to do. I've been married twenty wonderful years. I have raised my children to be independent. I graduated with honors from college and I started the local cancer group."

But then Janet's time began running out. Death began moving in, nipping away at her courage and sapping her hope and will to live. She continued fighting. She fought to live long enough to celebrate her youngest son's thirteenth birthday. She did not want to die on this special day of celebration. She was too weak to speak and was delirious most of the time at the end, but she would not stop fighting.

178

"Honey, you've fought so long, please give us one more day," Don asked her. "Can you make it through the birthday today?" It was hard to ascertain whether she could comprehend what he was saying, but Don felt she understood.

The next day, Don went to her and said, "Jannie, you did everything you wanted to do. You've won it all. You have watched our youngest son become a teenager. Now you're released. There's nothing left to do here. Just lie here and rest, because you're going on a long, exciting journey. I want you to wait for us on the other side, until we come."

She winced, as if to say, "No!"

Don reached down and kissed her, as he had done so many times before.

She looked up at him. Her face was calm and beautiful. For a fleeting moment, she smiled.

Then she died.

The battle was over. Janet had won.

By being courageous and honest about her dying, she had given her family the strength to go on living without her.

9

The Clergyman: Religion and Cancer

*"I asked God for strength, that I might achieve,
I was made weak, that I might learn humbly to obey . . .
I asked for health, that I might do greater things,
I was given infirmity, that I might do better things . . .
I asked for riches, that I might be happy,
I was given poverty, that I might be wise . . .
I asked for power, that I might have the praise of men,
I was given weakness, that I might feel the need of God . . .
I asked for all things, that I might enjoy life,
I was given life, that I might enjoy all things . . .
I got nothing that I asked for ————
but almost everything I had hoped for,
Almost despite myself,
my unspoken prayers were answered.
I am among all men, most richly blessed."*

The author of the poem above remains anonymous. But whoever he is or was, I can identify with him. When I first learned I had cancer, I blamed God. I cursed God. Then I refused to acknowledge His existence. I wondered how God could have inflicted such a terrible punishment on me when there seemed to be other people more deserving than I was. After all, I was happily married, the father of four children. Everything seemed to be going so well for us until I became ill. Then we lost all the money we had accumulated. I never considered the fact that we still had each other, which was the most important thing of all, which meant we were far from "poor."

Prior to the cancer, I thought my faith was strong enough to sustain me through the trials and tribulations of my life.

Religion was quite basic. There was Heaven and there was Hell as far as we were concerned. I had to decide where *I* wanted to go. The trouble was that I feared both God and the Devil, because Grandmother would tell me when I was bad, either that the Devil had me "by the shirt-tails," or that God would punish me for being a bad boy.

Another thing that bothered me was listening to preachers who ranted and raved about sin and salvation at revival meetings from the loudspeaker of our Atwater-Kent radio in the living room. I didn't think God's word had to be shouted about nor should little boys like me have to be scared to death before they would believe in God.

As the years have passed since my childhood, society has added many ingredients to the recipe of life. More technological advances have been made during the past twenty years than in all the previous years of mankind. Just the other night, a voice on a television commercial informed me that all the knowledge from rows of books on a library shelf shown in the commercial could be stored on a computer wafer the size of a coin. Had such a prediction appeared anywhere in the newspapers during my childhood years, I don't think anyone would have believed it.

We live today in an age of instant, mass communications. When President Lincoln was assassinated, it took two weeks for the news to reach Europe. When Neil Armstrong took his "giant leap for mankind," hundreds of millions of television viewers around the world saw it about one second later.

What do these comments have to do with religion? Our religious needs have become more complicated, too. We are constantly seeking answers to complex questions. For instance, is there life after death? Many of us aren't satisfied with faith. We want scientific proof. Our faith asks us to believe something we cannot see, touch, hear, feel or smell. We are asked to believe in love, too, but we cannot lay it on a table for all disbelievers to see.

Because some people want more than they seem to find in their churches and through orthodox religions, they turn to "cults" and to leaders outside the church. To meet the needs of disenchanted people in America, over one thousand cults have been established. Many of the leaders of these cults resort to various forms of religion to add credibility to their philosophies. Many of the cult leaders are egotistical misfits with a background in some vocation which has given them a superficial knowledge of people and their needs. Many of these leaders are charismatic and exert great influence over their followers. The leaders realize the importance of physically touching someone in need of love and friendship. They know that the majority of Americans are shy and insecure, quite different from the smug, over-confident exteriors they present to the public. They know how important it is to make individuals feel "wanted" and "important."

Unfortunately, many churches fail to realize how vital

warmth and love are in our daily lives. I have been to some churches where the congregations were as unfriendly as crowds at a department store sale. I have talked with seriously ill persons who have told me their pastors didn't support them. Was it because the ministers involved didn't care? No, I am sure it was because they didn't know, anymore than most of us do, how to cope with the problems associated with serious illness. They felt threatened. Similar frustrating experiences at doctors' offices and hospitals tend to drive patients into the arms of the quacks who welcome them with a pat on the back and lots of warmth and understanding, but offer false hope. Ineffectual, uncaring churches and ministers drive desperate people into religious cults.

I spoke at a church in Iowa once and afterwards several members of the congregation talked with me privately about their personal problems. Two of them were cancer patients who were reluctant to discuss their problems openly because they lived in a small community and hadn't decided yet whether they wanted anyone to know about their illness. Later, the minister of this church wrote a letter thanking me for sharing my time with his congregation. "If anyone in my church ever becomes a cancer patient, I'll know how to better help them with their problems," he added. I didn't tell him there were *already* two patients in his flock.

Who is to blame in the above case—the minister or the patients who didn't share their knowledge about their illness with the pastor? I don't know for certain, but I believe *all* were to blame. A patient should feel free to talk with his pastor about *any* problem. And a minister should not run away from people who face death because he feels threatened. The minister above all persons, should be able to improve communications in the family and support the patient and family during the illness. If a death occurs, he

should continue to support the family and offer grief coun-
selling and guidance. He can't do these things without
training. Training in helping the dying person should be a
mandatory course in *all* seminary curricula.

Most patients I talk with about religion tell me they feel
most comfortable with a clergyman who is interested in
them as a person, not as just a member of the congregation.

Clergymen should keep in mind that it is the patients who
are the real "experts" in the field of death and dying. No
one should try to tell someone else how to die, but they can
offer support to the dying person.

There is no way anyone who has not been affected can
really know what it feels like to be dying. (Yes, I know we're
all terminal, etc., but there *is* a difference!). However, you
should realize that you *can* offer many effective aids—
—love, friendship, and your hand holding the hand of someone who is dying.

This necessity for caring is what my feelings about real
religion are all about!

During my years in the United States Army, I quit going
to church. After I married Wanda, my faith was renewed.
As a newspaper editor in Illinois, I spoke at various churches while ministers were on vacation. I became a lay speaker
at two churches in Illinois for several months during a time
when the church elders were seeking a new pastor. I was
recommended for lay speaker's training so I could serve
full-time in the churches. I did not pursue this vocation
because I wanted to write and the newspaper job had
offered me an opportunity to do so.

After the diagnosis of my cancer, I realized my faith was
not strong enough to sustain me. In the past, I had turned to
God, especially when I needed help. I remember praying
one time when an Army transport airplane on which I was a

passenger developed engine trouble, near Wake Island in the South Pacific.

"God, if You will just get me through this one, I'll reform," I promised. "I'll go to church every Sunday. I'll be more compassionate toward the soldiers under my command."

We landed at Wake Island and the engine was repaired. The next day we landed near Tokyo. I soon forgot the promises.

But I couldn't forget the cancer. It was one problem I couldn't run away from nor dismiss from my mind. The thought of dying overwhelmed me. Why would God choose *me* to suffer from cancer? Why me? I could find no answers.

In the days following my discovery that I had cancer, I wasn't very hospitable toward ministers. It wasn't really their fault. They tried to help me. But I couldn't identify with what they were saying.

"Try to visualize Heaven as the wonderful place it is," a minister said to me. "Close your eyes and think about it and you will find that dying can be a great experience. Remember that Heaven is beautiful and you will have no pain, no troubles there."

"Why don't *you* go there, if it is that beautiful?" I asked him.

But *he* didn't want to go, he wanted *me* to.

I realize I was a difficult patient and not very responsive to offers of spiritual assistance, but I *did* need help. I just didn't know how to ask for it.

Three of the first clergymen to effectively help me were Norman Vincent Peale, whom I discuss elsewhere in this book; Don Turkelson, a Methodist minister who is now an Army chaplain; and John Vickers, pastor of the First Christian Church in Burlington and a member of the Make

Today Count board of directors (he is also the father of Paul Vickers, who married my daughter Tammy).

When Don visited me, he didn't introduce himself as "Pastor Don Turkelson" but I could tell he was interested in helping me cope with my emotional problems. During our first conversation, he told me that he, too, had some doubts about his own faith when his father died. I could identify with him and felt comfortable in talking with him about my own fears and doubts.

He was also interested in talking with other members of my family, realizing that they needed as much or more help than I did. He became a member of our local MTC chapter. Perhaps he was more aware of how to approach me because of some specialized training he had received at a large hospital, while working with terminally ill patients. In any event, he was one of the first ministers to really help me.

John Vickers visited me at my home after reading about our initial Make Today Count meeting. We had a lengthy discussion about cancer and death. John has taught philosophy at the local community college, and perhaps because of this background he can turn routine discussions about religion into interesting conversations. I have turned to him many times for help in seeking solutions to controversial questions in my mind about life and death.

When I blamed God for my illness, I also felt guilty about some of the things I had said. I had cursed God, saying that nothing he could do to me could be any worse than the cancer. Although Wanda never lost her religious faith, I reminded her it was *me* who had cancer, not her. During this time, it was John Vickers who reminded me that cancer might be God's enemy, too, and that I shouldn't blame Him for all my problems. That was the first thing anyone had said which made sense to me. Why couldn't cancer be *God's* enemy? And if this could be true, why not ask for *God's* help in fighting the cancer?

There was one obstacle in my mind with regard to asking for God's help. I couldn't forget all the derogatory things I had said about God on several occasions. But I decided to try anyway. One day, returning home from my first chemotherapy treatment, I realized my life had dropped to a level where I had to find a way to live despite the cancer or I had to "throw in the towel." I was so depressed I couldn't sleep much. Everything around me seemed to be a grim reminder of death. There were funeral processions everywhere I went, including my trip to the hospital. I searched the obituary columns of newspapers to find the names of fellow cancer patients who had died, so I could get an idea of how long people with cancer might live.

I asked God for help that afternoon. There was no sudden revelation. My life did begin to change, though, and I started to notice things around me again. As a matter of fact, I became more acutely aware of so many of the little things I had overlooked before—sunrises, sunsets, lilacs in bloom, children's laughter, the "fresh air" smell in my yard after a spring rain—and I was gradually able to accept the fact that I was a mortal.

I responded to the offers of help from pastors who cared about me as a human being. These clergymen helped me not only from a spiritual standpoint, but assisted me in coping with the emotional problems of depression, fear, anger and rejection.

"Go ahead and scream if you want to," one of them said to me one day. "I won't run away. I've had to scream, too, when I was too angry to hold everything within me."

Shortly after starting the Make Today Count organization, I met Vern Albrecht, a chaplain at Lutheran Medical Center in Omaha. Vern has talked with many patients and families during the years he served as a chaplain. He knows what it is like to help someone else *and* to need help. His oldest son, Tom, together with his son's girlfriend, were killed instantly in a car crash. The crash occurred two weeks before Tom's seventeenth birthday.

"There is really no way I can fully describe the impact and hurt this tragedy had on me, my wife, and five other children," Vern said. "But I can say we have never experienced any pain so far during our lives that is in any way comparable in its intensity to that of the two deaths."

I talked with Vern about helping families face tragedies such as the one he had experienced. "Do you think someone has to experience these things personally before they can understand and be of help to others?" I asked.

"I believe that personally entering and experiencing that dark valley of loss and grief can be of great help in understanding the pain of others who are experiencing it," he replied, "but I also believe it is not essential for a person who wants to help someone else who is hurting because of a tragic death. In fact, it may even interfere with the helping process if the person, whether it's a chaplain or anyone else, hasn't 'worked through' his own feelings about death.

"As a family, we were helped by people who had not experienced anything similar to our tragedy," Vern continued. "Others who helped us had suffered like we had.

"We were 'turned off' and even hurt more by a few persons who may have meant well, but apparently had so many hang-ups about death themselves that they tried to impose on us their easy answers and quick solutions to our deeply disturbing questions concerning such things as shock, guilt, anger, regression and confusion," Vern explained.

"What then should someone say or do to help families who are facing a tragedy?" I asked.

"There is no 'right' or 'wrong' thing to say," Vern said.

"There isn't even a need to say *anything* that speaks to the intellect, but the need is rather for sincere, human love. That love has a built-in message. That message is, 'Even though I don't fully understand how you feel, I care enough to come to you and try sharing your hurt as much as I can and as much as you will allow me to at this time. I'll leave you alone if I get any vibrations from you that you prefer to be alone, but I'll be ready to come back when you give me the signal.' "

I asked Vern to give me some examples of the help he and his family received at the time of his son's death.

"Our young pastor is the first to come to my mind. He came to our house early in the morning when he heard the news of Tom's fatal accident. He put his arms around us and all he could think of to say was, 'Vern, I don't know what to say.' His eyes, though, communicated a thousand times more of what we needed at the time, contrasted to a pastor-colleague who came with a radiant beam on his face, announcing, 'How happy we can now be to have a son in Heaven.' My wife later remarked, 'What did he want us to do, uncork the champagne bottles because our son was just killed?'

"Expressions of care came to our four younger children from their school classmates and teachers. This helped them. Our daughter, who was attending a university, missed this personal touch. My wife received help from friends where she worked. Our neighbors and many fellow church members reached out to us. I mention this because of how much it helped and how important it can be if we, as chaplains or pastors, can facilitate significant groups in the community to express care to persons suffering from the grief of death."

Vern spoke of the prayer-statement that was part of a memorial mass offered for Tom's girlfriend. The prayer stressed that nothing can actually fill the gap which is created when we are away from someone we love. Leaving the gap unfilled can strengthen the love. It is wrong, the prayer suggested, to say that God fills the gap. He keeps it empty so that our communion with another may be kept alive, even at the cost of pain.

"Some may feel the thoughts expressed in the prayer are irreverent and even blasphemous, to say that God cannot or does not fill the void," Vern said. "I believe the opposite. No person you truly love can be replaced. If this were possible, something would be taken away from the special God-given uniqueness of that person and of the original relationship."

Although clergymen can reinforce hope in seriously ill patients and their families, they should also be willing to help the patient prepare for death. Sometimes dying patients want to talk about dying. Clergymen should listen and then they will know when the patient reaches this stage. Most patients seem to sense when they are dying, and if we all will only listen, we, too, will know when the time has come to talk about death with them. Just don't try to say too much. Keep listening. All of us are tempted to inspire patients with our own preconceived ideas about death. Forget this approach. The two most important things are to listen and to show that you care. Don't hesitate to hold the patient's hand.

"What do you expect from someone who visits you?" I asked a young lady dying of cancer.

"Not a great deal," she replied. "I just want them to come into my room and sit beside me, where I can see them. I don't want them to stand at the end of my bed, and I don't want them to carry a clipboard or notebook as a sort of 'security blanket.' I hope they care about me. I know I am dying. What I don't know is how my visitors feel about my dying. I have accepted my coming death, but if someone else hasn't, it bothers me. It makes me feel guilty. My sister said to me recently, 'Please don't talk about dying. We all need you so much.' Well, I can't help it if I'm dying. I didn't choose to die at age twenty-six. But she makes me feel guilty, like I'm doing something wrong. What I need most now is love."

Love! That's the most important emotion of all when death is near. Nothing else matters *except* love.

"What is the most important thing anyone could do for you?" I asked a dying lung cancer patient.

"I just want to know someone loves me," she replied. "I want someone to hold my hand and care about me."

Isn't this what it is all about? Clergymen should look upon patients as human beings who are truly God's children. And they should remember the importance of love and compassion. One night, from a dying man's room, I called four ministers before I found one who would come to the patient's room.

"Who is his pastor?" one minister asked.

"He has none," I said.

"Well, why don't you try John Smith? He does this sort of thing."

The fourth minister I called came to the dying man's hospital room. He didn't shake hands, but put his arms around the two family members present. He didn't tell them everything would be all right, but told them he would remain with them as long as they needed him. The patient, who was semi-comatose, had been reaching toward his face as if something was bothering him. The minister detected what was wrong. The oxygen mask was cutting into the bridge of the patient's nose. He asked the nurse for some gauze which he placed beneath the mask. The patient relaxed. The minister held his hand and brushed the hair from his forehead.

When the clergyman left the room for a moment, one of the family members turned to me and said, "Isn't he a nice man? You would never know he is a minister."

The remark was meant as a compliment. The family felt comfortable with this person, even though he was not their pastor.

Since some people turn to God in desperation, asking Him for help when there seems to be no other hope for survival, faith healing is sometimes a final resort—a last attempt to thwart the progress of an illness and the facts of nature.

At the beginning, when I first learned about cancer, I did not believe in any form of faith healing. I have since changed my mind. I feel I am alive today because God has kept me alive. I know that many people have prayed for me during my illness and I believe in the strength and power of prayer. I cannot tell you whether the positive results of various forms of faith healing can be attributed to God, to the healing power of the human mind when we believe strongly in something or someone, or whether it is a combination of these two elements, plus a touch of something which we do not understand. I choose to believe it is a combination of things which sometimes pulls a patient from the arms of death, but that it is all done because of God's intervention.

It is difficult to substantiate actual examples of faith healing, because sometimes the facts get jumbled as the story is told. Sometimes patients think they are cured when they are actually only in a state of remission and the cancer is stabilized for an indefinite period. Sometimes the initial diagnosis was not correct and the patient has a type of cancer which can be stabilized for long periods of time. But in my own mind, there is no doubt about the effectiveness of faith healing, or the "laying on of hands," when performed by sincere healers or ministers. Actually, I feel, it is God who does the healing and the person who lays hands on the patient is a link between the ailing person and God.

In order for spiritual healing to work, the patient must have faith. This is the important factor in healing, for many of us have faith only when things are going well. There are many "middle-of-the-road Christians" whose faith is strongest when the sun is shining. When something goes wrong, they question God's will and even feel they are being punished for some imaginary sin.

Faith helps me cope with not only my disease, but the trials and tribulations of life itself.

I have written a prayer which has helped me when I am afraid or depressed. I would like to share it with you.

Give me the strength to face each night before the dawn
Let me count each passing moment
As I once marked the fleeting days and nights,
And give me hope for each tomorrow.
Let my dreams be dreams of the future.
But when life on earth is over,
Let there be no sadness—
Only joy for the golden days I've had.

193

10

"Burn-Out" Among Health-Care Professionals

NOW THAT CHRISTMAS is growing closer, I detect a note of sadness in many of the letters I receive. Yesterday, a letter came to me from a young mother whose two-month-old baby is dying of cancer. "I read about Make Today Count and I want to know if you believe in miracles?" she asked. "Can you help me? I don't want to lose my baby."

I am tempted to reassure this mother by telling her that miracles do happen and that her baby may live despite what the doctors have told her. But this would not be enough. Yes, there are spontaneous remissions, when cancer disappears. One person out of perhaps 100,000 survives terminal cancer. But along with whatever hope I offer the mother, I must reinforce my inspirational comments with compassion. I must let her know I care. I want her to know she is not alone. It would be wrong to promise this mother something I can't deliver. I hope her baby lives, but this may not happen. I must not give her *false* hope.

I am reminded of the tragedies I have known about as I read my mail this Christmas season. I am able to cope with the seemingly unbearable blanket of depression that begins to cover me after listening to stories of sadness and death because every person touched by tragedy has something to offer me in the way of hope and inspiration for myself. Let me explain: I can find nothing to make me feel good in the letter from the young mother whose baby is dying of cancer. But she has turned to me for help. I am needed. *This* makes my life worthwhile. There is no better therapy than helping others who are desperate. But the offer to help must be genuine, and if I am not sincere, the insincerity can be detected by the person I am trying to reach. Therefore, when I feel myself reaching the "burn-out" stage, which I do occasionally, I must get away for a while. I look for something to relax me. I don't have to go on a long trip, nor do I have to stay away from my work for long periods of time. But I have to be careful to not delay my decision to quit seeing patients and families temporarily.

Incidentally, by "burn-out" I mean the stage people reach when they are no longer able to effectively meet the needs of the patients or persons under their care. I hear more about this lately because professional persons are beginning to realize their limitations. I cannot recognize the signs of my own increasing depression because I become very agitated and short-tempered. I find it difficult to sleep at nights when I reach the point of losing my patience with people. I find it hard to cope with my feelings of desperation and helplessness, as I continue to watch people die without being able to do anything about it.

It took a long time for me to realize that I could not

control life and death. I am not responsible for the deaths of the patients I know. I cannot extend the lives of those I love just because I care. But I *can* control my personal involvement with them and make certain I emphasize the *quality* of the time, not the *quantity*. It also took me a long time to realize I must consider my own feelings. It is so easy for me to occasionally forget that I, too, am a patient. I must always remember the matter of my own mortality. It is not "they" who are dying; it is all of us. So at times I must learn all over again to accept the fact that I am going to die of cancer, unless something else should cause my death first.

Most professional persons have not come to terms with their own mortality or their personal feelings about death. We assume that nurses, doctors, medical social workers, therapists, psychiatrists, and psychologists are the "experts." They have been trained and we need them for obvious reasons when we are dying. But nurses, doctors, and all the rest of the people who care for seriously ill persons must realize that they, too, are human beings. Along with therapy, medical treatment, nursing care, and other professional help, the professionals must learn to dispense human kindness and compassion, and to admit their fallibility. This is what I have been talking about throughout the pages of this book.

I recently talked with a clinical psychologist who works with physically handicapped and chronically ill persons. He had graduated after four years of college and four years of graduate school and had served a one-year internship.

"How much of this training was of the type that would help you in your work with terminally ill persons?" I asked him.

"These issues were never addressed," he replied. "The issues I refer to are those that would help someone like me, with a patient who has an illness such as cancer, when I have not even been able to deal with thoughts of my *own* mortality. I realize that everyone is dying. But mental health training just doesn't prepare us for this issue. It has been my experience, and that of other psychologists with whom I am acquainted, that we professionals must work through our own feelings about death before we can really help others with their problems. When I helped organize a special cancer unit at a hospital, I cried more during that time than I ever had in my life. Why? Because I started thinking about my own death and my parents' death, and I had never thought about these things much before. But I *had* to think about death when I was around it every day. What I really needed then, and even now, was someone I could talk with about my own feelings. I am supposed to help other people, and I can do my job well, but *I* need help, too!

"I think psychology students should have help with their thoughts and feelings about death and serious illness after the first seven or eight months of training. If they don't get this help, they begin to build defenses to help them cope with the emotional challenges that confront them as they start to counsel terminally ill or physically handicapped persons. Right now, many students seek help from each other. Medical students, for example, look to other medical students for help as they wrestle with their personal fears about death and their feelings toward dying patients."

The psychologist concluded his remarks by saying that he felt schools should recognize the needs that he discussed and seek ways to strengthen the training program and to make consultants accessible to the students. These consultants could counsel the students concerning problems arising from their work with terminally or seriously ill persons.

I have talked with many professional persons who are responsible in various ways for the care of dying persons. Through these conversations, I have discovered that few of these persons have really been able to cope with their own feelings about dying. I would recommend that health professionals seek help in working through these problems. For centuries, people have been hiding their inadequacies and weaknesses behind titles and other protective cloaks. "I know all except myself," François Villon, the great French lyric poet, wrote before his death in 1463. But it is essential that we know ourselves before we can know others.

I was a guest in the home of a well-known psychiatrist. A cocktail party was arranged in my honor so I could meet some physicians, psychologists, and other psychiatrists who lived in the same city as my hostess. As the evening continued, we talked about dying patients and it occurred to me that the people in the room were telling me how to die, from their own professional viewpoints. No one was willing to concede their own mortality. I could even detect some masked criticism about my lack of credentials, which they felt I needed in order to work with other cancer patients.

"From what source do you draw upon when you help cancer patients with their emotional problems?" a psychologist asked.

"I remind you that I am a cancer patient, too," I replied. "Who else knows better than a cancer patient what it is like to live with cancer?"

I had a feeling everyone in the room that evening was refusing to confront me as a human being. They were resorting to the defensive tactic of hiding behind their professional identities. I did not feel comfortable with them. And I don't think they were very comfortable with me. Later, one of the psychiatrists present talked with me privately and the barriers that had existed previously fell away in the face of mutual candor. I had disliked this particular psychologist when I met him earlier, but I discovered he was actually a very warm, caring human being. Why can't professional persons in the health-care field allow themselves to approach patients and clients with more warmth and candor? Perhaps part of the fault lies with the rest of us, who help to place some of them on pedestals. We want our doctors to be omnipotent creatures who dispense medical miracles daily. We, as patients, must not only accept more responsibility for our well-being, but we must also recognize that modern medicine is not infallible or capable of limitless feats of lifesaving. We should be aware that over five thousand persons die every twenty-four hours in America, regardless of what is done for them.

I have become increasingly aware of efforts to help doctors and other health-care persons cope with their own emotional problems. During 1976, in San Diego, a U.S. Navy chaplain, Captain Bob Anderson (now retired), initiated a "rap session" for oncology physicians and nurses, so both groups could openly discuss not the emotional problems of patients, but rather their *own.* The group met once a week. Chaplain Anderson asked the members two major questions: "Why are you doing what you do?" and "What are the problems you have encountered?"

"In explaining *why* they chose to treat cancer patients, some of the oncologists recalled someone in their immediate family who had cancer," Anderson explained. "One of the major problems continues to be 'burn-out' which occurs when a person reaches the point where he or she can no longer cope with the emotional challenges involved in caring for seriously ill patients."

I asked Anderson to express his own views about the problem of "burn-out" among doctors specifically.

"I am sure it has something to do with the whole medical profession," he answered. "We push these guys to be 'God'! For instance, the doctors are told they are the upper five percent of humanity . . . and they probably are, from the standpoint of intelligence . . . but we forget they are human beings, too. Rarely are they allowed to express themselves as human beings."

"Have you noticed any change in individual attitudes on the part of the participants since the oncologists and oncology nurses started attending your sessions?" I asked.

"I can now see more warmth and openness between the nurses and doctors," he replied.

Since I spoke at two of these sessions while on lecture tours in San Diego, I asked Anderson if any changes in format had occurred since I had attended a meeting.

"We have expanded our enrollment," he said. "We now invite navy corpsmen, lab technicians, and other hospital personnel to meet with us. We have found that they, too, have encountered the problem of 'burn-out.' Technicians who operate the machines in the radiation department develop a 'cold' attitude toward patients. You must remember that in this department, nothing touches the patient and there is no one in the room during treatment procedures. In the X-ray unit, the technicians are not primary health-delivery persons since patients may come to them only once or no more than a few times. The personal contact is missing. So 'burn-out' in the treatment of seriously ill patients can occur with or without personal involvement."

When I spoke at the sessions in San Diego, I was impressed with the willingness of the physicians to admit their own shortcomings in some areas of medical practice where medicine does not have all the answers, and with the desire to share their own emotional problems associated with the treatment of cancer patients. Some of the discussion centered around the question of whether or not a physician can get "emotionally involved" with patients without paying too high a price. One doctor said that he remembered a time early in his career when he found he was becoming so emotionally involved with many patients that he couldn't effectively treat them from a medical standpoint.

Once again, I stress the importance of stopping the practice in medical schools of "dehumanizing" the students. Instead of promoting the omnipotent image, professors in the medical schools should encourage the students to be compassionate without becoming so emotionally involved that their efficiency as physicians is affected. For instance, there are many ways to deliver bad news to someone. I would like to give some examples:

A young attorney who belonged to one of our Make Today Count chapters underwent surgery to determine if a tumor in the abdomen was malignant. The operation took longer than his wife had anticipated. She was anxiously awaiting the results in the corridor outside the operating room. Finally, the surgeon opened the door, looked at the young woman, threw his hands in the air, and exclaimed, "Well, it's cancer!" Then he walked away. The woman never forgot the manner in which she learned about her husband's cancer.

In another case, an oncologist had some bad news for a patient and his wife. He chose a time when the patient's wife was in the hospital room with him.

"We are getting signals that your remission might be ending," the oncologist said. "However, I want you to know that there is a chance we can put you in another remission, through chemotherapy treatment. I am going to send you home for a few days, but I don't want either of you to think this has any significance. We are not going to abandon you. It's just that we are awaiting the results from some more tests. If any of these results are significant, I will call you. Remember, we can do some things for you from a medical standpoint. Although we all realize there is no cure rate for your cancer, it is still treatable."

In still another case, related to me by an emergency room volunteer, I was told about three accident victims who were brought to a hospital. The mother and one child were dead. A third child was in critical condition. Finally, the father was located. He knew nothing about the tragedy. Someone explained there had been an accident and his wife and two children were involved. When he arrived at the hospital, he was taken to an empty room near the emergency room, where a hospital employee told him his wife and one child had been killed, while one child had survived. Then the employee walked out of the room, leaving the grief-stricken man alone. Shortly afterward, the man started screaming and pounding on the walls. Perhaps no one knew what to do. Or they were unwilling to do anything to help the man. The volunteer, who was relating this story to me, went into the room and held the man in her arms. They cried together. Then the volunteer, although she was exceeding her authority, took the man to see the child who was still alive.

"He didn't even know which child had survived," she told me. "Once he saw his child and knew everything possible was being done for that child to keep him alive, he calmed down considerably. But I will never forget the fact that he was left all alone in that room, to cry and scream, without anyone to hold him or cry with him, until I went to him because I knew what it was like to lose someone you love."

Are we asking *too* much of the health-care profession when we insist its members treat us as human beings? I don't think so. The problems faced by health-care persons as a result of a lack of concern for patients are more devastating than the problems created by emotional involvement with the patients. What we *can* do is continue to seek ways to help the doctors, nurses, technicians, psychologists, and others cope with their personal problems, such as depression and "burn-out," resulting from this involvement.

A friend of mine from San Francisco, Dr. Charles Garfield, is a clinical research psychologist at the Cancer Research Institute there. He is also assistant clinical professor of medical psychology at the Schools of Medicine and Nursing, University of California, San Francisco. Since Charlie recently served as a consultant for a major university studying the problem of "burn-out," I asked him what people in the health-care field could do to help themselves before this stage was reached.

"There are many things that can be done to alleviate 'burn-out' among health-care professionals," he said. "Two major areas of prevention are individual and collective methods. Collectively, there can be support groups for professionals. Also, hospital employees should know more about the hospital system and how it works, from a functional point of view. Many workers feel oppressed because of a lack of equipment, too many working hours, understaffing, and so on. These persons must learn what possibilities exist for successful input into the hospital's decision-making process."

Dr. Garfield's suggestion that support groups be established for health-care persons strengthened the work being done by Bob Anderson in San Diego and in a few other areas of the United States. This recommendation also supports my contention that people must help themselves before they can effectively help others. But in order to help themselves, they need assistance in coping with the depression caused by watching so many patients suffer and die. I asked an ex-nurse in Seattle, who was working as a secretary, why she left the field of nursing.

"I couldn't bear to watch people die any longer," she said. "I was totally depressed when I quit."

She needed help before she reached the final stages of apparent "burn-out."

"I guess the best illustration of this type of help is the story *you* often tell," Charlie said to me. "I am talking about the need most of us, including professionals, have to know there is someone close enough to us whom we can call at three o'clock in the morning for emotional support when we are really 'down.'"

(Charlie was referring to the fact that I often ask people attending my lectures if they know of someone, other than a relative, whom they can call at 3 A.M. when they have a need to talk with someone. Not many people can name more than one or two persons with whom they would feel comfortable calling at this time of the morning.)

"How about individual ways someone can cope with approaching 'burn-out'?" I asked.

"One way is to not make any hard-and-fast rules about separation of work environment and home environment," Charlie replied. "In crisis situations, it is almost impossible to separate the two environments. We must have support from fellow-workers when we have personal problems and we must have support at home when our work becomes extremely stressful.

"Another successful way to cope with the stress of our jobs while caring for seriously ill patients is to pause for thirty seconds before going into a hospital room for a visit and focus on *yourself*. Ask yourself, 'What am I trying to accomplish with this visit and how can I be more helpful?' Most of us don't have thirty minutes to spare, but we do have thirty seconds."

Dr. Garfield paused for a moment before continuing. "There is one other thing I might mention in connection with 'burn-out.' When I was consulting with a university hospital committee composed of high-level, decision-making people studying this problem, I noticed some of these people were smiling during the conversations. They didn't seem to consider 'burn-out' of nurses, for example, as a major problem? Why? Well, they were seeing it as a problem, but certainly not as an economic one. After all, when a nurse earning $18,000 per year quits because she can't take it anymore, the hospital staff can find a young nurse willing to work for much less. So, for the decision-makers the problem of 'burn-out' is not necessarily a negative one. This is a specific issue, but a touchy one, of course."

Once again, I was reminded of the difficulty I have in reaching these decision-makers in hospitals who look at everything from a standpoint of economics and who resist changes that will probably not result in profit, but will improve the quality of life for the patients. As patients and families become more knowledgeable about these matters, they must lead the way to more effective and humane health care.

One of the ways this can be achieved is by assuming more responsibility for their own health through an insistence that they, as patients, be treated as human beings in doctors' offices and hospitals. Patients should ask if the Hospital Patient's Bill of Rights, which appears at the end of this book, is recognized by the staff. Patients and family members should report instances of rudeness and indifference on the part of the doctors and nurses to the hospital administrator's office.

Until health care professionals face the fact that compassion and caring are just as important as the physical therapies in the treatment of patients, we will continue to endure or witness callous and sometimes inhumane treatment from some professionals. If patients and family members make their emotional needs known to persons in the health care field, then it will become increasingly difficult for them to ignore those needs.

In an early chapter of this book, I discussed many of the problems faced by nurses who care for seriously ill persons. I do want to continue this discussion now, through a conversation I had with Mrs. June Eilers, R.N., an oncology nurse specialist who works at a large hospital in Omaha.

"Staff support and 'burn-out' are being discussed more and more in the health-care field," June said. "The question is, 'Who is taking care of the care givers?' I feel that hospital staffs in the health-care field need a strong support system, both at work and at home, to be more effective.

"Nurses need to know when to get away from their jobs and they must know they can no longer be effective if they don't make a break once in a while," June continued. "I think nurses should support each other more than they do. They need to listen to each other. They need outside interests and activities because death and dying can't be their whole life."

I asked June to tell me about some of the difficulties faced by nurses who care for cancer patients.

"I feel that care of the cancer patient, especially those with advanced disease, is much different than care of persons in the critical-care unit," she said. "In the critical-care section, you do all of those sophisticated, heroic things for the patient and there is always hope for recovery. You can see a light at the end of the tunnel. In the unit where cancer patients are located, the nurses know they will have to watch the majority of them die. The oncology nurses need to be able to stand up and say, 'I did a good job in caring for so-and-so. I feel good about what I did.' They shouldn't feel they failed because a patient they were caring for died."

Near the end of my conversation with June, she reminded me of something I often forget because of my busy work schedule.

"I know you have lots of things to do, Kelly, but if you

don't take care of *yourself*, it will be difficult to continue helping others."

It is a fact that many people feel I have things under control as far as my own life is concerned. This is not true. I become depressed easily. Today, for instance, I felt the enlarged node beneath my arm and it seemed larger (doesn't this always happen?!). Feeling the node again reminded me that I have an appointment at the University of Iowa Hospital Specialty Medicine Clinic in five days. The thought depressed me. Will they schedule me for more tests? Is the node actually larger, or am I just imagining it is? Above all, can I make it until next summer? We have planned a family vacation. Oh, there I go again—bargaining for more time!

I have been sitting in this den at home for two weeks, with only occasional visits to my office. I think I am beginning to get "cabin fever." I am going stir crazy. I wish I could talk with some of my friends. Yesterday, I caught myself talking to myself. I never thought this could happen so soon after I told everyone I needed solitude, but I do need people!

More than anything else, though, I want to finish this book. After all, I am recalling my experiences during visits to hundreds of hospitals, nursing and medical schools, medical conventions, and numerous other functions and facilities as I write these chapters. I don't want my thoughts, feelings, and recollections to remain buried in my mind or scattered on scraps of pages from airline magazines and restaurant menus. I have heard hundreds of stories from doctors, nurses, patients, family members, young children, technicians, and many others as I have traveled. I hope I can somehow make these stories as interesting for you as they have been for me. I especially hope I can show you, through the pages of this book, how things really are in the health-care field and what needs to be done to change certain practices. After all, we have one of the best health-care delivery programs in the world, so why not improve it? Why not be the first nation to remove the dehumanization aspects of health care? Why not transform patients back into human beings? And why not allow health-care professionals to be human themselves?

We all need to recognize that doctors, nurses, psychiatrists, psychologists, and others who try to keep us functioning are not supermen or women. They *are* human. They often hide their thoughts and feelings behind the facade of a white uniform, but they need help, too. We must not put doctors on pedestals and expect them to perform miracles for us. No one can push himself endlessly without encountering serious problems of his own.

The stress affecting doctors treating seriously ill patients also reaches nonphysicians in the health-care field. A federal study conducted recently of the occupations of mental patients when first admitted to hospitals disclosed six categories of health-care workers in the top twenty-two by frequency of admittance. First on the list were health technicians.

Professional health-care givers must be reminded that patients are people much like themselves. They should not be subjected to attitudes or acts that erode their dignity. Patients respond to compassion and react to indifference. A dying person needs to know someone else cares. All nursing schools in the United States should emphasize the importance of touching seriously ill patients. Nurses and doctors should be reminded that patients have different tolerance levels for pain and the answer is not to "let them grin and bear it," in the old American tradition.

I believe it will be the nurses in America who will continue to initiate and effect changes in our hospital systems. The younger nurses are seeking answers to questions not asked in the past: "What can we do for someone who is dying?" "Why should I get in trouble for telling a patient the truth?" "Why does the nursing supervisor insist we go by the clock to administer hypos when a dying person is suffering from pain? How can someone become addicted to narcotics in a few hours before death?" "Why are nurses expected to help cover up mistakes made by incompetent doctors?" "Why are nurses who try to make changes that will benefit patients considered troublemakers?"

The oncologists, radiologists, and other doctors treating cancer patients are also making changes. These doctors are directly exposed to the pain and suffering of patients on a daily basis. They are aware of the emotional problems associated with cancer and the need to help these people cope with them. Community physicians are not, since they are not exposed to cancer often enough to know.

In most hospitals, it is impossible for staff members to make changes unless these changes are approved by doctors on the hospital staff. After all, what is a hospital without doctors? But someday, I believe, hospitals will be operated for the benefit of the *patients*.

For aren't we *all* potential patients—doctors, nurses, and health-care professionals, too?

11

The High Cost of Cancer— And How to Reduce Its Expense

I TALKED with my editor, Jerry Gross, today and he seems pleased the chapters of this book are arriving at his office in New York on time. Most of the chapters seem to be flowing smoothly for me, but this particular one, "The High Cost of Cancer," is a real challenge. I have found there is not much information available relating to the cost of cancer. More issues are involved than just the medical costs of cancer. We must also consider loss of income for the patient and for family members who take care of the patient. Transportation, lodging, and other travel expenses for treatment at medical centers away from the patient's home are also involved.

We do know that the economic toll for the patient and the entire nation is devastating. Obviously, figures would have to be updated as hospital costs increase. The Health Insurance Institute, for instance, reports an average hospital cost per day of $151 in 1975.

Some estimates place the cost of lost earning power and productivity to the United States because of cancer at $15 to $25 billion per year.

Predictions for the future show an even gloomier picture for our nation's health bill. At the start of the twentieth century, America spent less than 3 percent of the gross national product on health care, but by the turn of the next century, in the year 2000, medical bills (including all forms of health care) will total $1 trillion a year, consuming nearly 12 percent of the GNP. These predictions were released in 1978 as part of a government-financed study sponsored by the National Institutes of Health.

(Did you ever wonder how much a trillion dollars really is? For one thing, the figure has twelve zeros. That much money in dollar bills would stretch around the earth more than 1,800 times. It would reach to the moon and back 250 times.)

Cancer costs will account for about $50 billion of the budgetary projections at the turn of the new century.

The study said that the total cost of illness in America, including such indirect costs as loss of income and lower production, will exceed $2 trillion by the year 2000.

It is obvious to me that we should be looking at preventive medicine more closely than we are now if we are going to effectively decrease medical costs. Consider the fact that during the next twenty-four hours 350,000 babies will be born around the world. In 1830 there were 1 billion people living on this earth. By 1930 there were 2 billion inhabitants. By the time you read these words, we will have passed the 4 billion population mark. World population is now doubling every thirty years. By the year 2000 there will be about 7 billion people living on our earth.

Doesn't it make sense to spend more research dollars in such slighted areas as diet and cancer? Shouldn't doctors be urged to encourage patients to assume more responsibility in looking for early signs of illness? For example, there is no way of knowing how many thousands of people today have cancer without realizing it. We must seek more ways to detect cancer in its early stages. Patients must have access to cancer screening clinics where the disease can be detected, and the patient must then be able to locate a physician who will treat him. The patients must have confidence in the medical profession. (Among complaints listed by patients about doctors are the following: Nurses and receptionists are not respectful toward patients; office hours are not adequate; medical problems are not explained in a language patients can understand; doctors do not like their decisions to be questioned; patients are kept waiting for long periods in rooms where facilities are inadequate.)

Nothing is accomplished if cancer is detected in a patient at a screening center and that patient fails to make contact with a physician who will treat him.

We have spent billions of dollars and over ten years' time researching the treatment of cancer. We can now successfully *treat* many cancer patients. But why not spend some of these research dollars on the most promising field of all: Cancer prevention. And why not more research on ways to help people live with cancer?

If we could improve methods of detecting cancer so it could be discovered earlier and if we could find ways to prevent it, we would drastically decrease the money spent on treating cancer symptoms.

Is the answer to some of our rising health cost problems a mandatory national health-insurance plan? We have been debating national health insurance in America for forty-six years. The problem of cost has been the influencing factor for deciding against it in most cases. Medicare and Medicaid programs for the poor and aged have been compromise solutions approved by Congress, but these plans are a long step from a national health plan for everyone. When we consider that probably 24 million Americans have no health insurance at all, it is evident we need *some* program to provide proper health care for those who can't afford it. The question is *what kind* of program we can *all* afford.

To further complicate the problem of trying to deliver proper health care for all Americans, we are now learning that about 18 million Americans who already have health insurance do not have adequate coverage for even basic medical care.

The ideal insurance coverage would insure the subscriber against all types of medical expenses, especially against catastrophic illnesses, such as cancer. Diagnosis of a serious illness such as cancer can be the start of many months of medical treatment, resulting in a complete depletion of finances. At least 40 percent of the population in the United States is uninsured against the high costs of catastrophic illness.

Since Medicare and Medicaid programs, costing taxpayers nearly $50 billion annually, do not adequately meet the needs of the users, and since millions of Americans are not prepared for catastrophic illness, we must seek other ways to provide adequate health care. There is no sound reason why any American should be denied reasonable health because of the cost. I am paying nearly $1,000 per year for my own health-care insurance, and it is a financial burden. But I cannot afford to be without it, so I will have to continue making the payments.

I believe that doctors and hospital administrative staffs must call a halt to rising doctor and hospital bills. They should police their own ranks. This would be a step in the right direction, while we continue to await a decision on a national health-insurance plan. During 1978 physicians' fees were rising at a rate of 9.6 percent, about the same as the previous two years. Primary-care physicians were leading the way in 1978 in pay hikes. The typical internist raised his first-visit fee by $6. The price of a history and physical by a family practitioner went up $10. These are medical costs that the patient generally has to pay out of his pocket. General practitioners boosted their charges for first-office visits, revisits, and physicals by $5 each. The median fee for a consultation in a psychiatrist's office was $55 in 1978 (how many patients needing help with their emotional problems can afford this fee?). The average fee charged by an otolarynogologist for a laryngectomy in 1978 was $1,100.

It is ridiculous that a patient in America may have to pay $50,000 or more for treatment of an advanced cancer. One month spent in a hospital by a cancer patient can cost that patient over $4,000 for just hospital costs alone. Physicians' services, drugs, and private nursing fees would represent extra charges.

I am sorry to inform you that unless you are very wealthy or have access to social service benefits as a low-income person, there is not much you can do to protect yourself or your family from the high costs of a prolonged illness such as cancer. But there are organizations that do offer some help.

SOCIAL SECURITY

I was unable to continue working because I was too ill, even prior to the diagnosis of cancer, so Wanda obtained employment at a local electronics factory. After a period of time, she became eligible for a group hospitalization insurance plan, which covered our family, too. When she was forced to quit work, to help care for me after my hospitalization, we were able to convert the policy. We did lose approximately 20 percent of the coverage because of the conversion to an individual policy, but I am thankful we do have insurance coverage.

Because of our total loss of income, I applied for Social Security disability payments. In order to qualify for Social Security disability income, you must have a disability that will keep you from working for a year or more. The amount of monthly payments depends on your previous earnings. Generally, there is a six-month waiting period after your disability before payments can begin. It is important to apply as soon after your disability as possible, since back payments are limited to the twelve months preceding the date of your application.

If you are under sixty-five years of age and have been receiving Social Security disability checks for two years or more, you qualify for Medicare protection to help pay hospital and doctor bills. If you want the medical insurance, too, you must pay a small monthly premium.

When you apply for Social Security disability, someone will ask you for medical evidence about your condition. I obtained this information from my doctors. Sometimes you may be asked to undergo additional medical examinations and tests, at government expense. (You will find detailed information about Social Security disability payments in Appendix A of this book that will include the facts you need to complete your application.)

When I learned I was in a remission and my cancer had been stabilized temporarily, I contacted my local Social Security office and reported that I felt I could work again. I was placed on a trial work period for nine months, to determine if I could be gainfully employed without major medical problems. At the end of the nine-month period, benefits under the Social Security disability program are often continued for an additional three months while a final determination is made about the person's ability to work. If the disability occurs within five years, benefits can start again beginning with the first month of disability.

Another support program available is the supplemental security income, which pays monthly checks to people in financial need who are sixty-five or older and to people in need at any age who are blind or disabled. Persons who have little or no regular cash income and who do not own much in the way of property or assets that can be turned into cash may qualify for supplemental security income. (Once again, refer to Appendix A for detailed information.)

VETERANS ADMINISTRATION

Although I didn't know it for several months, I also qualified for a non-service-connected disability pension, as a veteran. To find out if you are eligible, contact your local VA office or Veterans Affairs officer. The important thing to remember about this pension is that you need not be disabled because of something that occurred during your military service in order to qualify. (You should not confuse it with a service-connected disability pension, paid to veterans who are disabled because of something that occurred during military service.) Payments for the non-service-connected disability pension range from $5 to $483.75 per month, depending on your income, number of dependents, age, and periods of time you may be hospitalized in a VA hospital. My pension totaled about $127 per month, and during the period of time when I could not work, it helped me feed and clothe my family. The problem is that not many persons, including counselors, know about it.

The Veterans Administration also provides hospital care

on a bed-available basis for treatment of non-service-connected conditions, provided a veteran signs a statement of inability to defray the costs of equivalent care. The VA provides hospital or outpatient care when needed for all service-connected medical or compensable dental conditions. If outpatient care isn't available at a VA hospital or clinic, the VA may pay for this care by a hometown doctor or dentist. Be sure you get payment authorization in advance.

The VA will pay a $300 burial allowance for any eligible deceased veteran and $150 for plot or interment allowance if burial is not in a national cemetery. If the veteran dies of a service-connected disability, a burial allowance up to $1,000 may be paid. Widows should apply for benefits within two years after burial or cremation.

If the deceased veteran served after January 31, 1955, an American flag may be obtained at any VA office or from most local post offices, to drape the casket.

If a veteran's widow wishes to obtain a headstone or marker for the unmarked grave of the deceased, the VA will furnish one, upon request, if the last discharge of the veteran was other than dishonorable.

Educational benefits for the dependents of completely disabled veterans will be paid after death, if the veteran dies as a result of service or should die while completely disabled from service-connected causes. Both children and spouses are covered under this benefit.

There is a VA death pension for eligible widows or widowers and children or veterans of the Vietnam era. There is an income limitation for this pension. (See Appendix A for further information about veterans' benefits.)

Write, call, or visit any of the VA offices in the United States for assistance in applying for any veterans' benefits. Local representatives of various veterans' organizations also have information and application forms for these benefits. Blind veterans may obtain cassettes covering VA benefits by writing to the Blinded Veterans Association, 1735 DeSales Street, N.W., Washington, D.C. 20036, or by calling 202 347-4010.

MEDICARE AND MEDICAID

There are other resources available to patients and their families. I did not know where to turn for help at the time I was diagnosed, so I have spent much time since then identifying resource agencies available in most communities. For example, I briefly mentioned federal Medicaid and Medicare programs earlier in this chapter. But what do these two federal programs offer?

Medicaid is a financial assistance program designed by states operating within federal guidelines. The program offers payment for in- and outpatient care and services for certain needy and low-income persons. Also available is payment for nursing services, home health care, and, in certain states, drugs and additional services.

Medicare is a health-insurance program under Social Security, offering hospital and medical insurance. It is available to almost everyone sixty-five years of age or over, rich or poor. In addition, disabled persons who have qualified for Social Security disability income for at least two consecutive years can qualify.

CANCER CARE ORGANIZATIONS

The American Cancer Society is a national voluntary health agency conducting service and rehabilitation programs to help cancer patients and their families. Services vary from community to community.

218

If you are a leukemia, lymphoma, or Hodgkin's disease patient, contact *The Leukemia Society of America*, a voluntary health agency providing supplementary financial assistance to outpatients. Their program covers payment for certain drugs, laboratory charges associated with blood transfusion, X ray therapy for early Hodgkin's disease, transportation, and X ray therapy for cranial radiation for children with acute lymphocytic leukemia.

Cancer Care, Inc., is a voluntary Social Security agency devoted to serving advanced cancer patients and their families by providing supplementary financial disbursements in order to enable self-maintaining families to pay for nonmedical services for care at home. This aid helps pay for homemakers, housekeepers, practical nurses, and other special services. Persons living within the city limits of New York City and the surrounding fifty-mile radius may qualify for these benefits.

United Way services provide for such needs as day care for children, Meals on Wheels for homebound persons, visiting nurses, and rehabilitation. The services vary with locality. I would suggest you check with your local United Way agency for information on services available in your area.

The Salvation Army, a religious and charitable group, devotes full time to social welfare and religious activities. Emergency financial assistance is available on a limited basis. Similar agencies include Lutheran Social Services and Jewish Social Services.

If you or your spouse are presently on active military duty or have retired from service, the *Navy Relief Society, Air Force Aid Society*, and *Army Emergency Relief Agency* provide emergency financial assistance to qualified persons. The Navy Relief Society can be located at a naval installation or through the local Red Cross. Air Force Aid Society offices are found at air force installations, while Army

Emergency Relief information can be obtained at most army reservations.

Another organization, the *Associated Catholic Charities*, offers financial aid in a crisis, basically for Catholics, but this agency will accept requests for assistance from other needy persons.

I have called the *FISH (Friends in Service Here)* organization in my own community to assist cancer patients with transportation problems pertaining to medical services. They have been helpful in furnishing emergency gasoline allotments for needy patients who must travel away from home for treatment. They also offer other services, such as referral information.

In some cities, there are cancer and leukemia associations funded by United Way which offer referral services, homemaker and home health assistance, sickroom supplies and equipment, patient counseling, and home visitation. Several of these associations help support our Make Today Count chapters located in their area.

County departments of health provide such assistance as public health nursing, physical and speech therapy, and nursing home placement.

The *ENCORE* program at local YWCAs offers services designed to help mastectomy patients regain strength through swim and exercise programs. If you are interested, call your local YWCA office.

The Visiting Nurse Association in your community offers professional nursing care to qualified persons. This care generally includes services provided by registered nurses such as injections, dressings, catheter care, enemas, exercises, and special treatment. Trained health aides, supervised by registered nurses, can help you with such things as bathing, exercising, and walking. As a homemaker service, trained people will prepare your meals and do light housekeeping for you. On specified days of the week, hot noon meals will be delivered to you in your home.

Visiting Nurse Association therapists also help you with physical and speech therapy.

These services are available to all persons. Payment is often arranged through Medicare, Medicaid, the Veterans Administration, or private insurers. If you are not eligible under a private plan for financial aid, fees are determined by your ability to pay.

Home Health Care Services under Medicare may be available in your community. Under the Medicare program for people aged sixty-five or over, or for people who have been entitled to disability benefits for twenty-four consecutive months, Home Health Care provides skilled nursing and other services at home.

To qualify for federal payment, these services must be provided by home health agencies participating in the Medicare program.

Professional part-time nursing care is provided, as well as practical nursing care. Therapy services are available, including occupational therapy to help you in creative and self-care activities. Medical supplies and appliances to include oxygen, surgical dressings, gauze, wheelchairs, crutches, hospital beds, oxygen tents, air pressure mattresses, and trapeze bars may be provided.

Physicians' services are available if you are eligible for Voluntary Medical Insurance under Medicare.

If you qualify for home-care benefits, you should find out what your benefits are as far as the number of home visits authorized per calendar year. You may be entitled to at least 100 home visits in 365 days under your basic hospital insurance.

If you want to learn more about home health agencies, ask the people at your local Social Security office, your doctor, or check the telephone book for the nearest home health agency.

There are private providers of in-home health care for persons who can afford the services. However, in many cases the cost for a private provider may be covered by Medicare or Medicaid. You should find out if the state where you live recognizes private health-care agencies as providers of service. These services may also be provided by a personal insurance policy or Workers' Compensation. If you pay for the services yourself, check to see if it can be a deductible item from your personal income tax. Call your local Internal Revenue Service office for this information.

When a person has been hospitalized and needs to return home, but still must have some medical supervision and nursing care, some type of home health-care services are necessary. One lady wrote to tell me that her husband had died after a several-year battle with cancer. "I didn't know that much might have been done at home to ease the many types of anguish we had to cope with," she wrote. "Unfortunately, we didn't know where or how to ask, or even what to ask for, and little was brought to our attention. I found out about nursing services at home quite by accident during a phone call to the doctor's office about help in bathing my husband. When the nurse did come (very quickly), I was so overcome by the relief of communicating with someone understanding, sympathetic, knowledgeable, and obviously concerned that I wept uncontrollably for the first time. It seems to me that there is far too much that can be done to ease pain and help families care for patients, but which is never done because of lack of knowledge about where these services are available."

I remember visiting a lung cancer patient in my own community. He was sitting in a reclining chair in the front room of his home.

"Where do you sleep at night?" I asked him.

"In this chair," he replied.

When I asked him why he didn't make arrangements for a hospital bed in his home, he told me it would be too expensive. I explained that a local church had a hospital bed available free of charge on a loan basis. It was not in use, so I arranged to have it delivered to his home that same night. He died in it early the next morning.

"What a shame you didn't get it to him sooner," someone said, after I told him the story.

I think we accomplished something. He was comfortable for at least one night.

Home health care is practical from a financial viewpoint, too. Considering the high cost of hospital care, I think it is worth considering home health care because of this fact alone. But the psychological benefits derived from being cared for at home are also important to consider. Your doctor must make the medical decision as to whether or not the cancer patient can be cared for at home. The family must also decide whether they can cope with caring for a loved one at home. Family conferences should be arranged to determine what needs to be done for the patient and how it can be accomplished. Determine in advance what resources are available. Ask individual family members to be responsible for investigating various resources available.

As an example of how much money can be saved by caring for patients at home, compared to hospitalization fees, the Blue Cross and Blue Shield plan in Maryland reported in 1978 that its home care program had resulted in an estimated $250,000 in savings in its first two years of operation. The average hospital stay was slashed by a full ten days. In Rochester, New York, the local Blue Cross plan showed an average daily cost of $25 per patient as against the $200 it would cost in a hospital. Other states have reported similar savings.

Estimates indicate that as many as 10 percent of hospital patients and perhaps 25 percent of nursing home residents could be cared for in their homes.

As an indication of the growing interest in home health care, nearly three hundred hospitals operate their own home care agencies, for patients released from their hospitals.

I would recommend that you check the qualifications of staff members if you are considering a home health-care agency to help care for you. Find out if the service is certified by Medicare. Approximately 2,500 agencies in the United States are certified by the Department of Health, Education, and Welfare to provide health-care services in the home. This means the agency meets minimal federal standards and qualifies for Medicare reimbursement. But the lack of Medicare certification doesn't necessarily mean the agency doesn't provide quality service to patients. It could be located in a state that has no licensing laws. To be safe, check with your physician or hospital staff members.

Be sure to thoroughly investigate sources that will help you pay for home health-care services. If you don't, you may end up paying more money out of your own pocket for home health care than you would in the hospital for covered expenses.

The cost of caring for seriously ill children at home is far less than the cost of the same care provided in a hospital. If the child's doctor feels home care will provide the child with proper medical support, then the additional psychological benefits of the child being at home with those who love him make this approach even more sensible.

(I am talking about home care of terminally ill children who no longer receive active medical treatment. The main things that can be done for these children are to make them comfortable and to keep the pain under control.)

Visiting nurses can show the family how to care for the child, including how to give injections of drugs. Family members can even learn to administer the child's intravenous feedings.

Home care of dying children allows family relationships to develop. This would probably not happen in a hospital. Such development can result in fewer family problems after the death of a child.

If you are considering caring for someone you love in your home, you must realize it is not always easy. Family schedules must be adjusted. The patient's room must be in a quiet part of the house. A balanced diet must be provided. Someone must be responsible for medications. The patient must be allowed to care for himself, if this is possible. If the patient cannot bathe, feed, or shave himself, then someone must do it for him.

I know the challenge of caring for someone at home sounds like a formidable task, but I have talked with many persons who have done this and the majority of them feel they have benefited from it. Home care of a loved one diminishes feelings of guilt because families know they have done something to improve the quality of life for the patient.

Family members helping to take care of a loved one at home should always remember that help is available. Just the other day, a Make Today Count member called to tell me how depressed she was after taking care of her husband at home for two months. Prior to his arrival back home from the hospital, she told me how happy she was that he was coming home.

"How long has it been since you have been away from your home, visiting with friends, or doing something relaxing?" I asked her.

"Oh, I haven't left the house except to go shopping or pick up my husband's medicine!" she exclaimed.

She didn't realize trained persons could come to her home on a temporary basis to care for her husband while she was gone, or to help care for him even while she was home.

I believe there should be special community training programs for families who are contemplating caring for a loved one at home.

I also favor the establishment of a single central organization within each community to help families in locating resources available to them when a loved one is seriously ill. I believe hospitals should provide some sort of counseling service for patients and families, to help them with their financial problems and to acquaint them with the resources that might be available to them. Often, the problem is not to provide more resources for seriously ill patients and their families, but rather to let them know what is already available to them. For example, they could be informed of support programs such as Make Today Count, United Ostomy, and Reach to Recovery.

I hope that someday hospitals will help families obtain temporary housing when a loved one is hospitalized with a serious illness. For example, Children's Hospital at Stanford in Palo Alto, California, promotes involvement of parents in their child's treatment, and parents are allowed to remain overnight in the room of a hospitalized child. At St. Jude's Children's Research Hospital in Memphis, Tennessee, children receive care on an outpatient basis, when possible, and the child lives near the hospital in a motel room with one of his parents. If the family cannot pay, the institution pays for lodging and meals. When possible, the child lives at home and receives treatment from his family doctor, who consults with the hospital staff.

There are private medical and dental plans available in

some areas of the United States. Basically, you pay a flat fee per month as you would for insurance coverage, and when you are in need of hospitalization, either it is free of charge under your coverage or you pay a basic charge (two dollars under some plans) for each visit. The Kaiser Permanente Medical Center in San Diego is one example of this type of medical service.

Some private and religious foundations offer financial help to organizations that support patients and their families. You may want to check in your community to ascertain if there are any organizations offering specialized help with baby-sitting needs, financial assistance for transportation to and from medical centers, and other requirements not covered by your present insurance plan or any other resource.

During the years I have been involved with seriously ill patients and their families, I have found many needy people are reluctant to accept what they consider to be "charity." I would recommend they consider the fact that sometimes we do need help, and without this help we cannot hope to recover from a catastrophe such as cancer. Assistance is often available, if you will only make your needs known, and make the effort to locate the organizations that offer assistance.

12

Facing Death When There Is No Choice

"A PERMANENT CESSATION of all vital functions; the end of life," is the definition one dictionary gives for death. But considering our ability to keep people alive for long periods of time with artificial means, it is no longer acceptable to state that death occurs when the heart stops beating of its own accord.

Not long ago, I read of a device that probes deep inside the human brain to find the answer to a new question: When does "brain death" occur? The instrument consists of earphones that transmit "clicks" through nerve centers deep in the brain. Reactions are recorded on a graph and physicians can tell where the damage is located.

Why not use the heart as a basis for attesting to the death of a human being? The problem in using this determination of death is that doctors can use modern medical machinery to restart hearts that have quit beating. Other equipment can be used to keep lungs working until the body's own nervous system can start functioning again. Therefore, we need a method of determining when the brain function has deteriorated to a level where it cannot be resumed. If this "brain death" test can be legally used to establish the death of a human being, then doctors could cease artificial means of sustaining heart and lung functions without danger of violating laws when disconnecting equipment.

Just yesterday, I learned of a case involving a woman who was declared dead, but kept on life-support equipment because she had agreed to donate her kidney. An hour later she was alive, her doctors reported. Had it not been for the kidney donation agreement on her part, the life-support systems would have been disconnected and she would not be alive today.

Is this an isolated case? There is no way of determining this fact. Doctors and other health-care professionals are recognizing the new problems confronting them, stemming from the public's increasing awareness of such things as mercy killing, life-support systems, euthanasia, living wills, and death and dying processes. Doctors must search for new answers to such questions as: "Does a human being have the right to die and, if so, how can documents such as a 'living will' be legally recognized?" And "As doctors continue to make decisions concerning discontinuation of care, what criteria should be followed for ceasing life-support systems before brain death occurs?" In other words, who lives and who dies? How many human beings might have lived through a seemingly hopeless medical crisis if the life-support systems had been maintained?

On the other hand, how much anguish and financial drain on the part of loved ones could have been prevented if

229

doctors had either not used life-support systems in the first place or had given orders to disconnect them long before the family and patient suffered needlessly in the face of inevitable death?

And who "pulls the plug"?

During my lectures, when I discuss life-support systems, at least 90 percent of the persons in the audience raise their hands when I asked for a show of hands from those persons who feel life-support systems should be disconnected when there is no apparent hope for a normal life and there is reason to believe the patient may become a "human vegetable." But when I ask for a show of hands of those persons who would volunteer to "pull the plug," relatively few raise their hands.

What we need is a nationally accepted legal definition of death, plus some clear-cut guidelines for doctors to follow when making decisions involving life and death. After all, some of the doctors accepting such responsibilities have not accepted their *own* mortality, so how can they be expected to make rational or fair decisions involving other people's lives?

I would recommend a thorough study at the national level of the subjects of euthanasia, mercy killing, life-support systems and their use, and definitions of death. Theologians, doctors, lawyers, psychologists, nurses, patients, and family members who have experienced the lingering death of a loved one should be on the committee actively involved in the study. This select group should listen to testimony from both health-care professionals *and* patients and families. There are organizations, such as the Concern for Dying group in New York, that could be contacted and asked for comments and/or recommendations. The ultimate goal of this special committee would be to recommend a national plan for the care of dying persons in America, one that would include whether a person has a right to die and a new legal definition of death. Then doctors or patients and their guardians could be allowed to make the final decisions concerning the use or discontinuation of life-support systems, guided by the recommendations of the national committee. Also, these recommendations should be sent to each state so new laws defining death and other related matters could be passed. For example, in the Karen Quinlan case, which was widely publicized in the nation's press, the New Jersey Supreme Court ruled 7–0 that a person has a right to prevent his body from being invaded by life-saving measures and equipment. Also, these rights may be asserted by a guardian. A lower court in New Jersey had ruled that it is the physician, not the patient or guardian, who should decide the issue.

I feel we cannot permit the state to decide upon such personal matters as whether a person has a right to control his body. An individual should be allowed to decide whether or not to endure medical treatment when all hope of saving life is gone, or if the patient is unable to decide, then a guardian should assume this responsibility, as difficult as it may be to do so. If doctors are to decide these issues, then the laws should be clear about their responsibilities.

As we make these decisions, we should remember that the right to privacy is also the right to be let alone. The question is whether a dying patient or his doctor has the right to decide how long that patient might live or whether life-support equipment should be used in the first place. Or, if the patient is unconscious, does a doctor or guardian, or a previously signed living will determine whether the patient should be kept alive through artificial means or allowed to die?

In this age of advanced medical technology, we must remind ourselves that death is not an unnatural occurrence.

231

Death will eventually occur to all of us. Isn't the right to die as universally important as the right to live?

We can no longer ignore these matters as we continue to extend the lives of seriously ill patients. Recently, smallpox was reported to no longer be a threat anywhere in the world. At the turn of the century, the major causes of death in America included diarrhea, diphtheria, nephritis, tuberculosis, and senility. Today, these earlier causes of death are no longer considered to be a threat. Now, diseases of the heart, cancer, and strokes are the three leading killers, in that order. Antibiotics, antihistamines, cortisone, and antiviral drugs are changing the way we die. There is even a possibility that someday there will be a vaccine to "prevent" cancer.

In America the death rate fell to an all-time low in 1977 and life expectancy for the general population reached 73.2 years, the highest ever. So even though we continue to make advances in health care, we are unable to deal with the problems associated with dying. There are growing efforts to help patients learn to live with cancer and other catastrophic illnesses. There should also be new ways established to help people die when a continuation of life is no longer possible.

Before patients die, there are things that can be done to make their lives more comfortable. First of all, patients should never be allowed to feel they have been "sent home to die" without telling them they are not being abandoned and something can still be done for them. I talk with many patients who do feel this way, because of their relationships with doctors and hospital staff members.

Actually, much can be done for patients and their families if the physician chooses to look at the positive side of caring for the critically ill patient, instead of "writing them off." If a physician chooses to consider successful treatment without a probable cure an accomplishment instead of a failure, then the terminally ill patients can be helped considerably. Death represents failure to some physicians, though, based on the philosophy taught at medical schools.

Control of pain is probably the most important thing that can be done in making dying patients as comfortable as possible. Most of the patients I have talked with fear two things—pain and death. And the fear of pain was more often discussed than the fear of death.

Some physicians have tried treating pain not just as a symptom of a disease, but as a separate problem, and without resorting to drugs.

Although pain generally signals something is wrong somewhere in the body, once it becomes chronic some experimental programs indicate relief can be obtained from techniques such as self-hypnosis and relaxation. Also, biofeedback (a technique developed by some patients to gain a degree of control over body functions) has been used for tension and migraine headaches. These experimental approaches are still not universally accepted by physicians, but I feel that every method of relieving pain should be investigated.

Intractable (difficult to control) pain affects many, but not all, cancer patients. Until recently, little research was being done in the area of pain control. Now pain researchers are discussing possible new treatment methods and releasing some of the evidence produced by tests around the nation.

Heroin and marijuana have been suggested by some physicians as drugs that might ease the discomfort of cancer patients. There are indications that heroin relieves the pain suffered by many advanced cancer patients, while marijuana seems to alleviate the nausea often caused by the drugs used in chemotherapy treatments.

Since nausea prevents many patients from eating, resulting in forms of malnutrition, either marijuana, or a derivative of it, shows much promise, not as a treatment, but as a way to help make patients more comfortable.

At present, both heroin and marijuana are still classifed as drugs of criminal abuse. But it seems unlikely that a lung cancer patient, for example, who is suffering from excruciating pain intensified by coughing, would be guilty of criminal abuse if heroin was prescribed and used for the relief of pain.

However, there is one problem that may not have been anticipated when pain-killers were made available to terminally ill cancer patients. For instance, in Alabama during 1978, undercover agents were reported observing more and more heroin and morphine addicts turning to a lesser-known but highly potent drug called hydromorphone, popularly known as Dilaudid. It is a powerful pain-killer usually prescribed for cancer patients. Some financially desperate cancer patients are selling the drug to middlemen on the streets to help cover mounting medical expenses. The authorities are faced with the prospect of considering what to do with dying patients who violate drug abuse laws. Since the Dilaudid tablet sells for less than a dime with a legal prescription and for $40 on the street, the markup is tremendous. The drug is prescribed for patients by physicians at the rate of about one hundred per month.

One case in Alabama involved a lung cancer patient who sold the drug because he didn't want to leave his family with a large financial burden.

In another case, West Virginia state police didn't have the heart to arrest a woman dying of cancer and deserted by her husband who had turned to peddling marijuana to pay her high hospital bills. They made what they thought would be a routine "bust" and found the terminally ill woman was too sick to get out of her chair.

Some doctors feel we should not rush the passage of state laws authorizing the use of marijuana for the control of nausea and heroin for pain control until we further investigate their effectiveness. I agree with this approach, but I think we should continue to seek new and more effective ways of controlling pain.

Methadone, a drug used as a substitute for heroin in withdrawal treatment of addicts, has been used for controlling the pain of some cancer patients. The drug seems to work on the areas of the brain and spinal cord involved in the perception of pain. It doesn't make people drowsy like morphine does. Some studies have shown that methadone isn't addictive in cancer treatment, so it can be used effectively for patients who might be cured or who have hopes for a long survival.

Brompton's cocktail has attracted a lot of attention as a preparation for pain relief. I first heard about this mixture from Dr. Elisabeth Kubler-Ross. It is a drinkable combination of morphine, alcohol, cocaine, chloroform, and a syrup to make it taste better—although there are other combinations. The dosage has to be exact. It is generally made up by individual prescription for patients. Some doctors feel it is no more effective than other pain-killers, but I have talked with patients who were using it and many of them told me they were more coherent after taking it, compared to other forms of narcotics. Its effectiveness is still controversial.

One oncologist reported that he uses simple aspirin in many cases as a pain-reliever for cancer patients. Later, he resorts to codeine and then morphine, with Dilaudid as a final treatment, if the pain increases.

When I talk with newly diagnosed cancer patients who

235

express fear about potential pain, I stress that many patients suffer from little or no pain at all.

In discussing pain with both physicians and patients, I have discovered that the mind seems to play an important part in control. One oncologist told me he prescribed pain medication "as needed" for cancer patients and subsequently discovered that his patients did not require as much medication when they knew it was available to them. (There was still control exercised over the administration of the drugs.)

"I am more concerned about the comfort of dying persons," he told me, "than I am about addiction problems. After all, how addicted can someone become, if he has only a few weeks or months to live?"

But not all patients have such understanding and compassionate doctors. Some of my most heart-rending visits with patients have been those when someone in a hospital is suffering fron intense pain, while everyone nearby counts the seconds remaining until it is time for the next hypo.

It seems ironic and incomprehensible to me that the two things patients fear most—death and pain—are the two areas the least explored by the health-care professionals. And certainly persons involved in the care and treatment of patients have more difficulties coping with the issues associated with death and pain than with any other problem.

Judith Quattlebaum became so concerned about the lack of treatment for pain that she founded an organization called the Committee on the Treatment of Intractable Pain. From her office in Potomac, Maryland, she has waged a continuing campaign for more effective pain control in America.

The subject of euthanasia is often in the news in this age of candor about the subjects of death and dying.

What *is* euthanasia? The dictionary on my desk defines it as follows: "Act or practice of painlessly putting to death person suffering from incurable and distressing disease." Today, some people interpret the word to also mean the right to die, too. So some people today refer to *active* and *passive* euthanasia; active is the "mercy killing" aspect of the term, while passive represents many other acts, including "pulling the plug" and abortion. It becomes very confusing.

To me, euthanasia means inducing death to end suffering. This, of course, is unlawful and mercy killing is a crime. Nevertheless, an increasing number of people in America (over one-half, if the polls are correct) now feel that physicians should be allowed by law to painlessly end the life of a person with an incurable illness if the patient and family request it. Fifteen years ago, in 1964, only about one-third of the people in America favored euthanasia.

On the other hand, a poll of physicians indicated that the great majority of them felt patients should not have the right to ask doctors to end their lives.

I agree with the physicians who felt that patients and families should not be allowed to make decisions to end their lives. Most of us are not qualified to make these decisions alone. For instance, if a young person injured in a diving accident is paralyzed from the neck down and, because of the paralysis, asks a loved one to end his life, should the act of mercy killing, if carried out, be sanctioned? I do not think so. How many of us are aware of the advancements made in the rehabilitation of quadraplegics? Not enough to warrant making decisions involving mercy killing. However, I *do* feel *someone*, or a group of persons, should have the right to consider each case individually and decide whether euthanasia should be allowed. Certainly the patient, if possible, and the family, if there is one, should be a part of the decision-making process.

There is another aspect of euthanasia which we must consider: the act of euthanasia for deformed and retarded children at birth. The question always is this: *Who* makes the decision and how can it be legalized but still controlled? I think physicians must be the focal point of such decisions. The courts must someday consider laws which would allow certain forms of euthanasia involving retardation and other serious problems for newborn children, as well as for persons suffering from incurable diseases, for whom there is no hope.

All of us have heard something like this from cancer patients, I'm certain: "The doctors gave me six months to live and that was two years ago!" Certainly no one can predict the day of one's death. Generally, doctors can be reasonably sure when the end is apparently near. But even doctors can be mistaken.

Sally Wecksler, my literary agent who lives in New York City, told me the following story about her mother, a cancer patient:

"My mother's cancerous condition was deemed inoperable; however, the doctors recommended a series of radiation treatments to prolong her life. After one series, the doctors urged that my mother take additional treatments as they had found evidence that there was cancerous tissue in her chest. Although reluctant to do so, she finally agreed. The severity of the burns caused by the radiation made her extremely ill and her condition deteriorated until she collapsed and was put on the critical list. Her internist, a man in his late sixties, was most compassionate and advised us (father, brother, and myself) to place my mother in a fancy nursing home where she could be made comfortable and die in peace. His prognosis for Mother was six weeks to two months.

"I guess my father, brother, and I felt my mother deserved better after all the suffering she had gone through as a result of the treatment intended to prolong her life, and we called in a young doctor attached to another hospital. He did not promise a miracle, but said my mother could regain her strength and spend some years in comparatively good health. He also assured us that she would not suffer in the event there would be a relapse. Six or eight months after the first doctor had pronounced her end, my mother attended a relative's wedding and was among the first guests to rise and join a Hora which, I assure you, is a most vigorous dance.

"She lived three years beyond the illness, years of peace and tranquility. Her relationship with my father was never better and all treasured her company. What if we had let her go—in 'peace and comfort'—as the first doctor recommended? I do not blame him since he meant to be kind and had seen a great deal of suffering. But in projecting the end in his manner, he also downed my mother's spirits; the other doctor gave her hope and built up her will to live. I don't know what the right answer is, if one is faced with 'pulling the plug.' I just don't know who decides, who pronounces 'the end'."

I believe that more than one physician should be involved in the decision-making process when euthanasia is being considered. Perhaps each hospital could appoint several persons, including two or more physicians, to serve as a group who would make such decisions if laws could be enacted which would define and qualify euthanasia.

Another subject often discussed today is the "living will." To help make their feelings about their own death known, in the event they become terminally ill or are dying of an incurable illness, the living will in various forms, which can be signed by individual patients, has been promoted by various organizations. Among them is the Concern for Dying Educational Council in New York. (Their living will appears in Appendix D of this book.) Its legality has never been tested in a court case. As the Concern for Dying Council emphasizes, it stands as a written document signed by the patient, asserting his individual right to self-determination over his own body. If not legally binding, it is nevertheless an advisory document.

Millions of these living wills have been distributed throughout America in various forms, but the one prepared by the Concern for Dying Council seems to be the most popular version. The council recommends the will, once signed, be discussed with a doctor, family members, and/or a lawyer.

If persons signing the living will would like to add specific statements in the space provided for that purpose above the signature, the Concern for Dying Council suggests the following:

"I appoint _____ to make binding decisions concerning my medical treatment."

"I have discussed my views as to life-sustaining measures with the following who understand my wishes _____.

"Measures of artificial life support in the face of impending death that are especially abhorrent to me are:

a. Electrical or mechanical resuscitation of my heart when it has stopped beating.

b. Nasogastric tube feedings when I am paralyzed and no longer able to swallow.

c. Mechanical respiration by machine when my brain can no longer sustain my own breathing.

"If it does not jeopardize the chance of my recovery to a meaningful and sentient life or impose an undue burden on my family, I would like to live out my last days at home rather than in a hospital.

"If any of my tissues are sound and would be of

value as transplants to help other people, I freely give my permission for such donation."

If you would like a copy of the living will, write to the Concern for Dying, 250 West 57th Street, New York, NY 10019, or call 212 246-6962. There is no charge for the living will, but the Concern for Dying Council asks for a tax-deductible contribution, if possible.

Several versions of the living will, generally called the "Christian living will" and distributed by various religious groups, differ from the original in that certain statements and phrases are added stressing the Christian approach to death. My own version of a Christian will appears in Appendix D.

Another question faced by many of us is whether or not we should donate our organs and bodies for research. Human bodies are an indispensable aid in medical teaching and research. Human anatomy is the basis of all medical knowledge, and without the human body, it cannot be learned.

Some people question the possible religious objections to willing one's body to medical science, but the practice apparently is approved by Catholic, Protestant, and Reformed Jewish religious leaders in America.

Another question asked by persons who are considering the bequest of their bodies for research is whether or not they can later change their minds. The deed may be altered, canceled, or revoked by writing the medical school where the donation was made.

Some people still think they can "sell" their bodies to medical schools, but no medical school in America is permitted, by law, to purchase any person's body.

Bodies of donors are acceptable even though the eyes have been donated to an eye bank. If you are also considering the donation of your heart, kidneys, or other organs for transplantation, you should contact the medical school where the donation of your body is to be made to determine the need for bequests of this nature. Transplantation requires a special type of donor who must become available at exactly the right time, under the right conditions.

If you plan to be a donor, you should know that autopsied bodies are not acceptable. Also, physical condition, rather than age, is the most important factor.

Even though you make arrangements to donate your body to medical science, a funeral service can be held with the body in the casket at the chapel. However, the funeral director should know about the bequest before removal of a body to the funeral home.

After the scientific study has been completed, which may take from one to two years, the body will be cremated. Arrangements can probably be made for the medical school to return the ashes in a suitable container to surviving relatives or to a cemetery for final disposition.

I have not personally made arrangements for the donation of my own body. My own feeling is that the donation of my body for medical science purposes would violate my belief that the body should not be subject, even after death, to such things as would be done to it at medical schools. Thank goodness everyone doesn't feel this way or advancements in the field of diagnosis and treatment would be slowed considerably, since cadavers offer medical students an opportunity to study the human body firsthand.

I do believe much good comes from the donation of organs for transplant. However, this is once again a personal decision which should be made by individuals after much thought, during a time when they are healthy, or by families who feel some benefits should come from the death of a loved one. Because of transplants from donors, hundreds of persons are living and enjoying eyesight today in the United States.

A sample Deed of Disposition of Body for Scientific Purposes appears in Appendix D. You will also probably be required to furnish the medical school with a medical history.

I would suggest you check with your local or area medical school for laws and regulations pertaining to bodies donated for medical research, since there might be differences from state to state.

One person we never like to think about contacting is the funeral director. Because of the Federal Trade Commission's report on Funeral Industry Practices, released in June 1978, there has been a growing interest in funerals and how consumers can reduce the cost of dying in America. For instance, more persons are opting for cremation than ever before, but the problem is that most people do not understand the cremation process.

Cremation may take place almost immediately after death or following a conventional funeral with an open casket. If a conventional funeral is held, there will usually be charges for embalming, use of funeral home facilities, and a casket, so the total cost would be about the same as the cost of a conventional funeral with ground burial.

The cost of the cremation itself and the disposal of the remains is much lower. One funeral director I contacted quoted a price of $160 for the cremation, plus $54 for transportation; from $100 to $1,500 for the container; and from $100 to $795 for professional services. His minimum charge for a cremation was $314.

Traditional services at this same funeral home started at $695, which included embalming, casket, professional services, facilities, and two autos.

Final disposition charges for cremated remains vary from a niche in a columbarium at $50 to $750, to burial in a cemetery at a cost of between $50 and $150. Scattering of the remains can cost as much as $250 if done through commercial services.

Disposition without a prior service in the presence of the body is called "direct disposition," and is even less expensive. Direct cremation, like direct burial, eliminates the need for many services of the funeral director. The body usually need not be embalmed. There is no viewing so burial clothing and elaborate caskets are not needed. With direct disposition, the body is removed from the place of death, the necessary forms are filed, and the body is cremated or buried in an inexpensive, alternative container or plain coffin.

Another choice available is the "adaptive funeral," such as a memorial service out of doors without the body present; use of a family-built casket in a traditional service; or the viewing of remains on a permanent viewing dais instead of a casket, prior to final disposition.

Since I am aware of potentially high funeral costs and grief-stricken spouses who are forced to make decisions while undergoing an emotional trauma, I have already made my own funeral arrangements. I checked with my funeral director and found that I can be buried for about $600 to $700, the amount covered by the Veterans Administration and Social Security. There will be no guilt on the part of my wife, because I have already discussed my decision with her. I don't want her to be faced with a bill for several thousand dollars from a funeral director when I can be buried with simplicity and dignity for much less. After all, will I be remembered with more love if I have a funeral service costing $2,000 than one costing $600? I doubt it.

What about typical funeral arrangements and costs? What will you be confronted with if you must make arrangements for someone? What decisions must you make? I turned to the Funeral Industry Practices report mentioned earlier for answers to these questions.

First, you must contact a funeral home. Sometimes this is done by a hospital or nursing home employee, if death occurs outside the home, but in most cases relatives decide which funeral home to call.

When the funeral director receives your call, he will arrange for someone to pick up the body and take it to the funeral home. Then cleansing and embalming takes place, unless you have informed the funeral director otherwise. The embalming process involves replacing the blood with chemical fluids and the use of cosmetological techniques to make the body look more lifelike.

Several hours after the body has been taken to the funeral home, you will have to meet with the funeral director, probably at the funeral home, to "make arrangements." You will have to furnish certain vital statistics for the death certificate. Many times the funeral director will help you file papers so Veterans Administration and Social Security burial benefits can be obtained.

There are two basic questions confronting you, as you begin to arrange for the funeral. What will be the final disposition of the body, and what ceremonies and observances, if any, will be held in conjunction with the final disposition? You may wish ground interment; cremation with a scattering of the ashes or placing them in an urn which is buried, placed in a columbarium niche, or stored in some other location; mausoleum entombment; or donation of the body for medical research.

245

You must decide if there is to be visitation or viewing of the deceased before disposition of the body or whether disposition is to take place immediately. Do you want some form of religious or commemorative service to take place, and if so, will it be held with or without the presence of the body? If a funeral service is desired, will the casket be open or closed? Where will the services be held—at the cemetery, a church or temple, family home, or at the funeral home? Your decisions will affect not only the way in which friends and relatives observe the death but the cost of the funeral itself.

If you decide upon a traditional funeral, viewing hours must be established, the ceremony scheduled, pallbearers and clergy contacted, music and flower arrangements made, and a hearse and additional limousines arranged for, if necessary. If you do not have a cemetery lot, you must purchase a burial site.

After the arrangements conference, you will have to choose a casket if you have decided upon a traditional funeral. Most funeral homes have a casket display room with up to forty models available for inspection. There are four basic types of caskets: softwood, nonsealer metal, hardwood, and metal sealers. Hardwoods and sealers are generally costlier. Some funeral homes have alternative containers available, such as ones constructed from pressed-wood or fiberboard, which are less expensive.

After the selection of a casket, you may have to choose a burial container to be placed in the grave as a receptacle. This is a requirement of some cemeteries.

After these decisions have been made, the obituary notice must be written and given to the newspapers. This will be done by the funeral director. The grave opening must be ordered and plans made for the procession and graveside services. The body is dressed, placed in a casket, and taken to the room for visitation purposes. Flowers may be ordered and arranged.

In addition to funeral costs, you will have to pay cemetery fees for plots, an opening and closing fee, monument fee, installation charges, and some type of perpetual care fee.

The grave marker or monument is an additional charge, which can be as little as $75 and run as much as you wish to spend.

You may be faced with making decisions about "third-party" charges for the funeral, such as clergy honoraria, flowers, obituary notices, and death certificates. The FTC report shows the total average amount to be about $200 for these third-party charges. An average breakdown of third-party costs would be: clergy honorarium, $35; death certificates, $14; and flowers, $150.

There are memorial societies in the United States that offer packaged funerals and there is a St. Francis Burial Society in Washington, D.C., which, among other things, sells low-cost wood coffins and coffin kits and ash boxes for cremation remains. A contemporary coffin kit, which you must assemble yourself, costs $115; assembled, it sells for $160. If you want a traditional coffin kit, with the time-honored design, the cost is $130; assembled, the price is $185. A birch ash box for cremations costs $35, while a pine ash box sells for $24. Both are assembled. A contemporary-shaped coffin kit meeting Jewish Orthodox requirements sells for $150. Anyone can purchase these items. Freight is C.O.D. from point of manufacture.

Wanda walked into the den just as I finished typing the above paragraph and I explained the low-cost coffins and how they could be purchased by anyone.

"Do you mean you want to be buried in a wooden box?" she asked incredulously. "It wouldn't be safe!"

247

"What would you be protecting me from by purchasing a more costly casket?" I asked.

She couldn't think of any specific thing, but somehow she didn't feel it would be respectable to have me buried in a wood box. But this is the way I want it. I have worked hard to keep pace with the rising costs of inflation and I do not want to have a large bill for my funeral be the final bequest to my family.

Why do people wait to make arrangements for something they know will occur someday? I suggest you make your own funeral arrangements now, whether or not you are ill. Shop around. Write your wishes on a piece of paper and make certain your funeral director, attorney, and responsible members of your family or your relatives have a copy. There should be a form, like the living will, so people can plan their own funerals. I am not aware of such a form, so I drew up one myself. You will find it in Appendix D. I realize we all point out that funerals are for the survivors, but so are the bills to pay for the funeral!

(Incidentally, if you want to contact the St. Francis Burial Society, they are located at 1768 Church Street, N.W., Washington, D.C. 20036; telephone number 202 234-5613. I am not endorsing their products, but I feel there should be alternatives for all of us who are willing to make arrangements for our funerals and burials ahead of time, thereby relieving a grieving family of this future responsibility.)

"Putting my affairs in order" is a phrase I often hear from terminally ill patients, as they deal with the many problems associated with death. From a practical standpoint, there are things *all* of us should consider. After all, we never know when "our time" will come. Perhaps the best time to prepare for death is the time when you are still healthy and able to do what is necessary.

If you have an insurance policy, check the beneficiaries. I have talked with social workers who have told me of persons who have died without changing beneficiaries, causing complex problems for the survivors. You should have all your insurance policies in one place, with the names and telephone numbers of insurance agents.

If you are a veteran of the armed forces, all discharges and other military records should be together. These papers are important when the time comes to process claims for burial benefits and pensions.

If you do not have a will, your estate will be distributed among your heirs according to the law. This could cause trouble and expense for your loved ones. You should name a guardian for your minor children in the event you and your wife both die. Your will must be witnessed. I know there is a trend to "do it yourself" in our society, but I would suggest you contact an attorney for the drafting of your will, since it is one of the most important things you will do during your lifetime. Through your will, you plan for the disposition of everything you have accumulated during a lifetime.

A will is in effect until it is changed or revoked, but it may be revoked or changed as often as you wish. State laws governing wills vary, so I suggest you follow your lawyer's advice in the preparation of this document.

I also suggest you make certain your spouse or a responsible person knows the location of all your important documents, including tax returns (often needed in preparing tax returns required for settling estates); debtors and creditors; existent trust funds; personal property records; U.S. savings bonds; securities, such as stock certificates and bonds; checking and savings account records; real estate records; automobile ownership proof; employee benefits, such as pension records; and keys to safe-deposit boxes.

You should be certain that a responsible person such as your spouse or close family relative has the name, address, and telephone number of your lawyer.

Marriage licenses, naturalization papers, divorce records, birth certificates, and other personal documents should be quickly located in the event of your death.

Even important documents are easily lost. I suggest you place everything in manila folders or envelopes and store them in a filing cabinet. I have a fireproof filing cabinet in my den, which contains our important records. I have additional photostatic copies of most of our important records.

One thing many people feel they cannot prepare for is grief arising from the death of a loved one. The death of a child or spouse is the most traumatic experience that can occur in your life. But there *are* things we can do, prior to death, to ease the burdens of grief and guilt. The guilt we often feel after the death of a loved one because of imagined offenses or a sense of inadequacy is a terrible load to bear. We might ask ourselves, "Why did I spank my child just a week before she was killed?" or "Why did I argue with my husband the day before he died of a heart attack?"

There is no way to totally prevent guilt. But how we live our lives together affects our future feelings when death occurs.

Barbara Joan Grubman of Woodland Hills, California, is a widow. Her husband, Don, died in his sleep, at home, following a previous heart attack.

"There will be time," Joan told herself prior to her husband's death, "time for me to get the courage to talk with Don about the fact that he is dying. I will gather him and our two sons around me and we will mourn together."

After the heart attack, Don was able to return to work,

but as time went by he grew weaker. Still, Joan could not find the opportune moment to approach Don to discuss death with him. She consulted her best friend and explained her dilemma.

"I want to talk with Don about his dying," Joan said.

Her friend suggested that Joan make a list of all the reasons why she loved Don and then read them to him. The idea appealed to Joan. Late that night she compiled the list.

"Would you like to know all the reasons why I love you?" she asked her husband.

"Yes," he replied, his face lighting up.

"When you tell us you are going to do something, you keep your word." The list contained more reasons, but they were more personal. When she was finished, Don simply said, "Thank you," but the look in his eyes said much more.

A few days later, Don started speaking in Yiddish, using phrases he had first learned in his grandmother's house in the Bronx. On the evening of the same day, he said to Joan, "I must be dying. I remember all my Yiddish."

Three days later, he died. The farewell talk will never be forgotten; its words, like fine wine, will grow more precious with the passage of time.

You should do the important things that need to be done or say what you want to say, before death occurs.

Bill Bonner, from West Burlington, Iowa, who is a friend of mine, learned his younger brother, Chris, from Cottandale, Alabama, was dying from cancer. Both Bill and Chris loved to fish. The brothers were determined to enjoy some bass fishing while there was still time. Chris came to West Burlington and I went fishing with him and Bill at a farm lake nearby. I can still see a picture of Chris in my mind, casting a fly rod at the edge of the lake while the April sun slipped up on us from behind the faraway Iowa hills. And once Bill, Chris, and some friends spent a week on a houseboat, fishing and enjoying themselves. Bill still talks about these episodes of their lives together before Chris died.

Most of our friends and relatives don't want us to talk about the death of a loved one or express our grief openly. Most of them will give you a pat on the back and say, "Now, don't talk about it. It's best you forget." But it isn't best that you hold back your emotions. The grief is not going to disappear just because you don't talk about it. Relatives and friends should encourage a grieving survivor to talk about their sorrow if they want do do so.

Holding back your emotions may even cause problems for you in the future. I have met people who told me they had never grieved over the loss of a father, mother, or some other loved one, so the grief remains unresolved.

Don't shield children from the grief of death, either. Don't tell a child, after the death of a mother, that she has "gone away on a long trip." If the child wants to participate in the funeral activities, let him. Don't insist, though, if the child is reluctant. I would encourage you to cry with a child, if both of you are grieving. Allow the child to work through his grief. Not discussing the death of a loved one with a child will probably cause emotional problems later in life. And don't say, "God took your mother away." The child may blame God for the death. Don't evade the subject of death when talking with the child. Answer the child's questions honestly and if he wants to talk about the person who has died, allow him to do so.

We cannot change the reality of death. The loss of a loved one is a terrible shock for us. But death occurs. We cannot escape its touch. Making today count before death and learning to cope with it when and after it happens are the only effective answers to the problems associated with the loss of a loved one.

As I prepare to write the final words of the last chapter of this book, the calendar on the wall in my den indicates that only six more days are left until Christmas. I have noticed that Britty's eyes have been sparkling brighter than the Christmas tree lights these past few days.

I am reminded today, as the snow falls outside my window on the frozen ground, how important this day is for me. What if it were to be my last day? How would I live it? Just the same as I am now, I suppose.

My friend Mrs. Deanna Edwards, from Utah, who is a music therapist (which means she sings to seriously ill patients in hospitals everywhere), wrote this song, which expresses how I would feel if I had just one day left on earth:

*If I should wake up on a soft summer morning
With only one day left to live,
I'd cherish the moments, and notice each color,
I'd give all the love I could give.*

*I'd light one small candle to brighten the darkness
And shine in the heart of my friend.
I'd take time to notice the view from my window
And walk in my garden again.*

*If I had just twenty-four hours for living,
The things that don't matter could wait.
I'd play with the children and hear all their stories.
I'd tell you I love you, before it's too late.**

*Words and music by Deanna Edwards. Copyright Franciscan Communications Center, Los Angeles, California. Reprinted with permission.

What will it be like for my family, the first Christmas at home, after I die? Life must continue. The world will not change because I am gone. This is as it should be. After the sorrow must come new growth. My sons and daughters will, I hope, grow to maturity. Even my little Britty will someday be a man.

I hope that I never die completely. Perhaps memories will bring back to my family and friends, occasionally, an incident from the past we shared together:

Wanda and I walking along the Atlantic beach in New Hampshire, as the tide came in.

A summer day in Disneyland at Anaheim and the children's laughter and how we felt so close to each other in the car, on the way home.

Our eighteenth wedding anniversary together (one we thought we would never share) and the candlelight dinner at home.

I wonder if dreams ever die? I hope not. I would not want my dreams to die with me. And it is important to me that I remembered.

Somehow, my darling wife,
I will remember you.
And, perhaps, you will think of me.
when springtime shadows caress lovers on an evening
                    stroll;
City streets go to sleep just before the dawn;
Drops of rain fall softly against your window on a
summer night;
And you hear a song that breathes a breath of love
into your heart.

I will remember you
In a countless stretch of empty space,
When loneliness surrounds me like flowing clouds
                              in eternity.
And I will remember
the touch of you from some nameless moment in the
                              ancient past:
A candle's glow that reached to warm the very depths
of me; the remembrance of you as I held you in my arms
at early dawn.
Does love
disappear
in the awesome realm of eternity?
No, I think not,
because,
some night, while you sit thinking by the fireplace,
and our children's laughter
  mingles with the whispered sounds of untouchable si-
lence,
And your life,
like a singing river,
blends with your memories from the past,
and you hear our favorite song
as an autumn night descends . . .
then—perhaps—
                  You will remember me.

Tomorrow, God will give birth to a bright, new day. I hope I am a part of it. I do not know whether, after winter passes, spring will come again for me. I do not even know what tomorrow holds for any of us. But today, I will love, dream, hope, and live each passing moment until tomorrow comes.

13

On a
Personal Note

SOME TIME HAS PASSED since I wrote the first twelve
chapters of this book. The world has turned around a
few more times. Christmas Day has come and gone.
We have stored our artificial tree in the attic until next year
(Mark has asthma, so we don't use a real tree) and we are
talking about the arrival of spring already.

Not a lot has changed during the past few weeks. In this
morning's paper, I read another article offering "new hope
for cancer patients," and the headline is misleading, as
usual. We have accumulated some more Make Today
Count chapters, including one that will open soon in India.
Some researchers have developed a quick diagnostic technique for viral illness that they say could save us millions of
dollars in costs for health care. We are continuing to make
gains in the treatment of childhood cancer, with more than

half of all the children with leukemia surviving for more than five years, but cancer is still the leading cause of death by disease among school-age children. Our nation's health-care givers are still debating the effectiveness of cancer treatment as compared to cancer prevention. We continue to discover, during this age of advanced medical technology, new diseases for which there is no known cause or cure. In the field of mental health, suicide by children of kindergarten and grade school ages is a growing problem. Many doctors are beginning to realize the importance of allowing more time for communications in the physician-patient relationship. In the field of cancer treatment, catheterization (the inserting of catheters or tubes through arteries) is taking the place of surgery in some cases when internal organs, such as adrenal glands atop the kidneys, need to be destroyed. The federal government has apparently convinced representatives of organized medicine that there should be a voluntary effort to cut down on the unnecessary use of diagnostic X rays to prevent possible irreparable harm. Millions of Americans continue to become the victims of drugs prescribed for them, with 57 million prescriptions for Valium and 15 million for Librium written in 1977, strengthening my belief that we are not treating the diseases in many cases, but merely covering up the symptoms. Plans are under way by the federal government to phase out the use of nitrite, a meat preservative suspected of causing cancer, forcing us to ask ourselves whether we want to die of cancer or food poisoning. A new generation of Americans, the younger brothers, sisters, and offspring of the rebels who shocked us ten years ago with their violent demonstrations of protest and different life-styles, is emerging. And a massive study of American workers indicates a growing number of them, especially college graduates, are dissatisfied with their jobs.

257

Despite our existence in a complex world, the threat of a thermonuclear war hanging over our heads, and a constant bombardment of the suspected causes of cancer ranging from grilled hamburgers to the air we breathe, I remind you that the sun still comes up in the morning and goes down at night, just as it did when Genghis Khan and his Golden Horde and Julius Caesar and the Legions of Rome walked the earth. Despite our fears and anxieties, our hang-ups and depressions, we still have reason to be thankful we are alive. Even though we may yearn for the "good old days," the fact is that we live in a world our forefathers could only have dreamed about. Yes, we must pay a price for the standard of living we enjoy in America and elsewhere, but the world will never be perfect. If we continue moving too rapidly along the route of scientific advancement, without proper checks and balances, then the common sense of the people in America will slow progress down until we can all catch up and examine what has taken place. I still believe in the power of the people.

I have visited with my doctors once more at the University of Iowa Hospital since completing this book. The enlarged node beneath my arm has grown no larger. The doctors are not convinced now that I am losing my remission. No one, except God, really knows what is happening to me from a medical standpoint. I have another appointment at the hospital in a month, but meanwhile no chemotherapy has been scheduled for me.

I do not know what God has in mind for me in the days ahead. I live one day and one night at a time. The empty drug bottles keep piling up in the medicine cabinet. I check each morning beneath my arms, around my neck, and in my groin for new signs of tumors.

As I contemplate the future and my potential role in it, I am often reminded of the words of the late Senator Hubert

Humphrey, on the occasion of the opening of a Make Today Count chapter in Honolulu: "The concern and prayers of my family and friends and the thoughtfulness of those who have also experienced cancer in their lives have given me comfort and encouragement during trying times. . . . I have only one prayer, but it is constant—'Keep me alive while I live.' "

To help *me* live, I have tried to master the secret of measuring time not by the passing years, but by acts and deeds; not by hours that tick away on the faces of millions of clocks, but by the sight of a sunrise or the touch of a hand upon mine.

How can I, a cancer patient who expected to be dead long ago, explain to someone else what it is like to awaken, early in the morning, and watch the fingers of the sun peel away the layers of darkness in the sky above me, while my wife and children still sleep? How can I describe the way I feel high on life, without the benefit of drugs or alcohol, while my heart still beats within me, as I watch the birth of another day—a gift from God—to be enjoyed and appreciated?

The last words of one of England's queens were these: "All my possessions for a moment of time." Material accumulations cannot purchase a sunset or one last moment for someone who is dying, but you possess the priceless commodity of time, making you a wealthy person.

Previously in this book I emphasized many of the practical things that can be done by and for seriously ill patients and their families. Now I would like to tell you, through my own experiences, about some of the important but less tangible ways the quality of your own life can be improved, whether or not you are ill.

I cannot paint a beautiful picture of life for you, leaving out the ugliness. It takes dirt to grow a rose. I have been with cancer patients while they vomited from the side effects of chemotherapy until I thought they were dying. I have comforted lung cancer patients as they coughed up clots of blood from their disease-ravaged lungs. I have held the hand of a little boy who was celebrating Christmas in September because he probably wouldn't be alive in December, and I cried when his fragile hands couldn't hold a toy. And I have learned about humility and compassion in hospital rooms across the United States and Canada.

I have learned to forgive others for real or imaginary wrongs and to realize that when I am wronged, it is the other person who really has a problem, not myself.

I have learned the importance of caring and sharing, because of all the Make Today Count people who have been helping others help themselves.

I have learned to not wait until tomorrow to do something I want to do. How many times have *you* put something away so you can enjoy it later, only to find that "later" never comes?

I have learned the significance of love and found it to be the most valuable asset of all, the only thing that really matters when nothing else is left to us. Only today, I saw love in the eyes of my wife, Wanda, and felt it later when Mark, Lori, Britty, and Tammy kissed me good night. It took me so long to admit how difficult it was for me to say, "I love you." Now love comes freely and I am not ashamed or embarrassed to express my emotions, for I am more concerned about being human than I am about being "masculine."

I have learned to appreciate the simple beauty of life around me, for I have searched for and found a single violet in springtime, nestled in the green grass in my backyard, and I have heard the call of a mourning dove on a quiet summer night in Iowa.

I have discovered the meaning of friendship because of my many Make Today Count friends and I realize how important it is to know there is someone who will not run away from you when your life has been touched by tragedy.

I have learned what my faith in God actually means to me and I know I will never again have to walk through the valley alone. He will be with me. I feel His presence somewhere in the bright morning sunlight and during the darkest hours of a winter night. He has opened my eyes to a radiant new world. He has touched me, a lone cancer patient, at a time of personal tragedy and has shown me that the road need never end as long as I have the desire to walk or crawl up the next steep hill.

If you are a person living with a life-threatening illness, remember that you cannot alter the course of destiny, but you *can* change your own attitudes toward life and death. You have one lifetime left to live, just as I do. Please don't waste it. If you are not ill, why wait until the fingers of death tap you on the shoulder before you become aware of life? Heed the words of Charlotte "Tiki" Galt, whose death by cancer at a young age I told you about earlier: "Go feel, live, love; don't be afraid. No one knows, and if they do, why care? for you are you."

I have so many things yet to do before I die. I want to walk along a beach somewhere, with my wife and children, and feel the soft, damp sand between my toes. I want to witness the resurgence of spring once again and feel the sun on my back as I walk through a woods in Iowa. I want to feel the first drops of rain from a summer shower and see another rainbow blossom in the sky.

I want to feel young again, and laugh and play, if only in my dreams. I want to relive some of my childhood, through images in my mind created by memories from the past.

Grandma ... Grandma ... can you hear me from where you are? Do you remember? Do you remember when the snowdrifts encircled our farmhouse and I cried because I thought they would reach the rooftop and we would never see daylight again? And do you remember, Grandma, when Grandpa brought you a bouquet of wild red roses which he picked from the bushes near the creek, in the woods by the country schoolhouse? I saw you wipe a tear from the corner of your eye with your apron, the first time I had ever seen you cry openly. Before, I had only heard the sound of muffled sobs coming from the darkness of your bedroom when you thought I was asleep. And remember, too, how I cried when I cut my finger on a pocketknife and thought I was going to die? But I'm not afraid anymore, Grandma. I have seen death and now I know for whom the bell tolls.

I pray to God that I be allowed to live with quality and dignity in my life until the bell stops its tolling and I am no more.

APPENDIXES

Appendix A

Glossary

ALKYLATING AGENT—One of a group of highly reactive
    chemical compounds representing an important class of
    anticancer drugs.
ANTIBIOTIC—An antibacterial substance produced by a living
    organism. An example would be fungus.
ANTIMETABOLITES—Used in chemotherapy treatment. Resemble
    metabolites, the nutrients a cell needs for growth.
    Mimic normal nutrients so closely that they are taken
    up by the cell through mistaken identity. Examples:
    5-fluorouracil, methotrexate.
BENIGN—Not malignant.
BIOPSY—The removal and microscopic examination of tissue
    from a living body for purposes of diagnosis.
BONE MARROW—Where body manufactures white blood cells
    that combat infection, red blood cells that prevent
    anemia, and platelets that help to clot blood and
    promote healing of breaks in the skin.

BONE MARROW BIOPSY—The act of removing a bit of marrow from a bone to determine possible cancerous involvement.

CANCER—A malignant tumor of potentially unlimited growth that expands locally by invasion and systemically by metastasis.

CANCER CELL—A cell of the human body so altered that it reproduces abnormally. (Also known as "mutant cell.")

CARCINOGEN—A cancer-causing agent.

CARCINOMA—A cancer growth.

CHEMOSURGERY—The use of chemicals to remove tissue.

CHEMOTHERAPY—Treatment by chemicals. Drug treatment for cancer.

CLINICAL—Pertaining to care and observation of sick people.

COBALT-60—A radioactive isotope of the cobalt element; an important source of gamma radiation used in radiotherapy.

COLOSTOMY—A temporary or permanent opening in the stomach wall to permit elimination of wastes.

DNA—One of the two nucleic acids found in all cells. The other is RNA. These two elements exert primary control over life processes in all organisms.

ELECTRON—Negatively charged atomic particle.

ESTROGEN—A hormone affecting the monthly cycle of changes taking place in the female genital tract.

HEMATOCRIT—A ratio of volume of packed red blood cells to volume of whole blood.

HEMOGLOBIN—An iron-containing protein respiratory pigment occurring in the red blood cells.

HODGKIN'S DISEASE—A form of cancer affecting the lymphatic and other tissues that play a part in an individual's ability to fight infections.

HORMONE—Chemical product of the endocrine glands of the body which, when secreted into body fluids, has a specific effect on other organs.

ILEOSTOMY—An opening in the small intestine, performed by surgery.

IMMUNITY—The body's ability to resist or overcome infection; it varies from person to person and from one time to another.

IMMUNOLOGY—The biologic discipline that concerns itself with the study of immunity.

IONIZING RADIATION—Radiation that tears molecules apart, leaving their fragments electrically charged. Used in radiation therapy.

LAETRILE—Cyanide-containing compound derived from pits of fruits such as apricots and used by some persons for cancer treatment. Considered by most doctors as a "quack" therapy but allowed as a treatment under specified terms in some states. (Also known as "vitamin B$_{17}$" or "amygdalin.")

LEUKEMIA—Cancer of the blood-forming organs, characterized by a marked increase of the white blood cells and their precursors.

LEUKOCYTE—Any of the white or colorless nucleated cells that occur in blood.

LYMPH—A nearly colorless liquid composed of excess tissue fluid and proteins, found in the lymphatic vessels of the body.

LYMPHANGIOGRAM—A test whereby a dye is injected into the body's lymph system and traced through X-ray techniques as it flows through the body; used to determine extent of cancer.

LYMPHATIC SYSTEM—Circulatory network of vessels carrying lymph and the lymphoid organs such as the lymph nodes, spleen, and thymus that produce and store infection-fighting cells.

LYMPHOCYTE—A colorless weakly motile cell produced in lymphoid tissue.

LYMPHOMAS—Cancers of the lymphatic system.

LYMPHOMARCOMA—A cancer arising in lymphatic tissue.

MALIGNANT—Tending to produce death or deterioration.

MAMMOGRAPHY—X-ray examination of the breasts.

MASTECTOMY (RADICAL)—Removal of breast and muscles beneath the breast down to wall of chest. Removal of lymph nodes beneath arm.

METASTASIS—The transfer of disease from one part of the body to another.

METASTASIZE—To spread by metastasis.

NEOPLASM—Any abnormal growth, usually a tumor.

NEUROBLASTOMA—A malignant tumor of the nervous system, composed of immature nerve cells.

NEUTRON—An electrically neutral or uncharged particle of matter found in the nucleus of an atom.

ONCOLOGY—The study of tumors.

OSTOMY—A body opening performed by surgery.

PALLIATIVE—To reduce the violence of a disease; providing relief.

PALPABLE—Capable of being touched or felt.

PAPILLOMA—Benign tumors, such as a wart, occurring in the skin or the lining of the internal organs.

PAP TEST (or "pap smear")—A technique that involves the microscopic examination of cells collected from the vagina or other body cavity.

PHARMACOLOGY—The science of drugs.

PLACEBO—An inactive substance given to patients in controlled evaluation of drugs. "Sugar pills."

PLANT ALKALOIDS—Chemotherapy drugs, derived from extracts of the common periwinkle plant. Examples: vinlastine sulfate and vincristine sulfate.

PLATELETS—Disk-shaped particles in the blood which play a role in coagulation.

PSYCHIATRY—A branch of medicine that deals with mental, emotional, or behavioral disorders.

PSYCHOLOGY—The study of the mind and human behavior.

RADIATION—The release of energy from matter through waves, such as ultraviolet or X rays, or energetic particles, such as neutrons or electrons.

RADIOLOGY—The use of radiant energy (such as X rays and radium) in the diagnosis and treatment of disease.

Glossary

RADIUM—An intensely radioactive metallic element found in minute quantities in minerals.

REMISSION—A diminution or abatement of the symptoms of a disease; also the period during which such abatement occurs.

SPONTANEOUS REGRESSION (OR REMISSION)—Tumors that disappear for unknown reasons.

TOXIC—Poisonous.

TUMOR—An abnormal mass of tissue.

URINARY OSTOMY—A surgical opening in the urinary tract.

WHITE BLOOD CELL—A blood cell that does not contain hemoglobin.

X RAYS—Penetrating radiations of the same general nature as light, but of an extremely short wavelength.

Appendix B

General Information About Cancer

There is no way I can furnish you with all the resources that are available to you, but in this appendix you will find a rather complete cross section of organizations supporting the seriously ill patient, as well as books, pamphlets, and brochures which may be of help to you and your family. Some are free; others are for sale. I am promoting none of the items, nor do I necessarily endorse the organizations listed. However, I have tried to be selective.

I would like to remind you that organizations have their addresses changed occasionally and even telephone numbers may change. The list in this appendix is as up-to-date as possible at the time of this writing. I hope you will be able to find some help in these pages. Nothing like this was available when I was first diagnosed as a cancer patient.

Hot Lines for Information About Cancer

If you have questions about cancer and don't know where to turn for an answer, try dialing one of the following numbers. The Cancer Information Service Hot Line numbers (most of which are toll-free numbers) are sponsored by the National Cancer Institute, which is a branch of the National Institutes of Health. The services are free. When you call, you will reach a staff person who has received special training in answering questions in layman's terms. I visited one of the centers in California and was impressed with the staff members on duty and the supervisory personnel. Incidentally, callers can remain anonymous unless they request more detailed, written information to be sent to them.

California:	From Area Codes 213, 714, 805: 1 800 252-9066. Rest of California 213 226-2374.
Colorado:	1 800 332-1850.
Connecticut:	1 800 922-0824.
Delaware and New Jersey:	1 800 523-3586.
District of Columbia:	202 232-2833. (Includes D.C. suburbs in Maryland and northern Virginia.)
Florida:	1 800 432-5953. Dade County: 305 547-6920.
Illinois:	1 800 972-0586. Chicago: 312 346-9813.
Maine:	1 800 225-7034.
Maryland:	1 800 492-1444.
Massachusetts:	1 800 952-7420.
Minnesota:	1 800 582-5262.
Montana, New Mexico, and Wyoming:	1 800 525-0231.
New York State:	1 800 462-7255. Erie County: 716 845-4400. New York City: 212 794-7982.

Appendix B

North Carolina:	1 800 672-0943. Durham County: 919 286-2266.
Pennsylvania:	1 800 822-3963.
Texas:	1 800 392-2040. Houston: 713 792-3245.
Washington State:	1 800 562-2875. Seattle metro: 206 284-7263.
Wisconsin:	1 800 362-8038.

If you live in an area not listed above, you should call the national CIS number: 1 800 638-6694.

OTHER INFORMATION SERVICES

In addition to CIS offices funded by the National Cancer Institute, several institutions across the nation sponsor local telephone services to provide cancer information to the public. All use NCI information materials. They include:

Kansas:	Mid-America Cancer Center University of Kansas Medical School Kansas City, KS 913 588-5280
Michigan:	Michigan Cancer Action Now Michigan Cancer Foundation Detroit, MI 313 462-9191
Ohio:	Cancer Center, Inc. Cleveland, OH 1 800 362-1454 (toll-free for northeast Ohio residents) Ohio State University Comprehensive Cancer Center Columbus, OH 614 422-5022

272

COMPREHENSIVE CANCER CENTERS

Comprehensive cancer centers are being formed in several areas of the United States. These centers cooperate with local physicians, community hospitals, medical schools, and other medical centers to form a nationwide system for the prevention, diagnosis, and treatment of cancer.

A patient's family physician is in the best position to detect the presence of cancer through regular, periodic examinations. However, when the presence of the disease is suspected or established, the physician may wish to consult cancer specialists. Comprehensive cancer centers offer consulting services to physicians and also provide new scientific information about cancer to keep practicing physicians abreast of research advances.

Treatment for some patients is best given in comprehensive cancer centers and other cancer centers, where teams of highly trained, experienced specialists can jointly determine and administer the most effective therapy or combinations of therapy. Other patients may not require the extensive research and clinical facilities available at these centers.

A list of comprehensive cancer centers follows. Most of these institutions are presently meeting the criteria, but some of the more recently named centers are not yet able to offer the total range of services. New centers are being added.

Physicians may contact one of the center directors listed to arrange for consultation with appropriate specialists, to obtain information about research advances, or to request that a patient be admitted. Members of the *general public* wishing information may get in touch with the centers by writing or calling the contact person. If the person listed is no longer at the center, ask for the new director or contact person.

273

Colorado Regional Cancer Center. Director: Charlene P. Holton, M.D., Colorado Regional Cancer Center, Inc., 1655 Lafayette Street, Suite 301, Denver, CO 80218. 303 832-3031. Contact: Mr. Roger Shaffer, Director of Education and Information, Colorado Regional Cancer Center, Inc. (same address and telephone number as above).

Comprehensive Cancer Center for the State of Florida: University of Miami School of Medicine, Jackson Memorial Medical Center. Director: C. Gordon Zubrod, M.D., Department of Oncology, c/o Department of Medicine, University of Miami School of Medicine, P.O. Box 520875, Biscayne Annex, Miami, FL 33152. 305 547-6096. Contact: Beth Strunk, R.N., Center House—Roof Garden, 1400 N.W. 10th Avenue, Miami, FL 33136. 305 325-6563.

Duke University. Director: William W. Shingleton, M.D., Director, Comprehensive Cancer Center, Duke University Medical Center, Box 3814, Durham, NC 27710. 919 684-2282. Contact: Diane McGrath, Ph.D., Communications Coordinator, Duke University Medical Center, Box 2914 CHS, Durham, NC 27710. 919 286-5697.

The Fox Chase and University of Pennsylvania Cancer Center. Director: Timothy R. Talbot, M.D., Fox Chase Center, 7701 Burholme Avenue, Fox Chase, Philadelphia, PA 19111. 215 342-1000 ext. 402. Contact: Mr. David Bennett, Public Information Officer (same address and telephone number as director, except telephone extension is 408).

Fred Hutchinson Cancer Center affiliated with the University of Washington. Director: William B. Hutchinson, M.D., Fred Hutchinson Cancer Research Center, 1102 Columbia Street, Seattle, WA 98104. 206 292-2931. Contact: Mrs. Nancy Wright, Communications Coordinator (same address as director), telephone 206 292-2925.

Georgetown University, Howard University. Directors: John F. Potter, M.D., Vincent T. Lombardi Cancer Center, Georgetown University Hospital, Washington, D.C. 20007. 202 625-7118; and Jack E. White, M.D., Cancer Research Center, Howard University Hospital, College

of Medicine, Washington, D.C. 20059. 202 636-7807.
Contacts: Ms. Eleanor Nealon, Assistant Director of
Public Relations, Georgetown University Medical Center, 3800 Reservoir Road, N.W., Washington, D.C.
20007, 202 625-7683; and Francis E. Miller, Cancer
Research Center, Howard University Hospital, College
of Medicine, Washington, D.C. 20059. 202 745-1406.

Illinois Cancer Council. Director: Samuel G. Taylor III, M.D.,
Rush-Presbyterian—St. Lukes Hospital, 1753 West
Congress Parkway, Chicago, IL 60612. 312 942-6028.
Contact: Mrs. Lorraine Hannah, Illinois Cancer Council,
37 South Wabash, Suite 507, Chicago, IL 60603. 312
346-9813.

Johns Hopkins University. Director: Albert Owens, Jr., M.D.,
Oncology Center, Johns Hopkins Medical Institutions,
Baltimore, MD 21205. 301 955-3300. Contact: Mrs. B. J.
Norris, Director/Public Relations, Johns Hopkins Medical Institutions, Baltimore, MD 21205. 301 955-6680.

Mayo Foundation. Director: David T. Carr, M.D., Mayo Comprehensive Cancer Center, Mayo Clinic, Rochester, MN
55901. 507 282-2511 ext. 3261. Contact: Bruce Douglass, M.D. (same address and telephone number as director, except telephone extension is 3922).

Memorial Sloan-Kettering Cancer Center. Director: Lewis
Thomas, M.D., Memorial Sloan-Kettering Cancer Center, 1275 York Avenue, New York, NY 10021. 212
879-3000 ext. 2086. Contact: Mr. T. Gerald Delaney,
Director of Public Affairs (same address and telephone
number as director, except telephone extension is
2381).

Roswell Park Memorial Institute. Director: Gerald P. Murphy,
M.D., Roswell Park Memorial Institute, Buffalo, NY
14203. 716 845-5770. Contact: Mr. Merl Solomon, Public Information Officer (same address as director). 716
845-5746.

Sidney Farber Cancer Center. Director: Emil Frei III, M.D.,
Sidney Farber Cancer Center, 35 Binney Street, Boston,
MA 02115. 617 734-6000 ext. 3140. Contact: Mr. Darwin C. Farber, Director of Planning and Development

(same address and telephone number as director, except telephone extension is 3177).

University of Alabama. Director: John R. Durant, M.D., Cancer Research & Training Center, University of Alabama in Birmingham, University of Alabama Hospitals & Clinics, 619 South 19th Street, Birmingham, AL 35233. 205 934-5077. Contact: Ms. Jan Walker, Comprehensive Cancer Center, 205 Mortimer-Jordan-Hall, University of Alabama in Birmingham, University Station, Birmingham, AL 35294. 205 934-2651.

University of Southern California/LAC Cancer Center. Director: G. Denman Hammond, M.D., Associate Dean, University of Southern California, School of Medicine, 2025 Zonal Avenue, Los Angeles, CA 90033. 213 226-2008. Contact: Gordon Cohn, Director of Health Sciences Development (same address as director). 213 226-2094.

The University of Texas System Cancer Center. Director: R. Lee Clark, M.D., The University of Texas System Cancer Center, M.D. Anderson Hospital & Tumor Institute, 6723 Bertner Avenue, Houston, TX 77025. 713 792-3000. Contact: Ms. Jane H. Brandenberger, The University of Texas System Cancer Center, Texas Medical Center, Houston TX 77025. 713 792-3030.

University of Wisconsin. Director: Harold P. Rusch, M.D., Director of Wisconsin Clinical Cancer Center, 7010 University Hospitals, 1300 University Avenue, Madison, WI 53706. 608 262-3850 or 262-1686. Contact: Mrs. Naomi French, Public Information Officer (same address as director). 608 262-0046.

Yale University. Director: Jack W. Cole, M.D., Yale Comprehensive Cancer Center, Yale University School of Medicine, 333 Cedar Street, New Haven, CT 06510. 203 432-4122. Contact: Mr. Henry Mandel, Administrative Director for Regional Activities (same address as director). 203 436-0517.

International Association of Laryngectomees (IAL)

Sponsored by the American Cancer Society, the IAL assists local clubs (named variously as "Lost Chord," "Anamilo," "New Voice") in their efforts toward total rehabilitation of the laryngectomee. IAL was formed in 1952 and presently has clubs located throughout the country and abroad.

At the request of the physician, the rehabilitated laryngectomees from this volunteer organization visit the laryngectomy patient in the hospital following and sometimes before the operation to help him emotionally and to encourage him to attend supportive club meetings. Speech therapy is a major component of the group's activities. Spouses of club members provide pertinent information to the patient's spouse and family. Other IAL projects include:

1. Seminars or institutes for prospective teachers.
2. A national program of special education in first aid and artificial respiration for laryngectomees.
3. A registry of laryngectomized esophageal speech instructors.
4. A program to inform employers about reemployability of laryngectomees.
5. Financial assistance, the type of which varies in individual divisions.

Further information may be obtained from the International Association of Laryngectomees, 777 Third Avenue, New York, NY 10017.

Reach to Recovery
(Breast Surgery Patients)

The Reach to Recovery program, administered by the American Cancer Society, offers emotional support, physical rehabilitative services, and other forms of nonmedical assistance to mastectomy patients. With the approval of the physician, specially trained volunteers who have themselves undergone this operation visit the patient either in the hospital or in her home during the postoperative adjustment period. Advice on breast forms (prosthesis) and clothing as well as basic exercises may be of particular interest to many patients at this time. Patients should, of course, discuss their individual exercise plans with their physicians.

For additional information on this program, inquiries should be directed to the American Cancer Society, Inc., 777 Third Avenue, New York, N.Y. 10017, or the nearest chapter or state division.

Ostomy Rehabilitation Program of
the American Cancer Society, Inc.

Emotional and social rehabilitation of ostomates is the primary purpose of physician-approved visits to the cancer patient by carefully trained volunteers who themselves have successfully adjusted to ostomy surgeries.

An ostomy is any type of opening in the body, while a colostomy is an opening into the colon or large intestine performed through surgery. A urinary ostomy is an opening in the urinary tract of the body, and an ileostomy is an opening into the small intestine.

With emphasis on the quality of living, program services, which are provided at no cost to the patient, are directed toward helping the ostomate adjust to the everyday experiences of work, marriage, travel, and recreation. Other program offerings include ostomy therapy training.

Further information is available through the nearest chapter or state division of the American Cancer Society, Inc., or the national headquarters at 777 Third Avenue, New York, N.Y. 10017.

The United Ostomy Association

The United Ostomy Association promotes rehabilitation services to ostomy patients and professional education. The association assists in the formation of new groups; offers advice to individuals needing help; and provides for the exchange and dissemination of ostomy information through brochures, manuals, and the *Ostomy Quarterly*, a magazine sent to all members and subscribers.

Local groups provide person-to-person assistance in the hospital or out of the hospital for new ostomates of all ages. Mutual aid and moral support among its members are emphasized through chapter meetings, which include educational programs and discussion sessions.

The executive director's office of The United Ostomy Association, 1111 Wilshire Blvd., Los Angeles, CA 90017, functions as a clearinghouse for addresses of ostomy mutual-aid groups all over the world. Addresses of individual enterostomal therapists and of stoma clinics may also be obtained from the Los Angeles office.

Candlelighters
(Childhood and Adult Cancer)

The Candlelighters was formed in April 1970 by a group of parents of young cancer patients in the Washington, D.C., area. Their efforts are primarily directed toward obtaining consistent and adequate federal support for cancer research and helping families of cancer patients cope with the emotional stresses of their experience. Currently, there are one hundred Candlelighters chapters across the country, and several others are in the process of being formed.

To benefit young cancer patients and their parents, these groups conduct a wide variety of activities, such as collecting blood, distributing bibliographies of available information, presenting seminars with outstanding medical and research experts, and sometimes even assisting researchers. Members also receive the national newsletter from Washington. Direct financial assistance to individuals and families is not available.

To obtain further information about the Candlelighters and its activities, write to Candlelighters, 123 "C" Street, S.E., Washington, D.C. 20003, telephone 202 483-9100 or telephone 202 544-1696.

Leukemia Society of America, Inc.
(Leukemia, Hodgkin's disease,
leukemia-related lymphomas, and multiple myeloma)

The Leukemia Society of America helps outpatients in need of financial assistance to obtain the following services:

1. Drugs for the care, treatment, and/or control of leukemia, Hodgkin's disease, leukemia-related lymphomas (such as Burkitt's), and multiple myeloma.

2. Laboratory services for blood processing, cross-matching, typing, and transfusing for patients with these diseases.

3. Up to $300 per individual in the first stages of Hodgkin's disease.

4. Up to $300 per individual for cranial radiation in acute lymphocytic leukemia.

5. Transportation of patients.

In addition, the society's continuing education program is directed toward both professionals and the public, utilizing such methods as seminars, printed and visual materials, and the mass media.

Individuals desiring further information on this national voluntary health agency may contact the Leukemia Society of America, Inc., 211 East 43rd Street, New York, NY 10017, 212 573-8484; or they may contact the nearest chapter.

Make Today Count, Inc.

Founded in 1974 by Orville E. Kelly, Make Today Count provides practical and psychological assistance to families and patients with cancer and other serious illnesses through group meetings that allow them to share mutual problems. A primary aim is to help these persons live each day as fully and happily as possible. In addition to group discussions, the organization offers printed and visual materials, personal correspondence, a home visitation program, and advice on how to obtain various benefits such as Social Security, Veterans Administration, etc.

Approximately two hundred chapters of Make Today Count are either in operation or being developed throughout the country and abroad. Information related to existing chapters or organizing new ones may be obtained from

Rodney Wittkamp or Orville E. Kelly, Make Today Count, Inc., P.O. Box 303, Burlington, IA 52601, 319 754-7266. Make Today Count chapters are located in the following cities. Call the local hospital, cancer agency, or look for a listing in the telephone book for chapter contacts. Numbers beside some cities indicate the number of chapters in that city.

Arizona: Phoenix, Scottsdale.

Arkansas: Little Rock, Rogers.

California: San Diego (8), Santa Barbara, Van Nuys, Canoga Park, San Gabriel, Los Angeles (2), Torrance, Downey, Ontario-Pomona, Long Beach (2), San Pedro, Central Orange County, Redding, Crescent City, Whittier, Ventura.

Colorado: Fort Collins.

Connecticut: Manchester, Niantic.

Delaware: Milford, Wilmington.

Florida: Fort Lauderdale, Tampa, Pensacola, Fort Walton Beach, West Palm Beach, Naples.

Georgia: Cordele, Savannah.

Hawaii: Honolulu, Wailuku.

Illinois: Arlington Heights, Joliet, DeKalb, Oswego, Belleville, Decatur, Batavia, Centralia, Morton Grove, Oak Lawn, Itasca, Chicago Heights, Lombard, Park Ridge, Elgin, Streator, Chicago (3), Mt. Prospect, Melrose, Dixon, Harvey, Evanston, Peru, Evergreen Park.

Indiana: Terre Haute, South Bend, Fort Wayne, Evansville, Richmond, East Chicago.

Iowa: Burlington, Iowa City, Mason City, Cedar Rapids, Ames, Des Moines, Storm Lake, Fort Dodge, Davenport, Newton, Pocahontas, Sioux City.

Kansas: Larned, Kansas City.

Kentucky: Owensboro, Ashland, Louisville.

General Information About Cancer

Louisiana: Shreveport, Baton Rouge.

Maryland: Baltimore, Silver Spring, Cheverly, Frederick, Hagerstown, Salisbury, Cumberland.

Massachusetts: Foxborough, Cambridge, Beverly.

Michigan: Battle Creek, Kalamazoo, Midland, Allegan, Orchard Lake.

Minnesota: Waseca, St. Cloud.

Missouri: Cape Girardeau, Fort Leonard Wood, St. Joseph, Columbia, St. Louis (4).

Montana: Butte, Missoula, Billings.

Nebraska: Omaha, Lincoln, O'Neill, Grand Island.

Nevada: Reno.

New Jersey: Lebanon, Edison, Boonton, Somerset County, Matawan, Willingboro, Summit, Lakewood.

New Mexico: Las Cruces.

New York: Pawling, Liverpool, Elmira, Richmond Hill, Clifton Spring, Hampton Bays, Rochester, New York City, Huntington, Staten Island, Rockville Centre, Hornell.

North Carolina: Durham.

North Dakota: Dickinson.

Ohio: Kenton, Rittman, Sandusky, Tiffin, Alliance, Dayton, Springfield, Youngstown, Columbus, Eaton, Wright Patterson AFB, Wadsworth, Xenia.

Oklahoma: Oklahoma City (2), Tulsa, Edin.

Oregon: Medford, Portland, Grants Pass.

Pennsylvania: Philadelphia, Pittsburgh, Chester, West Bridgewater, Butler, Sharon, Sellersville, West Reading.

South Carolina: Charleston.

Tennessee: Nashville, Jackson, Martin, Bolivar.

Texas: Hale Center, San Antonio, El Paso, Longview, Corpus Christi.

Virginia: Fairfax, Roanoke, Newport News, Staunton, Mount Vernon.

Washington: Tacoma, Gig Harbour.

283

West Virginia: Shenandoah Junction.

Wisconsin: Fond du Lac, Madison, Milwaukee, LaCrosse, Oshkosh, Wausau.

Canada: Calgary, Alberta; Saskatoon, Saskatchewan.

Australia: Newcastle.

Make Today Count Films, Books, and Brochures Available to the Public

1. Film, *Make Today Count*, a professionally produced, twenty-eight-minute, full-color documentary dealing with the problems Orville Kelly encountered when he first discovered he had cancer. The film also covers the initial efforts involved in organizing the MTC movement. Scenes of Orville Kelly's talks with patients are actual conversations. There are no actors or actresses. It can be obtained either through purchase or rental from MTC Film Dept., Box 303, Burlington, IA 52601, or from Brigham Young University Media Marketing, Salt Lake City, UT 84602.

2. Book, *Make Today Count*, by Orville Kelly, published in both hardcover and trade paperback. Both books are published by Dell Publishing Co., New York. The hardcover edition is $7.95 plus $.90 postage and handling, and the trade paperback is $3.95 plus $.90 postage and handling. Order through your local bookstore or from MTC Book Dept., Box 303, Burlington, IA, 52601.

3. *Newsletter.* An eight-page tabloid, with photos and articles, published eight times each year. Annual subscription fee is $10.00 and the fee is tax-deductible. Order through MTC office in Burlington.

4. Brochures: *Let's Face It* and *Make Today Count*. The *Let's Face It* brochure was written for advanced cancer

patients who realize there is little hope for recovery. Contains excerpts from letters written to Orville Kelly from patients, family members, and professional health-care persons. The *Make Today Count* brochure contains a description of the MTC program and its goals.

5. Make Today Count *Organizational Manual.* Contains material from various Make Today Count chapters designed to help new chapters organize with minimum effort. Covers most aspects of MTC chapter operation. Cost: $4.00 plus $1.00 postage and handling.

FINANCIAL ASSISTANCE TO INDIVIDUALS

Social Security Disability Income

If you have a disability that will keep you from working for a year or more, you may be eligible for Social Security benefits.

Monthly benefits can be paid to:

- Disabled workers under sixty-five and their families.

- Unmarried persons disabled before age twenty-two who continue to be disabled. These benefits are payable when a parent (or in certain cases a grandparent) receives Social Security retirement or disability benefits, or when an insured parent dies.

- Disabled widows, disabled widowers, and (under certain circumstances) disabled surviving divorced wives of workers who were insured at

death. These benefits are payable as early as
age fifty.

If a worker dies after a long period of severe disability,
but hadn't applied for benefits, his or her survivors may
apply within three months after the death of the worker.
Disability benefits are payable on the basis of credit for
work under Social Security.
Disabled dependents and survivors get benefits based on
the earnings of the worker.
Generally, to have disability protection for yourself and
your family, you need Social Security credits for at least five
years out of the ten-year period ending when your disability
begins.
If you become disabled before age thirty-one, the requirement ranges down with age to as little as one and a half
years. There are special provisions for people who meet the
Social Security definition of being blind.
If you are a worker or a person disabled in childhood, you
are considered "disabled" under Social Security if you have
a physical or mental impairment that prevents you from
doing any substantial gainful work and is expected to last
(or has lasted) for at least twelve months, or is expected to
result in death.
If you have an impairment that prevents you from doing
your usual work, then your age, education, and work experience also may be considered in deciding whether you are
able to engage in any other type of work. If you can't do
your regular work but can do other substantial gainful work,
generally you will not be considered disabled.
Vocational factors such as age, education, and work experience cannot be considered in deciding whether a widow or
widower is disabled.
A person whose vision is not better than 20/200 even with

glasses (or who has a limited visual field of 20 degrees or less) is considered "blind" under the Social Security law. If he or she is not working, monthly benefits generally can be paid.

For more information on special provisions for blind people, ask your Social Security office for a copy of *If You Become Disabled.*

Cash benefits (payable in July 1977 and later) range from $114.30 to $622.30 monthly for a disabled worker. If there are other dependents, family benefits can be as much as $1,089. The amount depends on the worker's average earnings under Social Security over a period of years.

The law provides that payments to a disabled worker and family members or to a disabled widow or widower generally cannot begin until the sixth full month of disability. A person disabled in childhood may be eligible for benefits as soon as a parent begins getting retirement or disability benefits, or dies after having worked long enough under the law to make payments possible.

It is important to apply soon after the disability starts because back payments are limited to the twelve months preceding the date of application.

A person who has recovered from a disability that lasted twelve months or more may be eligible for some back benefits. But if application is made more than fourteen months after recovery, no benefits are payable.

People under sixty-five who have been entitled to disability checks for two consecutive years or more have Medicare protection to help pay hospital and doctor bills. There's no monthly premium payment for hospital insurance protection, but people who want the medical insurance part pay a monthly premium.

Everyone who applies for disability benefits—whether monthly benefits are payable or not—is considered for services by the state vocational rehabilitation agency. Such services include counseling, teaching of new employment skills, training in the use of prostheses, and job placements.

These services are generally financed from state-federal appropriations. In some cases, however, Social Security pays the cost of rehabilitating disability beneficiaries.

If you are disabled and can't work, you should call any Social Security office right away. The people there can give you more information about applying for disability benefits. If you can't get to the office because you are hospitalized or housebound, a Social Security representative will visit you or take your application on the phone.

You will be asked to provide medical evidence about your condition when you apply. This evidence is usually a medical report from your doctor, hospital, clinic, or institution where you have been treated. If there is a charge for a medical report, you are responsible for paying it.

Additional medical information may be needed to determine whether you are disabled under the law. If this information is not available in the records of your own physician, you may be asked to undergo additional medical examinations and tests. The cost of these supplemental examinations will be paid by the government.

You can shorten the time it takes to complete your application if you have the right information ready when you apply. Some of the information needed is listed below.

Even if you don't have all of the information, don't wait to apply. The Social Security representative can suggest ways for you to get any other facts needed for your application.

Information you will need:

1. Your Social Security number.

2. When you last worked (month, day, year).

3. When you became sick or injured (month, day, year).

4. What kind of illness or injury you have.

5. If you are no longer disabled, the date you recovered or returned to work (month, day, year).

6. Names, addresses, and telephone numbers of doctors, hospitals, institutions, or clinics that treated you for your disability and the dates you were treated.

7. If you are a veteran and received medical care in a service or VA hospital, your service serial number and your VA claim number.

8. If you have been working, a list of the kinds of jobs you worked at most in the ten years before you became disabled.

9. Names, Social Security numbers, and dates of birth of your spouse and children.

10. Your workers' compensation number, if you have filed a claim for workers' compensation.

11. A telephone number at which you can be reached.

Rehabilitation: From the start, vocational rehabilitation workers and others who work with disabled people have played an important role in shaping the Social Security disability program.

Program provisions have been developed with the advice of rehabilitation counselors, social workers, psychologists, and experts in related fields. Members of these professions are still consulted on policies and procedures for measuring work potential and work performance and for encouraging rehabilitation.

Determinations of disability for Social Security purposes are made by disability evaluators and physicians working in an agency of the claimant's home state. Usually this is the same agency that administers the vocational rehabilitation program. This is fitting, for a major objective of the disability program is to encourage disabled persons to undertake rehabilitation and become self-supporting.

Rehabilitation services are generally financed by state-federal funds. In some cases, however, Social Security pays the costs of rehabilitating those receiving disability benefits. This should save Social Security money because in the long run the cost of rehabilitating beneficiaries is expected to be less than the expense of paying them benefits.

Over the years, many thousands of disability claimants have been successfully rehabilitated. In addition, still more thousands of beneficiaries have been taken off the disability benefit rolls because of recovery or return to work.

At the time a person's disability claim is decided, he or she is also considered for rehabilitation services. All people applying for disability benefits, whether or not they are found eligible, will be considered. Those who are considered good rehabilitation prospects are interviewed and offered services by the state vocational rehabilitation agency.

It is the worker's present vocational capacity, rather than the ability he or she may attain after receiving vocational rehabilitation services, that is considered in determining whether the person is "disabled." Benefits may be withheld, however, if rehabilitation services are offered and the disabled person refuses them without good cause.

Benefits to disabled people are stopped if they show they can do substantial gainful work and are, therefore, no longer disabled within the meaning of the law or if the person recovers medically (whether or not he or she has a job). Benefits payable to a disabled person who gets checks on another's earnings record also may be stopped by marriage.

It is sometimes difficult to predict whether a severely impaired person will be able to keep on working for any length of time. Therefore, the decision as to whether a beneficiary's work is substantial and gainful is usually put off until he or she has worked for at least nine months (not necessarily consecutive). Meanwhile, benefits continue. These nine months are known as the "trial work period." (The "trial work period" provisions apply to most disabled workers and people disabled in childhood, but not to disabled widows and widowers.) It gives the person a chance to fully test his or her ability to work, confident that benefits will continue without interruption while working.

In order to help the beneficiary adjust to being self-supporting again, benefits are continued for three months— the months in which the person is determined able to work and two additional months.

All the pertinent facts about a person's work are considered in determining whether a beneficiary's work is substantial gainful activity—skills, experience, responsibility, hours, productivity, and pay. Earnings of at least $230 a month—and sometimes less—will ordinarily demonstrate an individual's ability to engage in substantial gainful activity. However, if it is necessary for someone to help the person with work assignments, the dollar value of this assistance is not counted in figuring the person's actual earnings.

Although the amount of earnings is significant, other factors are taken into consideration. For example, if a person shows he or she can do more work or if the work is about the same in amount and quality as nondisabled workers in the community who do similar work for a living, then he or she may be demonstrating the ability to perform substantial gainful activity.

A worker in a sheltered workshop with low earnings is not considered to be doing substantial gainful work. It is not necessary to compare his or her work with that of nondisabled workers.

Substantial gainful work for a person who is self-employed is evaluated about the same way as that of a salaried person. All the pertinent facts about his or her work are considered—skills, experience, responsibility, hours, productivity, and earnings. However, business income is influenced by economic conditions, the value of unpaid services of family members, etc. Accordingly, more emphasis may be placed on the self-employed person's ability to work and less emphasis on the amount of his or her earnings.

If the disability recurs within five years, benefits can start again with the first full month of disability. The person does not have to wait five months as he or she did the first time. People disabled before age twenty-two and disabled widows and widowers whose benefits are stopped can again get benefits if disability recurs within seven years.

If you should have any questions about Social Security disability benefits, contact your local Social Security office.

Supplemental Security Income (SSI)

Another federal program is the supplemental security income, which pays monthly checks to people in financial need who are sixty-five or older and to people in need at any age who are blind or disabled. Benefits change, but at the time of this writing, a blind or disabled person should receive $177.80 a month, while a married couple could receive $266.70 a month. Some persons might get more or less than these amounts, depending on other sources of income and whether or not the state might add money to the federal payment.

In most states, a person who becomes eligible for supplemental security income is also eligible for Medicaid and social services provided by the state, as well as federal food stamp allotments.

What are the qualifications for supplemental security income? People who have little or no regular cash income and who do not own much in the way of property or assets that can be turned into cash may get SSI. Also a factor in disability benefits is the severity of the illness. To be considered disabled, a person must be unable to work because of an impairment which has lasted (or is expected to last) for at least twelve months, or which can be expected to result in death.

A single person can have assets up to $1,500 and still get checks. The amount for a married couple is $2,250. Not everything owned counts as an asset. A home doesn't count. The federal government does not ask for liens on the homes of people who get SSI. Personal effects and household goods also do not count as assets in most cases. Insurance policies and autos may not affect eligibility either, depending on their monetary value.

People can have some income and still get SSI. The first $20 per month generally isn't counted. People who work while receiving SSI can earn as much as $65 per month without any reduction in SSI checks.

Although the supplemental security income is administered by the Social Security Administration, it is not the same as Social Security. The money for SSI checks comes from general funds of the United States Treasury, while

Social Security benefits are paid from contributions of workers, employers, and self-employed persons.

Veterans' Benefits

Hospitalization: The Veterans Administration provides hospital or outpatient care when needed for all service-connected medical or compensable dental conditions. The treatment will be given at one of the many VA hospitals or clinics, or the VA may pay for outpatient care by a hometown doctor or dentist. Generally, the VA cannot authorize payment for services of hometown doctors or dentists not approved in advance.

Certain persons who were administratively discharged under other than honorable conditions may be furnished health care for any disability incurred or aggravated during active-duty service in line of duty.

Hospital care from the VA is provided on a bed-available basis for treatment of non-service-connected conditions, provided the veteran signs a statement of inability to defray the costs of comparable care. The statement of inability to pay is not necessary for applicants who are sixty-five years of age or older, or who have compensable service-connected disabilities, or who are receiving VA pensions. Hospital care is not available to the person whose entire period of service was in an active-duty-for-training status, unless he or she was disabled from a disease or injury incurred or aggravated in line of duty. Such disabled veterans are eligible for medical services on the same basis as other veterans with service-incurred diseases or disabilities.

Veterans receiving additional service-connected disability compensation or allowance, or increased non-service-connected disability pension based on their need of regular aid and attendance or by reason of being permanently housebound, or having a disability rated at 50 percent or more from a service-connected disability, may be furnished necessary outpatient treatment, including drugs and medicines, for any medical disability.

Dental services on a one-time completion basis may be furnished veterans with service-connected but noncompensable dental conditions which were incurred in service and existed at time of separation provided application is made within one year after separation, except the one year is extended in certain cases of correction of a disqualifying separation.

Ambulatory care may be furnished to veterans who are eligible for VA hospital care and who do not otherwise have entitlement to outpatient care providing the following conditions exist: An application is made for hospital care and a medical determination indicates that hospital care is reasonably necessary, but might be avoided by providing ambulatory care, or hospitalization would become necessary in the immediate future if the condition remained untreated.

Reimbursement of burial expenses: VA will pay a $300 burial allowance for any eligible deceased veteran. In addition, a $150 plot or interment allowance will be paid for a veteran not buried in a national cemetery. For veterans who die of service-connected disabilities, a burial allowance up to $1,100 in lieu of any other burial benefit will be paid. The veteran must have been discharged under conditions other than dishonorable and have been either a wartime veteran, or a peacetime veteran in receipt of service-connected compensation at time of death, or discharged or retired for disability incurred in line of duty. Claim must be filed within two years after permanent burial or cremation.

Burial flag: An American flag may be issued to drape the casket of a veteran of service after January 31, 1955. After the funeral service, the flag may be given to the next of kin

295

or close friend or associate of the deceased. Flags are issued at any VA office and most local post offices.

Interment in national cemeteries: The VA operates the National Cemetery System. The interment of a deceased veteran of wartime or peacetime service whose last period of service (other than for training) terminated other than dishonorably, or the spouse, widow, widower, or minor children of an eligible veteran, will be authorized in any national cemetery in which space is available. One gravesite is authorized for interment of eligible members of a family unit. There is no charge for a grave in a national cemetery. Cemetery employees will open and close the grave, and a headstone with appropriate inscription for each decedent buried in a grave will be provided by the government. Application should be made only at the time of death of the veteran (or that of an eligible dependent) by contacting the superintendent of the nearest national cemetery.

Transportation of deceased veteran to a national cemetery: The VA may pay the cost of transportation of a deceased veteran for burial in a national cemetery when: (1) The veteran dies of a service-connected disability; or (2) the veteran was in receipt of (but for the receipt of retired pay or disability pension would have been entitled to) disability compensation. Payment shall not exceed the cost of transportation to the national cemetery nearest the veteran's last place of residence in which burial space is available.

Headstones or markers: The VA will furnish, upon request, a headstone or marker to be placed at the unmarked grave of a veteran whose last discharge was other than dishonorable. If interment is in a national cemetery, a headstone or marker is automatically furnished. The headstone or marker is shipped, without charge, to the person or firm designated on the application.

Educational assistance for dependents: If you are completely disabled from service-connected causes, should die as a result of service, or should die while completely disabled from service-connected causes, the VA will pay up to $311 per month to help educate your spouse and each son or daughter. These payments are usually provided for children between the ages of eighteen and twenty-six and their marriage is not a bar to this benefit. In some instances, handicapped children may begin a special vocational or restorative course as early as age fourteen. Spouses and children of service personnel who have been missing in action or captured in line of duty for more than ninety days are also eligible for these educational benefits. For further information, call or write your nearest VA office.

Non-service-connected death pension: VA's death pension may be paid to eligible widows or widowers and children of veterans of the Vietnam era with ninety or more days' service or who were separated from such service for a service-connected disability, who have died of causes not related to their service. For payment of death pension, the term "veteran" includes a person who has completed at least two years' honorable service but whose death in such service was not in line of duty.

Special telephone service: Consult your local telephone directory under United States Government, Veterans Administration, for the number to reach a VA representative. Toll-free telephone service is available in all fifty states.

WHERE TO FIND
INFORMATION ABOUT CANCER

*National Cancer Institute Publications**

Single copies of the following publications are available without charge from the Office of Cancer Communications,

National Cancer Institute, Bethesda, MD 20014. Quantities can be purchased from the Superintendent of Documents, U.S. Government Printing Office, Washington, D.C. 20402.

The National Cancer Institute. DHEW Pub. No. (NIH) 75–792, rev. 1975 (E)
A booklet discussing the history, organization, and program of the National Cancer Institute.

Cancer: What to Know, What to Do About It. DHEW Pub. No. (NIH) 72–211, rev. 1972, leaflet. (E) $5.50 per 100 copies.
Basic facts about cancer and possible signs of early cancer. This leaflet is also available in Spanish as *Cancer: Lo Que Debe Saber, Lo Que Se Debe Hacer*, DHEW Pub. No. (NIH) 75–718.

Progress Against Cancer of the Bladder. DHEW Pub. No. (NIH) 75–722, rev. 1974, leaflet. (E)
Information on the causes, symptoms, diagnosis, and treatment of cancer of the bladder.

Progress Against Cancer of the Bone. DHEW Pub. No. (NIH) 75–721, rev. 1974, leaflet. (E)
Information on cancer of the bone, including diagnosis, cause, treatment, and research.

Progress Against Cancer of the Breast. DHEW Pub. No. (NIH) 75–328, rev. 1974, leaflet, (E)
Discusses detection, diagnosis, and treatment of breast cancer as well as causes and prevention of the disease.

Progress Against Cancer of the Colon and Rectum. DHEW Pub. No. (NIH) 75–95, rev. 1974, leaflet. (E)
Discusses the symptoms, diagnosis, and surgical treatment for cancer of the colon and rectum. Research being conducted to develop better methods of diagnosis and treatment is also discussed.

Progress Against Cancer of the Larynx. DHEW Pub. No. (NIH) 75–448, rev. 1974, leaflet. (E)
Discusses the symptoms of early laryngeal cancer, the importance of early diagnosis and treatment, and rehabilitation of the laryngectomy patient.

*(E)—pamphlets graded for easy reading
(M)—pamphlets graded moderately difficult

Progress Against Cancer of the Lung. DHEW Pub. No. (NIH) 75-526, rev. 1974, leaflet. (E)
Includes discussion of causes, diagnosis, treatment, and prevention of lung cancer, the most common cause of cancer death among American men.

Progress Againt Cancer of the Mouth. DHEW Pub. No. (NIH) 75-118, rev. 1974, leaflet. (E)
A discussion of the symptoms, diagnosis, and treatment of cancer of the mouth as well as factors contributing to the disease.

Progress Against Cancer of the Prostate. DHEW Pub. No. (NIH) 75-528, reprinted 1974, leaflet. (E)
A discussion of the symptoms, diagnosis, and treatment of cancer of the prostate, one of the most common forms of cancer among men.

Progress Against Cancer of the Skin. DHEW Pub. No. (NIH) 75-310, rev. 1974, leaflet. (E)
Discusses the detection, diagnosis, treatment, and causes of this most common form of cancer. Also discusses research under way.

Progress Against Cancer of the Stomach. DHEW Pub. No. (NIH) 75-527, rev. 1974, leaflet. (E)
Discusses the incidence, symptoms, diagnosis, and treatment of stomach cancer.

Progress Against Cancer of the Uterus. DHEW Pub. No. (NIH) 75-171, rev. 1974, leaflet. (E)
Describes the highly reliable cell examination, Pap smear, for detection of uterine cervical cancer. Discusses the nature and treatment of uterine cancer and research on the disease. Illustrated.

Progress Against Hodgkin's Disease. DHEW Pub. No. (NIH) 75-172, rev. 1974, leaflet. (E)
Basic facts about Hodgkin's disease, its symptoms, diagnosis, and treatment. Illustrated.

Progress Against Leukemias, Lymphomas, and Multiple Myeloma. DHEW Pub. No. (NIH) 75-329, rev. 1974, leaflet. (E)
Discussion of cancer of the blood-forming and lymphoid organs.

Childhood Leukemia—A Pamphlet for Parents. DHEW Pub. No. (NIH) 72-212, rev. 1972, 26 pp. (E)

Prepared for parents of children with leukemia to contribute to their understanding of the disease and its treatment. Information is divided into four major parts: normal blood and its proper functioning; leukemia and its treatment; the child with leukemia; and the parent of a child with leukemia. This pamphlet is also available in Spanish as *Leucemia Infantil — Folleto para los Padres*, DHEW Pub. No. (NIH) 74–368.

The Leukemic Child. DHEW Pub. No. (NIH) 75–863, 1975, 30 pp. (E)
A mother's story of coping with the problems of having a leukemic child, and her advice for other parents in the same situation.

Treating Cancer. DHEW Pub. No. (NIH) 75–210, rev. 1972, 27 pp. (E) $.45
Answers some of the questions often asked about surgery, radiation, and chemotherapy, and their uses in the treatment of patients with cancer.

Feeding the Sick Child. DHEW Pub. No. (NIH) 75–795, 1975, 20 pp. (E)
Designed specifically for parents of children with cancer, this booklet offers numerous tips for parents of finicky eaters. Recipes are included.

Breast Self-examination. DHEW Pub. No. (NIH) 75–649, rev. 1974, 12 pp. (E)
Illustrations and text provide step-by-step explanation of how to perform breast self-examination.

Cancer Rates and Risks. 2nd ed. DHEW Pub. No. (NIH) 75–691, 1974, 108 pp. (M) $1.80
Text, charts, and graphs present trends in cancer incidence and mortality in various population groups. Factors associated with high or low risks of cancer are discussed.

The Cancer Story. DHEW Pub. No. (NIH) 74–232, rev. 1973, 52 pp. (E) $.85
A simplified version of *Science and Cancer*, discussing diagnosis and treatment, research and causation, the cell, hormones and nutrition, and the search for anticancer drugs.

Progress Against Cancer, 1970. 98 pp. (E)
A report by the National Advisory Cancer Council dealing with research on chemical carcinogenesis. Topics discussed include

smoking and cancer, hazards in the environment, tests of suspect chemicals, and research on cancer cells.

Progress Against Leukemia, Research Report. DHEW Pub. No. (NIH), rev. 1975. (E)
A discussion of the current expanded research effort to determine the causes of leukemia and the advances that have been made in the treatment of this disease.

Drugs vs. Cancer, Research Report. DHEW Pub. No. (NIH) 75–786, rev. 1975, 17 pp. (E) $.15
Information on the status of cancer chemotherapy. A discussion of the intensive effort being made to develop new drugs for treating cancer. An up-to-date list of the anticancer drugs now in use is included.

Booklets and Reports Available from Various Sources

Brain Tumors and Spinal Cord Tumors, Hope Through Research. DHEW Pub. No. (NIH) 73–504, reprinted 1973, 22 pp. (E)
Available from the National Institute of Neurological Diseases and Stroke, National Institutes of Health, Bethesda, MD 20014. An illustrated booklet discussing various types of brain tumors, their symptoms, treatment, and the research under way.

Candlelighters. Leaflet (E) Available from Candlelighters, 123 "C" Street, S.E., Washington, D.C. 20003.
Describes the Candlelighters, an organization of family members of cancer patients, and their goals: to obtain adequate federal support for cancer research and to help members deal with the emotional stresses of their experience.

A Primer on New Drug Development. DHEW Pub. No. (FDA) 74–3021, 1974, 7 pp. (E)
Available from Consumer Inquiries, HFI–10, Food and Drug Administration, 5600 Fishers Lane, Rockville, MD 20852.
Provides a view of how new prescription drugs are developed, thoroughly tested in both animals and humans under carefully controlled circumstances, then approved by the Food and Drug Administration for general marketing.

Cancer. Barbara J. Culliton and Wallace K. Waterfall. 1975. 36 pp. (M) Available from the American Association for the Ad-

vancement of Science, 1515 Massachusetts Avenue, N.W., Washington, D.C. 20005. $2.50 ($2.00 for AAAS members.)
An overview of nonscientists of the nature of cancer, its manifestations, pain, psychology, and treatment. The booklet also conveys some of the background, flavor, and expectations of cancer research.

Magazine, Newspaper, and Journal Articles

The following articles may be available in medical or public libraries.

Cancer Cause and Prevention

"Impact of Cancer (U.S. 1970–2000)." Frank J. Rauscher, Jr. *Preventive Medicine*, 1:293–9, 1972. (E)
An article by the former director of the National Cancer Institute dealing with the possibility of achieving a 90 percent reduction in cancer deaths in this century by (a) identifying environmental elements which lead to different rates in different countries and (b) identifying persons susceptible to cancer.

"Upon Man and Beast—Adventures in Cancer Epidemiology." Michael B. Shimkin. *Cancer Research*, 34:1525–35, July 1974. (E)
Address by the president of the American Association for Cancer Research, March 27, 1974, at the association's annual meeting. A review of findings and cancer causation gained over the years through studies of population groups.

"Environmental Determinants of Human Cancer." Samuel S. Epstein. *Cancer Research*, 34:2425–35, October 1974. (M)
Based on introductory remarks to a Symposium on Environmental Determinants of Human Cancer, March 30, 1974. A review of carcinogenicity as a public health hazard and problems in recognition of chemical carcinogens. Conflicts between health goals and economic goals are also discussed.

"Cancer and the Environment: Groping for New Remedies." Robert Gillette. *Science*, 186:242–5, October 18, 1974. (E)
Deals with the problems of testing and regulating man-made carcinogens, some of which are used so pervasively, in so many ways, as to be an almost inescapable part of American life.

"Chemical Carcinogenesis: A Long-neglected Field Blossoms."
Thomas H. Maugh II. *Science.* 183:940–4, March 8, 1974. (M)
Discusses research to identify cancer-causing chemicals and the
new emphasis placed on investigations of the interaction between
chemical and cell. Chemicals—in the workplace, in the environment, and in the diet—may be the single most important cause of
human cancers.

"Annals of Industry: Casualties of the Workplace." Paul Brodeur.
The New Yorker, pp. 44–106, October 29, 1973; pp. 92–142,
November 5, 1973; pp. 131–50, November 12, 1973; pp. 87–149,
November 19, 1973; pp. 126–79, November 26, 1973. (E)
A five-part series telling how dangerous working conditions in the
asbestos industry were allowed to go unchecked, thus resulting in
asbestosis and cancer in some workers. These articles won a 1973
Sidney Hillman prize and Columbia University's 1974 National
Magazine Award for reporting excellence.

"Fiber Carcinogenesis: Is Asbestos the Only Hazard?" Mearl F.
Stanton. *Journal of the National Cancer Institute,* 52:633–4,
March 1974. (M)
Suggests that carcinogenicity of a particle may depend on its
structure rather than its physiochemical composition. Asbestos
causes cancer when it separates into fibers with exceptionally
small diameters but substantial lengths.

"A Reporter at Large. Smoking Still." Thomas Whiteside. *The
New Yorker,* pp. 121–48, November 18, 1974. (E)
Informative, 16-page article on the rise in cigarette consumption
despite a ban on radio and television advertising. The author
suggests reasons why the ban has failed to discourage smoking
and recommends other methods.

"Drinking Water: Another Source of Carcinogens?" Jean L.
Marx. *Science,* 186:809–11, November 29, 1974. (E)
A report on studies undertaken to determine whether chemicals in
drinking water present a cancer hazard to man.

"The Delaney Clause: Should It Be Changed?" Ernest L. Wynder
et al. *Preventive Medicine,* 2:123–70, 1973. (E–M)
Ten articles presenting contrasting views on whether the Delaney
Clause should be retained or changed. The Delaney Clause, a part
of the 1958 Food Additive Amendment of the Federal Food,
Drug, and Cosmetic Act, provides "that no additive shall be

deemed to be safe if it is found to induce cancer when ingested by man or animal, or if it is found, after tests which are appropriate for the evaluation of the safety of food additives, to induce cancer in man or animal."

"FDA Turns Back Bid to Reinstate Cyclamates." *Science*, 186:422, November 1, 1974. (E)
Discusses the Food and Drug Administration's ban on cyclamates, which was ordered after research indicated that cyclamates might cause bladder tumors in mice.

"Dietary Fiber and Disease," D. P. Burkitt et al. *Journal of the American Medical Association*, 229:1068–74, August 19, 1974. (M)
Postulates that the fiber-depleted American diet could play a part in the prevalence of appendicitis, diverticular disease, cancer of the colon, and other noninfective diseases.

"Comments on Carcinoma of the Colon and Rectum." Justin J. Stein. *Cancer*, 34:799–80, September 1974. (E)
Discusses the incidence and possible causes of cancers of the colon and rectum.

"Cancer vs. What You Eat." Jerry E. Bishop. *Science Digest*, pp. 10–14, March 1974. (E)
Explains why some researchers believe a link exists between colon-rectal cancer and the meaty, fat-heavy American diet.

"Beef and Bowel Cancer." *Newsweek*, pp. 80–1, February 18, 1974. (E)
Discusses population studies that suggest a link between beef consumption and cancer of the colon.

"The Rise of Cancer in Black Men." Jack Slater. *Ebony*, pp. 92–100, July 1974. (E)
Reports figures showing that the cancer death rate in black males has doubled and that cancer incidence is greater in black men than in any other segment of the U.S. population. Possible reasons for the increase are discussed.

"The Organic Food Myth." Thomas H. Jukes. *Journal of the American Medical Association*, 230:276–7, October 14, 1974. (E)
Misconceptions about "health foods," vitamins and "natural" fertilizers are discussed.

"Heavy Drinking Adds to the Risk of Cancers of Mouth and Throat." *Journal of the American Medical Association*, 229:1023–4, August 19, 1974. (E)
Summarizes information on the association between alcohol and cancer presented in the Second Special Report to Congress of the National Institute on Alcohol Abuse and Alcoholism.

"Stilbestrol and Vaginal Cancer," B. D. A. Benton. *American Journal of Nursing*, 74:900–1, May 1974. (E)
Discusses the increased risk of vaginal cancer in adolescent daughters of women who took diethylstilbestrol (DES) during pregnancy. Detection and diagnosis of the disease are described.

"Brink of Tragedy." Elisabeth Keiffer. *Good Housekeeping*, pp. 85–155, July 1974. (E)
Relates the personal experience of a woman who developed adenocarcinoma of the vagina, and explains the association found between DES taken during pregnancy and vaginal cancer in female offspring.

"Radiation-induced Cancer." Robert W. Miller. *Journal of the National Cancer Institute*, 49:1221–7, November 1972. (M)
A review of studies of cancer in atomic bomb survivors and others exposed to ionizing radiation.

"Bask, Don't Burn: Running the Risk of Skin Cancer." J. C. G. Conniff, *New York Times Magazine*, pp. 12–13, July 7, 1974. (E)
Warns sunbathers that the sun's ultraviolet rays can lead to skin cancer and premature aging of the skin. Explains the anatomy of a sunburn and gives suggestions for ways to enjoy the sun without burning.

"Time Bombs: Old Treatments' Risks Spur Wide Searches for Former Patients." J. S. Lublin. *Wall Street Journal*, June 4, 1974. (E)
Reports that X-ray therapy twenty to thirty years ago for tonsillitis, acne, or enlarged lymph nodes, adenoids, or thymus, may be the cause of some benign thyroid tumors today. Thyroid cancer is being found in a few former patients.

"Of Mice and Men: Alarm over Plastics." *Time*, p. 64, October 14, 1974. (E)
Discusses federal regulation of the use of pesticides aldrin and

dieldrin and the limitations established for worker exposure to vinyl chloride gas.

"The Case Against the Trauma-Cancer Link." *Medical World News*, p. 52B, July 7, 1974. (E)
Summarizes a report by a team from the Mayo Clinic in Rochester, Minnesota. The Mayo group says its review of the literature revealed no evidence to suggest that a single, uncomplicated trauma can cause cancer.

"Leukemia: Much Is Known, but the Picture Is Still Confused." Thomas H. Maugh II. *Science*, 185:48–51, July 5, 1974. (M)
Discusses evidence that some form of virus is involved in the etiology of leukemia. Current methods of leukemia treatment are also discussed.

Cancer Detection and Diagnosis.

"Cancer: Where We Stand Today." *Medical World News*, pp. 55–65, March 22, 1974. (M)
Describes current diagnostic procedures for cancers of the lung, colon, rectum, breast, pancreas, stomach, cervix, prostate, bladder, and kidney, as well as for leukemia and lymphoma.

"How to Protect Your Family from Cancer." Jane E. Brody. *Woman's Day*, pp. 58–114, November 1974. (E)
Discusses cancer prevention and new methods of early detection.

"New Gains in Fighting a Common Cancer Killer; Colon-Rectal Cancer." *Good Housekeeping*, pp. 153–4, August 1974. (E)
Describes two new detection techniques for colon-rectal cancer: a simple, at-home test for occult blood; and the doctor's examination with a colonoscope. Leads on the causes of the disease are also discussed.

"A Hectic Week for Breast Cancer Researchers." *Medical World News*, pp. 19–22, October 25, 1974. (E)
Recounts advances in breast cancer detection and treatment presented at a National Cancer Institute meeting on September 30, 1974.

"Breast Cancer Research: Problems and Progress." Jean L. Marx. *Science*, 184:1162–5, June 14, 1974. (E)
Discusses factors that may increase a woman's risk of breast cancer. Also discusses breast cancer detection techniques and

various surgical and chemotherapeutic methods of controlling the disease.

"What Women Don't Know About Breast Cancer." *Consumer Reports*, pp. 264–8, March 1974. (E)
Facts on breast cancer incidence and mortality, and directions for breast self-examination. A list of twenty-seven breast cancer screening centers across the United States is also given.

"The Cancer Women Can Defeat." Clifton R. Read. *Family Health*, pp. 26–49, March 1974. (E)
Discusses the Pap test for early detection of uterine cervical cancer and the dramatic drop in mortality from that disease as a result of the test.

"Value of Mammography in Reduction of Mortality from Breast Cancer in Mass Screening." Philip Strax et al. *American Journal of Roentgenology, Radiation Therapy and Nuclear Medicine*, 117:686–9, March 1973. (M)
Reports that the mass screening program of the Health Insurance Plan of Greater New York achieved a one-third reduction in the breast cancer death rate. The important role of mammography in screening is shown.

Cancer Treatment and Rehabilitation.

"Yes, You Can Survive Cancer." Jane E. Brody. *Woman's Day*, pp. 74–146, October 1974. (E)
Seven-page article on improvements in treating major types of cancer. Advances in radiotherapy and chemotherapy are emphasized.

"Coping with Cancer." *Time*, p. 80, October 14, 1974. (E)
National Cancer Institute research on new methods of breast cancer treatment are discussed. The article also describes the American Cancer Society's Reach to Recovery program, in which women who have had mastectomies counsel women who have just had the operation.

"The Continuing Breast Cancer Controversy." Culliton and Marx. *Science*, 186:246–7, October 18, 1974. (E)
Presents preliminary results from controlled clinical studies undertaken to determine the most effective traatment for localized breast cancer and breast cancer that has spread to lymph nodes.

"Breast Cancer: Fear and Facts." *Time*, pp. 107–10, November 4, 1974. (E)
Factors that seem to make a woman more likely to develop breast cancer are discussed. The article also covers detection, diagnosis, and types of surgical treatment, as well as the mastectomy patient's fear of rejection.
"Osteogenic Sarcoma Beginning to Yield." L. Boston and G. McBride. *Journal of the American Medical Association*, 228:1218–20, June 3, 1974. (M)
Discusses advances in chemotherapy and immunotherapy for this bone malignancy.
"Young Teddy Kennedy Is Walking Proof of Major Advances in Prosthetics." Lester Davis. *Today's Health*, 52:44–7, November 1974. (E)
Describes improvements in new artificial limbs which are enabling amputees to lead more active lives.
"When Cancer Strikes at Children." Rona and Laurence Cherry. *New York Times Magazine*, p. 80, April 7, 1974. Discusses common types of childhood cancer and the psychological effect of the illness on the family.
"The Inevitable Prostate Problem." *Medical World News*, pp. 27–35, December 20, 1974. (M)
Questions on the diagnosis and treatment of prostate cancer are answered by the chairman of the Veterans Administration's Cooperative Study of Prostate Cancer and by a member of the National Prostate Cancer Study Group.
"Comeback After Cancer." Clifton R. Read. *Family Health*, pp. 22–42, March 1974. (E)
Tells how the International Association of Laryngectomees, the United Ostomy Association, and the Reach to Recovery Program help rehabilitate patients recovering from cancer.
"Cancer Therapy: How You Can Gauge Adequacy of Treatment." *Medical World News*, pp. 38–44, May 17, 1974. (M)
An article directed to physicians discussing optimal therapy for major types of cancer and how to obtain the best available treatment for patients.
"Cancer Chemotheraphy: Now a Promising Weapon." Thomas H. Maugh, II. *Science*, 184:970–4, May 31, 1974. (E)
Discusses advances in treating leukemias, lymphomas, and child-

hood cancers with chemotherapy. A discussion of drug screening and the ways antitumor agents interfere with the replication of cells is also presented.

"Chemotherapists Find Two or More Drugs Are Better." Joseph Hixson. *Chemical Week*, pp. 26–30, July 31, 1974. (M)
Researchers show new gains against cancer by use of specific drug combinations.

"Cancer Immunotherapy Starts from Scratch." *Medical World News*, pp. 39–52, February 23, 1973. (M)
An article discussing preliminary results from clinical trials of the immunotherapeutic agent BCG.

"The Necessity for Combined Modalities in Cancer Therapy." Daniel S. Martin. *Hospital Practice*, pp. 129–36, January 1973. (M)
Discusses the benefits of immunotherapy used in conjunction with the other cancer treatment modalities: surgery, radiation, and chemotherapy.

"Cancer Immunotherapy." Melvin J. Silverstein and Donald L. Morton. *American Journal of Nursing*, pp. 1178–81, July 1973. (M)
Describes antigen-antibody reactions, active and passive immunotherapy, and current use of the immunotherapeutic agent BCG.

"Plant Medicine." Gerald Jonas. *Family Circle*, pp. 98—103, October 1972. (E)
Tells how the National Cancer Institute is systematically testing a variety of folk medicines, home remedies, and thousands of previously untried plants in an effort to find substances with anticancer effect.

"The Fatal Choice, Cancer Quackery." Charlotte Isler. *RN*, pp. 55–9, September 1974. (E)
Describes false promises of "cancer-cures" that lure many patients into trying unproven treatments, costing them their lives. Scientific standards for testing new treatments are explained and education programs to protect patients from quackery are discussed.

Cancer Biology

"What Is Cancer: What Forms Does It Take? How Does It Kill?" Thomas H. Maugh II. *Science*, 183:1068–9, March 15, 1974. (E)

Brief article defining the four major types of cancer (leukemias, lymphomas, sarcomas, and carcinomas); the three characteristics all cancers share (hyperplasia, anaplasia, and metastasis); and the secondary conditions that are the chief cause of death in cancer patients.

"The Lines of Cancer Research." *Medical World News*, pp. 34–42, July 12, 1974. (E)
Several important areas of basic research are discussed, including cell membranes, immunology, and virology. Discusses controversy over how much of the cancer appropriation should be spent on making optimal care available now and how much should be spent for basic research.

"Cancer and the Body's Defense System." Joan Arehart-Treichel. *Science News*, 103:408–9, June 23, 1973. (M)
Reports that research on cancer and research on immunology have converged into study of the body's complex strategies against foreign invaders.

"Body's Defenses Could Be a Key to Cancer Riddle." Harold Schmeck, Jr. *Smithsonian*, pp. 26–32, January 1974. (M)
Text and illustrations explain the main components of the human immune system and the roles they play. Discusses research on ways to fortify the natural immune response so that it will become a weapon against cancer.

Reference Sources of Information About Cancer

Where one begins in his pursuit of information on any aspect of cancer depends, of course, on how much he already knows.

Encyclopedias contain general articles on cancer that will orient the reader in the field. Most of these articles will suggest related subjects for further study.

The New York Times Index, published every two weeks, is also available in many libraries. This index lists the newspaper's news and feature articles by subject and summarizes the most important ones.

The *Reader's Guide to Periodical Literature* is available in many libraries; monthly supplements keep it up to date. The guide lists articles from popular, semiprofessional, and professional magazines. Under the general topic of cancer, other headings direct the reader to closely related fields. The nature of the periodical in which a cited reference appears suggests its level of difficulty. Readers familiar with cancer as treated in newspapers and popular magazines can move on to professional magazines such as *Science, Medical World News*, and *Scientific American.* Ultimately, one's search for information on cancer will take him to professional journals such as the *Journal of the National Cancer Institute*, the *Journal of the American Medical Association, Cancer*, and *Cancer Research.*

Various guides and indexes help the reader find information in professional journals. One example is *Index Medicus*, published monthly by the National Library of Medicine and available in many medical libraries. This publication indexes articles appearing in English and other languages in more than 2,000 medical journals. Titles are listed by subject and author, thus enabling the reader to seek information on the topic of his special interest or to trace the works of research investigators in cancer.

The National Cancer Institute's Office of Cancer Communications: The major source of information for the public and a substantial source for health professionals. The Office of Cancer Communications does not provide references or scientific journals for the public, nor does it give specific medical advice to patients. However, it does provide general information on cancer treatment and research, and the names and telephone numbers of institute clinicians and others participating in the National Cancer Program with whom attending physicians may consult.

The American Cancer Society, 777 Third Avenue, New

York, NY 10017, is a large voluntary agency, which supports research, conducts programs of public and professional education, and provides service to cancer patients. The society is organized in divisions and local units throughout the country.

The Leukemia Society of America, Inc., 211 East 43rd Street, New York, NY 10017, supports research and provides services to patients with leukemia, Hodgkin's disease, and lymphoma. This society also has chapters across the country.

Information on local cancer programs can be obtained from the various state health departments.

Cancer Teaching Aids

The following publications constitute a group of science teaching aids developed by the National Cancer Institute with the cooperation of the National Science Teachers Association:

Science and Cancer, a paperback book recommended for use by the teacher.

The Cancer Story, a booklet prepared for general student use.

A Teaching Guide—Science and Cancer, prepared by members of the faculty of Kansas State Teachers College for the National Science Teachers Association.

A Portfolio of display photographs, illustrating cancer research experiments, equipment, and facilities.

These publications are available free of charge to science teachers from the Office of Cancer Communications, National Cancer Institute, Bethesda, MD 20014.

The National Cancer Institute has also developed two 16-millimeter color films which are useful as teaching aids in high school science classes:

Progress Against Cancer, a 28-minute color film explaining how modern research has solved many of cancer's mysteries and improved the patient's chance to survive.

Research to Prevent Cancer, an 18-minute color film which is a shortened version of the film listed above.

These films are available on a free-loan basis from the following regional film centers of Association-Sterling Films:

> 512 Burlington Ave., La Grange, IL 60525
> 600 Grand Ave., Ridgefield, NJ 07657
> 25358 Cypress Ave., Hayward, CA 94544
> 8615 Directors Row, Dallas, TX 75247
> 324 Delaware Ave., Oakmont, PA 15139
> 410 Gread Rd., Littleton, MA 01460
> 7838 San Fernando Rd., Sun Valley CA 91352
> 5797 New Peachtree Rd., Atlanta, GA 30340
> 6420 West Lake St., Minneapolis, MN 55426
> 915 NW Nineteenth Ave., Portland, OR 97209

Free Brochures on Various Types of Cancer

The following brochures are available free of charge from: Office of Cancer Communications, National Cancer Institute, Bethesda, MD 20014; telephone 301 496-5583.

1. What You Need to Know About Cancer
2. What You Need to Know About Cancer of the Bladder
3. What You Need to Know About Cancer of the Bone
4. What You Need to Know About Cancer of the Brain and Spinal Cord
5. What You Need to Know About Cancer of the Breast
6. What You Need to Know About Cancer of the Esophagus
7. What You Need to Know About Hodgkin's Disease
8. What You Need to Know About Cancer of the Kidney
9. What You Need to Know About Cancer of the Larynx

313

10. What You Need to Know About Adult Leukemia
11. What You Need to Know About Childhood Leukemia
12. What You Need to Know About Cancer of the Lung
13. What You Need to Know About Non-Hodgkin's Lymphoma
14. What You Need to Know About Melanoma
15. What You Need to Know About Cancer of the Mouth
16. What You Need to Know About Multiple Myeloma
17. What You Need to Know About Cancer of the Ovary
18. What You Need to Know About Cancer of the Pancreas
19. What You Need to Know About Cancer of the Prostate
20. What You Need to Know About Cancer of the Skin
21. What You Need to Know About Cancer of the Stomach
22. What You Need to Know About Cancer of the Testis
23. What You Need to Know About Wilms' Tumor
24. What You Need to Know About Cancer of the Uterus

Principal Medical Libraries in the United States

National Library of Medicine
Bethesda, MD 20014
Regional Medical Libraries:

New England Region (Conn., Me., Mass., N.H., R.I., VT.)

Francis A. Countway Library of Medicine
10 Shattuck Street
Boston, MA 02115

New York and Northern New Jersey Region (N. Y. and the eleven northern counties of N. J.)

New York Academy of Medicine Library
2 East 103rd Street
New York, NY 10029

Mideastern Region (Pa., Del., and the ten southern counties of N. J.)

Library of the College of Physicians
19 South 22nd Street
Philadelphia, PA 19103

Mid-Atlantic Region (Va., W.Va., Md., D.C., N.C.)
National Library of Medicine
8600 Rockville Pike
Bethesda, MD 20014

East Central Region (Ky., Mich., Ohio)
Wayne State University Medical Library
4325 Brush Street
Detroit, MI 48201

Southeastern Region (Ala., Fla., Ga., Miss., S.C., Tenn., P.R.)
A. W. Calhoun Medical Library
Emory University
Atlanta, GA 30322

Midwest Region (Ill., Ind., Iowa, Minn., N.D., Wis.)
John Crerar Library
35 West 33rd Street
Chicago, IL 60616

Midcontinental Region (Colo., Kan., Mo., Neb., S.D., Utah, Wyo.)
University of Nebraska Medical Center
42nd Street & Dewey Avenue
Omaha, NB 68105

South Central Region (Ark., La., N.M., Okla., Tex.)
University of Texas Southwestern Medical School at Dallas
5323 Harry Hines Blvd.
Dallas, TX 75235

Pacific Northwest Region (Alas., Ida., Mont., Ore., Wash.)
University of Washington
Health Sciences Library
Seattle, WA 98105

Pacific Southwest Region (Ariz., Ca., Hawaii, Nev.)
Center for the Health Sciences
University of California
Los Angeles, CA 90024

Appendix B

Nutrition For the Cancer Patient

Food Selection, Diets, Recipes

1. *Blenderized Diet.* By Jerry Kukachka. Developed during a
period when the author's husband was recovering from extensive surgery and radiotherapy, the diet emphasizes nutritionally balanced meals that are appealing in taste, smell, and
color. Hints are given for blending, freezing, liquefying, and
seasoning various foods. A typical daily menu is offered,
along with recipes for several high-protein main dishes and
desserts.

Source: University of Wisconsin Clinical Cancer Center,
Public Affairs Office, 1900 University Avenue, Madison, WI
53705. Telephone: 608 262-0046.

2. *A Diet Guide for Chemotherapy Patients.* 1976. A nutritionally balanced diet is recommended for patients undergoing
chemotherapy. Emphasis is on a high-protein diet and ample
fluid intake. The basic four food groups are explained, along
with tips to maintain appetite and prevent or control diarrhea.

Source: Ellis Fischel State Cancer Hospital, Business 70 and
Garth Avenue, Columbia, MO 65201. Telephone: 314 449-
2711.

3. *A Guide to Good Nutrition During and After Chemotherapy
and Radiation.* By Saundra Aker, Gail Tilmont, and Vangee
Harrison. 1976. Patients undergoing chemotherapy or radiotherapy can use this guide to select the best foods in the
correct amounts for gaining or maintaining weight. Side
effects from the therapy and possible solutions are discussed.
Progressive lists of liquid to soft foods are included. Also in
the booklet are a calorie guide, recipes, a list (by trade name)
of nutritional supplements. Cost: $2.00 per copy for 1–5
copies, $1.50 per copy for 6 or more; payable to Adult
Leukemia Center.

Source: Fred Hutchinson Cancer Research Center, Research
Kitchen, 1124 Columbia Street, Seattle, WA 98104. Telephone: 206 292-6301.

4. *Nutrition for Patients Receiving Chemotherapy and Radiation Treatment.* 1974. A high-protein diet is often an important factor in a cancer patient's response to chemotherapy or radiotherapy. Recipes for high-protein beverages, snacks, and desserts are featured in the booklet. The preparation of liquid formulas for oral, tube, and nasal feedings is described; and sample menus, information on diet supplements, and a brief bibliography are included.

Source: American Cancer Society, local units.

5. *Nutritional Guide for Patients Receiving Upper and Lower Abdominal Radiation Therapy.* Compiled by C. Persigehl. 1976. Prepared for patients receiving upper and lower abdominal radiation therapy, the nutrition guide lists foods recommended or disallowed for restricted residue diets. Ways of increasing the protein and caloric content of the diet are explained, and names of commercial diet supplements are listed. High-protein, nutritionally balanced sample menus are provided, along with suggestions for making the foods attractive and palatable, controlling diarrhea, and coping with nausea and vomiting. Cost: $1.

Source: Mountain States Tumor Institute, Dept. of Patient and Family Support, 151 East Bannock, Boise, ID 83702. Telephone: 208 345-1780.

6. *Progressive Blenderized Diet.* Information on nutrition, meal patterns, commercial supplements, and food preparation (including seasoning) is compiled for patients requiring liquid or soft diets. The blenderized diets and suggested meal patterns are arranged progressively—from liquid tube feedings, to modified, full liquid, to puree soft, to mechanical soft, to natural soft. Cost: $.50.

Source: Shands Teaching Hospital and Clinics, Dept. of Food and Nutrition Services, University of Florida, Gainesville, FL 32610. Telephone: 904 392-3575.

7. *Restricted Fiber Diet; High Protein Liquid Diet.* The diet is designed to decrease the amount of bulk while also providing adequate protein, vitamins, and other nutrients to maintain good health. Lists of foods to include daily, lists of foods to avoid, special directions for preparation, and a high-protein liquid diet are given.

317

Source: University of Wisconsin Clinical Cancer Center, Public Affairs Office, 1900 University Avenue, Madison, WI 53705. Telephone: 608 262-0046.

8. *Soft and Blended Foods (for Head and Neck Radiation Patients).* Compiled by C. Persigehl. Revised 1976. Recipes and sample menus for high-protein, soft diets are suggested for patients having head and neck radiation therapy. Lists of recommended foods, names of commercial high-protein formulas, information on the preparation of tube feedings, recommended dietary allowances, and a table showing the caloric and protein content of some common foods are included. Cost: $1.

Source: Mountain States Tumor Institute, Dept. of Patient and Family Support, 151 East Bannock, Boise, ID 83702. Telephone: 208 345-1780.

Home Care

9. *Home Care Guide for Patients with Head and Neck Disease.* Wisconsin Head and Neck Network. 1976. Tube feeding is one of the topics in this guide to postoperative self-care for patients who have had tracheotomy, laryngectomy, or other head and neck surgery. Stoma and wound care, suctioning, and oral hygiene are also discussed.

Source: University of Wisconsin Clinical Cancer Center, Public Affairs Office, 1900 University Avenue, Madison, WI 53705. Telephone: 608 262-0046.

Food Tolerance

10. *Feeding the Sick Child.* By Mikie Sherman. 1976. Sick children frequently reject nourishing food because of odor, texture, color, or sweetness; and therapy causes such side effects as loss of appetite, nausea, and vomiting. A relaxed, open, and innovative attitude toward the child's nutritional needs may alleviate problems. Guidelines to good nutrition are included, along with recipes and a list of child-oriented cookbooks.

Source: National Cancer Institute, Office of Cancer Communications, Bldg. 31, Rm. 10A18, 9000 Rockville Pike, Bethesda, MD 20014. Telephone: 301 496-6641.

11. *Food for Those Who Hesitate ... Tips ... Tips That They Might Tolerate.* By Jane E. Helsel. 1976. The booklet offers diet and nutrition tips and selected recipes to patients having chemotherapy. Recommendations are given for (1) the size and timing of meals, (2) kinds of foods easy to swallow or tolerate, and (3) ways to increase protein and caloric intake. The suggestions should be especially helpful to patients experiencing a general loss of appetite or side effects such as nausea, vomiting, sores in the mouth and throat, constipation, or diarrhea.

Source: Duke University Comprehensive Cancer Center, Cancer Information Services, 200 Atlas Street, Durham, NC 27705. Telephone: 919 286-2214.

Cancer Information Clearinghouse

The Cancer Information Clearinghouse is a service of the National Cancer Institute's Office of Cancer Communications. The clearinghouse collects and disseminates information on materials, programs, and resources relating to public, patient, and professional education. It provides routine information searches, referral services, topical bibliographies, special information packages, current awareness services, and selective dissemination of information on cancer education.

The clearinghouse serves organizations engaged in public, patient, and professional education. Public contact is not encouraged.

To request assistance or to submit information to the clearinghouse, contact:

Cancer Information Clearinghouse
Office of Cancer Communications
National Cancer Institute
7910 Woodmont Avenue, Suite 1320
Bethesda, MD 20014

Telephone: 301 496-4070

*Cancer-Causing Agents That May Be Associated With Various Occupations**

Below are some suspected causes of cancer in the workplace. Not everyone, of course, will develop cancer if exposed to these agents, but incidence of cancer among workers exposed to these agents is above average. Generally, laborers, miners, and transportation workers have an above-average rate of death, while farmers have a comparatively low rate.

Agent	*Sites of Cancer*
Arsenicals	Skin, lung
Auramine	Bladder
Coal tar, pitch	Skin, lung
High boiling petroleum oils	Skin
Shale oils	Skin
Tars	Skin
Creosote oils	Skin
Anthracene oils	Skin
Soot (carbon black)	Skin
Mustard gas	Lung
Cutting oils	Skin, possibly respiratory and upper alimentary tract
Various combustion products	Lung
Chromates	Lung
Asbestos	Lung, pleura, peritoneum, GI tract
Sunlight	Skin
Aromatic amines	Bladder, possibly biliary tract, salivary glands
Xray and radium	Skin, lung, leukemia
Nickel	Lung, nasal cavity
Isopropyl oil	Lung, larynx, nasal sinus
Radioactive chemicals	Bones, nasal sinus
Bis (chloromethyl) ether	Lung
Vinyl chloride	Liver

*Source: U. S. Department of Health, Education, and Welfare.

CHEMOTHERAPY TREATMENT FOR CANCER

Over forty drugs or chemicals have been developed for use in the chemotherapy treatment for cancer. Twenty to forty thousand new materials are screened each year in a search for drugs and chemicals that show anticancer activity. Perhaps twenty new agents out of the thousands tested each year show promise enough to be considered for further development. Some agents tested show considerable anticancer activity but are too toxic for use on humans in the treatment of cancer.

The majority of new materials tested for possible use in the chemotherapy program are synthetic compounds. The remainder are natural products from fermentation, plant and animals sources.

In about 15 percent of the cases of clinical cancer, chemotherapy drugs can produce cures. In the remainder of the cases, the drugs often temporarily inhibit the growth of cancer cells, relieve pain, and extend the lives of cancer patients.

Drugs and chemicals used in the chemotherapy program are toxic and produce a variety of side effects in *some* but not all patients. (Some of the side effects are shown elsewhere in this Appendix.) Because of these potential side effects, the patient receiving anticancer drugs should be monitored closely by physicians. Physical examinations and blood counts should be conducted.

How does chemotherapy work? The drugs enter the body's bloodstream, by intravenous injection or indirectly (orally) by absorption through the stomach or tissues, and are distributed to all parts of the body. Cells that divide rapidly, such as tumor cells, take up most of the drug. The drugs act on the tumor cells by interfering with the duplication and growth of these cells. The intent is to eventually destroy these cells. Unfortunately, anticancer drugs affect normal rapidly dividing cells as well as the cancer cells. Normal cells that might be affected include those in the bone marrow, the gastrointestinal tract, the reproductive system, and the hair follicle. However, normal cells have a tremendous capacity to regenerate themselves and return to a normal state. Doctors closely monitor the effect of the chemotherapy drugs on your normal cells and blood.

An "ideal" anticancer drug would destroy the cancer cells without harming healthy cells and tissue. However, finding this perfect drug would be like discovering a pill that, when swallowed, would make one ear fall off while leaving the other one intact, according to one physician.

Aside from the problem with toxicity, anticancer drugs also eventually lose their effectiveness against cancer in some cases, for reasons that are not entirely understood.

Chemotherapy drugs, used singularly or in combinations, show considerable promise in the treatment of cancers. Several successful drug combinations have been developed. One regimen is known as MOPP (Mustargen, Oncovin, procarbazine, and prednisone). About 75 percent of patients with advanced Hodgkin's disease show a disappearance of the cancer when treated with the MOPP regimen. Chemotherapy drugs are also being used in combination with radiation therapy and surgery with promising results.

During the early days of the chemotherapy program for cancer, physicians generally withheld early use of the drugs, feeling that the majority of solid tumors that the drugs were effective against were slow-growing in nature, allowing the patient to live a comfortable life for a period of years. Today, the trend is to start chemotherapy treatment early to prevent further spread of the cancer cells. This is known as "adjuvant chemotherapy." Early responses indicate that patients receiving early treatment can expect to live longer, without disability, than was possible prior to the introduction of this type of therapy.

If you are a patient receiving chemotherapy drugs, you should call your doctor if you have any symptoms that worry you, but especially in the following circumstances:

1. fever (temperature of 100° or over).
2. development of any rash.
3. any kind of bleeding that persists unusually long.
4. any pain of unusual intensity of distribution, including headaches.
5. shortness of breath, inability to "catch" your breath.

POSSIBLE SIDE EFFECTS OF INTRAVENOUS DRUGS FOR CANCER CHEMOTHERAPY

Drug	*Possible Side Effects*
Alkylating Agents:	
Cyclophosphamide	Nausea and vomiting; loss of hair; hemorrhagic cystitis; possible jaundice
Mechlorethamine	Severe vomiting (30–60 minutes after administration); blistering; diarrhea; anorexia
Thiophosphoramide	Pain at injection site
Antimetabolites:	
Cytosar	Bone marrow depression; nausea and vomiting
Flourouracil	Bone marrow depression; nausea and vomiting; bloody diarrhea; inflammation of the mouth (and

323

	ulceration); gastrointestinal ulceration and hemorrhage
Methotrexate	Bone marrow depression; inflammation of the mouth; gastrointestinal ulceration; diarrhea; nausea and vomiting; possible fever; liver dysfunction
Antibiotics:	
Adriamycin	Inflammation and ulceration of the mouth; bone marrow depression; loss of hair; cardiac toxicity—premature ventricular contractions and congestive heart failure; blistering; thrombophlegitis at injection site
Bleomycin	Fever, *immediate* on injection; nausea and vomiting; major toxicity—pulmonary fibrosis which can be fatal; skin lesions
Dactinomycin	Severe nausea and vomiting; bone marrow depression; occasional loss of hair; occasional skin eruptions; inflammation of the mouth; gastrointestinal disturbances; blistering
Daunorubicin	Cardiac toxicity—refractory congestive heart failure; bone marrow depression; fever; nausea and vomiting; blistering; diarrhea
Mithramycin	Nausea and vomiting; bone marrow depression; fever; bleeding syndrome
Mitomycin C	Nausea and vomiting; bone marrow depression; diarrhea; blistering
Alkaloids:	
Vinblastine	Mild nausea and vomiting; bone marrow depression; occasional loss

	of hair; neuromuscular toxicity—in high dosage; possible diarrhea or constipation; blistering
Vincristine	Nausea and vomiting; neuromuscular; loss of hair; oral ulcerations; constipation; abdominal pain; jaw pain; blistering; injection site irritation
Miscellaneous Agents:	
L-Asparaginase	Nausea and vomiting; fever; hypersensitivity reactions; confusion; blood dyscrasias; bone marrow depression
Bis-Chlorethylnitro-sureal (BCNU)	Nausea and vomiting; bone marrow depression; flushing of face
Guanazole	Bone marrow depression; liver toxicity; occasional hypoglycemia; progressive weight loss
Imidazole Carboxamide (DIC)	Severe nausea and vomiting; bone marrow depression; liver toxicity; occasional fever; "flu"-like syndrome
6-mercaptopurine Ribonucleoside	Bone marrow depression; severe oral ulceration

Appendix C
The Patient

If you have needs, let them be known. No one can anticipate your needs or communicate with you effectively if you remain silent. Do not be afraid to accept help. We all need help at some time during our lives.

You must remember that cancer is many different diseases—over one hundred—and some types are more deadly and devastating than others. Therefore, you must not assume that a diagnosis of cancer necessarily means an early and painful death. Ask your physician to explain the type of cancer you have. It is *your* cancer, and it is a violation of your rights if you are not told the truth when you seek it. Your physician has no right to withhold the truth from you, I believe, since it is *your* life in the balance.

You must also realize that with proper and effective medical treatment, you may have years of life left to you, or you may even be cured. Did you know that physicians now feel that some twelve to fifteen types of cancer, even in the final stages, may be successfully treated? It is too early to tell with certainty about most cases of cancer because all the results are not yet available and only time will prove their theories, but *there is hope.*

Do not try to find someone to blame for your cancer. It is not your fault, your doctor's fault, or the fault of your family. Nor did God, I believe, cause your cancer. I believe cancer is God's enemy, too, and He is on my side. Realize that many people have learned to live despite this disease, with limitations, and that from suffering can come accomplishments.

If you expect honesty from others, be honest with them and with yourself.

Realize that hope can be kept alive through your attitude, your faith, and proper medical treatment. Chemotherapy, and its side effects of today, can lead to a remission in the future.

Realize, if you have a family, that your loved ones have their own unique problems with which to cope. If you turn your anger against them, it makes it terribly difficult for them to support you or to face their problems.

If you are a cancer patient living alone, realize your problems are different from those of someone with a family. But there are things you can do to ease your loneliness. Seek out self-help groups and become involved in their work. Helping others is an effective therapy for loneliness.

Often, friends will shun you—not necessarily because they don't care about you, but because they don't know what to do or say. They feel uncomfortable because they are afraid they might upset you or your family by saying the wrong thing. You can help to put them at ease by letting them know how you feel.

Let your doctor know of any changes in your health or of any new pains. On the other hand, don't automatically associate every new pain or discomfort with cancer. Something else may be causing your problems. Do not *assume* anything about cancer. Seek medical facts.

If you are being treated for cancer and the prognosis seems good, don't become obsessed with death. Your chance for long-term survival may be greater than some of the people who are worrying about *you*.

Realize your limitations, but also be aware of your capabilities. Do not assume, when you leave the hospital, that you are going home to die. Ask your doctor what you are physically capable of doing. Many cancer patients continue working, even while undergoing chemotherapy or radiation therapy. Realize there are things that you can do to keep your body in better health. Some patients become so terrified, following a diagnosis of cancer, that they do not eat or rest properly. This can result in very real health problems, even without the presence of cancer.

It does little good to ask, "Why me?" You will get no answers.

Do not accept lengthy depression as inevitable.

Realize that depression can be a tolerable emotion, unless it becomes overwhelming. Most healthy people also become depressed at times. But learn to find ways to ease your depression. Find reasons to live. Discover new pleasures. Many cancer patients find a release for their feelings in writing poetry or books, or in music or painting. Others discover that helping people is a very effective therapy.

Let your doctors know you want to be a part of your own treatment. Tell them you want to cooperate with them and to have a part in your own destiny. After all, it is *your* cancer and *your* life.

Consider whether or not you are *really* protecting your loved ones if you decide to be brave and pretend "everything is all right" when it isn't. Chances are, your spouse can cope better with the truth than with deceit and "game-playing." Be honest with your children, too, because they cannot respond to your need for understanding if they are not aware of your disease and the prognosis.

Communicate with persons around you. If some of your friends cannot accept your cancer, find new friends. But give persons a chance to accept what has happened to you.

Consider some of the practical problems resulting from a serious illness. No one, except God, really knows when you will die. However, certain arrangements for your funeral can be made, and a will can be drawn up through your attorney. Check your insurance policies and the beneficiaries you have listed. When these things have been done, you can go on with the business of living.

Learn about the different resources available in your community. Ask about the visiting nurses program and learn what can be done should you face a financial emergency, such as needing gasoline for your auto in order to go to a hospital out of town and back home again. If you are being treated at a hospital some distance from your home, be sure to make an attempt to find a physician in your area who will accept you as a patient.

False hope can come in many forms. Consider the financial costs of unproven methods for treating cancer. Some unorthodox treatments sound appealing, but are often costly and ineffective. Testimonials alone from "cured" cancer patients are generally not accurate. Many of these persons have also been treated with chemotherapy, surgery, or radiation.

If things are going well for you, and then something goes wrong, do not panic. A relapse may not signal the end at all. Give your physicians a chance to employ their skills and the latest treatments for cancer at their disposal.

Realize that there are diseases other than cancer that can be treated, but not cured. Hypertension is one; diabetes is another.

If you do not want pity, do not ask for it.

If you are one who feels God will cure you if you believe strongly enough and pray long enough, know that faith and prayer are extremely important; but do not turn away from God when things do not go well. Do not feel you are being punished by God because you have not been a good person. Once, I blamed God for my cancer; but when I turned to Him for help when I had reached the bottom, I discovered that from despair and suffering can come new dreams and a new life. Do not seek success and happiness so eagerly and intently; relax, reach out to others; *truly* be a good person; and, perhaps, happiness will find *you!*

If you do not want extraordinary measures used to keep you alive unnecessarily (when there is no hope for reasonable life), then let your family, pastor, and physicians know how you feel. At least they can consider your feelings if they must make a decision in the future.

Do not try to hide your illness. Cancer is a disease, not a form of punishment. If we are ever able to erase the social stigmas and misconceptions surrounding cancer, we, as patients, must speak out in our defense. We should not be considered the lepers of this century.

Sooner or later, as a cancer patient, you will probably encounter persons who feel that cancer might be contagious. It is these persons who have problems, not you. Their fear of cancer overrides their common sense.

Realize the importance of love. Those who love you need

to express this love and you need to tell others how much you love them. Do not wait until tomorrow.

If you consider the quality of your life and make each day count in some way, you have just as long to live as anyone else—the rest of your life.

Remember, you are not alone; there are others who care about you.

SUGGESTIONS FOR FAMILY MEMBERS OF CANCER PATIENTS FROM WANDA KELLY

Be honest with each other. But do not try to force the conversation into one discussion area, since the patient may not wish to talk about his disease or the prognosis.

If the diagnosis *is* cancer, do not assume this means that death is inevitable. Even if the cancer is incurable, this does not mean the patient will die tomorrow. Often, patients can be treated successfully for certain types of cancer. And still other patients may live several years with some cancers.

Many times a spouse or relative of a patient instructs the physician: "If it's cancer, we don't want them to know it!" The reasoning behind this statement is that the patient will be spared the anguish of knowing about his disease. In reality, the patient generally knows but is unable to talk about his problems.

One initial reaction to a diagnosis of a serious illness such as cancer is a reluctance to face reality. Pretending the illness isn't present will not make it go away. A disease such as cancer is too big to "sweep under the rug."

Communicate with each other as a family. Communications often cease following the diagnosis of a serious illness. But more problems can result from not talking about the illness than from facing it openly.

If you, as a family member, have questions about your spouse's illness, ask a physician. Do not listen to well-meaning, but ill-informed, friends and relatives who try to tell you where to seek treatment and offer suggestions for living with the illness.

If you need support, seek community resources that are available to you. Many organizations offer short-term assistance on an emergency basis to families in need. Check with your Social Security office and Veterans Affairs or Veterans Administration office to determine if a pension might be available to your spouse if he served in the Armed Forces. He might qualify for the pension, whether the illness is service-connected or not.

If the patient in your family is a child, realize that many families disintegrate when a seriously ill child is involved. Be aware that many emotional problems that may have been lurking below the surface of your marriage before the illness may come to the surface when you are faced with cancer. Some parents are able to strengthen their marriage; others cannot. But it does little good to blame each other for what you might have done to prevent your child from having cancer.

As a family member, you will probably have to live with guilt at some time during the illness. You may blame yourself for not having been a better wife, husband, or parent. You may remember things you have done that were wrong. Guilt will not change things at all. We are all human and we make mistakes. If *you* were the patient, your spouse almost surely would also feel guilty about mistakes from the past—things like arguments and harsh words spoken to each other. Remember that life is not perfect and we cannot change the past. We will all continue to make mistakes.

Sometimes family members become very angry because it is *they* who have to cope with a serious illness in the family. Why did it have to happen to them? Children of cancer patients sometimes become angry because they have to lead restricted lives at times due to their father's or mother's cancer. But learn to talk about these problems. Once I talked with a young lady who tearfully told me she once wished her father, a cancer patient, would "just hurry up and die and get it over with!" Her father did die, and she suffered terrible feelings of guilt. She actually felt she had caused her father's death.

Consider the possibility of caring for your loved one at home. Some physicians urge families to allow the patient to return home if they desire. Bedrooms can be converted into home care rooms. Visiting nurse services and other resources are often available. And the patient may be happier.

Some mothers and fathers do not tell their children that one of the parents has cancer. I would recommend the child be told in most cases, unless the child is too young to understand. Once the children do know, there can, of course, still be problems. Here are some remarks from children of cancer patients, made at a special Make Today Count meeting in Omaha, Nebraska: "I wonder how much longer Mom will be around?" "The uncertainty drives me nuts!" "Some of my friends won't come to my house anymore." "It hurts me when Dad can't do things with me anymore." "Mom sure yells at me a lot." Being honest with your children won't make all your problems disappear, but it will generally make it easier to cope with them.

Some family members feel cancer may be contagious. Talk with your physician about this misconception. Still others may worry about the hereditary aspects of cancer. Once again, question your physician about this fear, since no blanket statement should be made that cancer cannot be inherited.

333

Other fears center around financial problems and the possibility of the patient's death from the disease. But these fears should be discussed as a family because the patient needs family support during this period of time, and hiding the truth tends to separate the family and halt communications.

If a patient is able to continue working and functioning as a human being, do not discourage him by assuming all cancer patients should "go to bed." Once again, a talk with your physician should alleviate your fears. Even though the patient is physically able to work, there may be barriers to his continued employment. Employment practices may prohibit employment of cancer patients in some instances. Employers sometimes assume, for example, that cancer patients, even though recovered, might have a higher rate of absenteeism. There may be fringe benefits for life and health insurance which would make an employer reluctant to hire a cancer patient. There seems to be no uniform policy as to how employers treat cancer patients. However, many employers seem to feel that all cancer patients sooner or later will die or return to the hospital. If you, as a family member, anticipate some of these problems, perhaps you will be better able to cope with them if they occur.

PATIENT'S BILL OF RIGHTS*

I.   The patient has the right to considerate and respectful care.

II.   The patient has the right to obtain, from his physician, complete current information concerning his diagnosis, treatment, and prognosis in terms the patient can be reasonably expected to understand. (When it is not medically advisable to give such information to the patient, the information should be made available to an appropriate person on his behalf. He has the right to know by name the physician responsible for coordinating his care.)

III.   The patient has the right to receive from his physician information necessary to give informed consent prior to the start of any procedure and/or treatment. Except in emergencies, such information for informed consent should include, but not necessarily be limited to, the specific procedure and/or treatment, the medically significant risks involved, and the probable duration of incapacitation. Where medically significant alternatives for care or treatment exist, or when the patient has the right to such information concerning medical alternatives, the patient has the right to such information. The patient also has the right to know the name of the person responsible for the procedures and/or treatment.

IV.   The patient has the right to refuse treatment to the extent permitted by law, and to be informed of the medical consequences of his action.

V.   The patient has the right to every consideration of his privacy concerning his own medical care program, case discussion, and consultation.

VI.   The patient has the right to expect that all communications and records pertaining to his care should be treated as confidential.

VII. The patient has the right to expect that within its capacity a hospital must make reasonable response to the request of

*Reprinted with permission from American Hospital Association, 840 North Lake Shore, Chicago, IL 60611.

a patient for services. The hospital must provide evaluation, service, and/or referral as indicated by the urgency of the case. When medically permissible, a patient may be transferred to another facility only after he has received complete information and explanation concerning the needs for and alternatives to such a transfer. The institution to which the patient is to be transferred must first have accepted the patient transfer.

VIII. The patient has the right to obtain information as to any relationship of his hospital to other health-care and educational institutions insofar as his care is concerned. The patient has the right to obtain information as to the existence of any professional relationships among individuals, by name, who are treating him.

IX. The patient has the right to be advised if the hospital proposes to engage in or perform human experimentation affecting his care or treatment. The patient has the right to refuse to participate in such research projects.

X. The patient has the right to expect reasonable continuity of care. He has the right to know in advance what appointment times and physicians are available and where. The patient has the right to expect that the hospital will provide a mechanism whereby he is informed by his physician, or a delegate of the physician, of the patient's continuing health-care requirements following discharge.

XI. The patient has the right to examine and receive an explanation of his bill regardless of source of payment.

XII. The patient has the right to know what hospital rules and regulations apply to his conduct as a patient.

THE DYING PERSON'S BILL OF RIGHTS*

I have the right to be treated as a living human being until I die.

I have the right to maintain a sense of hopefulness however changing its focus may be.

I have the right to be cared for by those who can maintain a sense of hopefulness, however changing this might be.

I have the right to express my feelings and emotions about my approaching death in my own way.

I have the right to participate in decisions concerning my care.

I have the right to expect continuing medical and nursing attention even though "cure" goals must be changed to "comfort" goals.

I have the right not to die alone.

I have the right to be free from pain.

I have the right to have my questions answered honestly.

I have the right not to be deceived.

I have the right to have help from and for my family in accepting my death.

I have the right to die in peace and dignity.

I have the right to retain my individuality and not be judged for my decisions which may be contrary to beliefs of others.

I have the right to discuss and enlarge my religious and/or spiritual experiences, whatever these may mean to others.

I have the right to expect that the sanctity of the human body will be respected after death.

I have the right to be cared for by caring, sensitive, knowledgeable people who will attempt to understand my needs and will be able to gain some satisfaction in helping me face my death.

*Reprinted with permission from Amelia J. Barbus, Assistant Vice-president/Patient Services, Northern Michigan Hospitals, Inc., 416 Connable Street, Petoskey, MI 49770.

Appendix D
Last Words

Questions and Answers About Funerals

How much does a funeral cost? The total average funeral costs range from $1,000 to $1,400. Cemetery and miscellaneous expenses bring the total average to about $2,000. About $4 billion is spent annually by Americans on funeral costs.

Are there cheaper ways to be buried? Try a memorial society. You can contact the Continental Association of Funeral and Memorial Societies at Suite 1100, 1828 "L" Street, N.W., Washington, D.C. 20036; telephone 202 293-4821. There are memorial societies in almost all states today.

What are memorial societies? Societies are nonprofit organizations established by consumer groups or churches. They are run by their members, who pay a one-time fee.

The society contracts with a funeral director to bury its members at a modest price.

How much money can I save with a memorial society? A memorial society can probably save you $500 or more in funeral costs.

Must I use limousines from the funeral home? No. You can make arrangements for transportation through friends and relatives.

Is embalming necessary? Embalming, or replacing the body's blood with a formalin (formaldehyde) solution, is not a long-term preservative. It does make the corpse more presentable for a brief period of time. Some states require that a corpse be embalmed after a specified period of time, usually ranging from twenty-four to seventy-two hours, unless it has been buried, cremated, or refrigerated. No state has an absolute legal requirement that remains must be embalmed in all circumstances. Since it is "usual practice" to embalm the corpse, few people question it. Without embalming there can't be a viewing of the body, and if there is no viewing, all the other trappings of an expensive funeral are unnecessary. The cost of embalming is about $150, which includes cosmetics.

Are pallbearers paid? The six pallbearers usually get $25 each.

Who arranges for the death certificate and is there a charge? The funeral director generally arranges for the death certificate. The cost is $2 or less.

Who gives newspapers and radio stations the obituary? The funeral director generally does this.

Where can I purchase a low-cost casket? The St. Francis Burial and Counseling Society, Inc., offers assembled coffin kits which you assemble yourself at prices ranging from $115 for contemporary pine to $185 for an assembled pine coffin. This organization also markets ash boxes for cremations, ranging from $25 to $35 in price. A book, *How to Build Your Own Coffin*, is available at a cost of $2.50. The address is: St. Francis Burial & Counseling Society, 1768 Church Street, N.W., Washington, D.C. 20036.

Last Words

INDIVIDUAL FUNERAL ARRANGEMENT FORM

Name_____Address _____
City_____State_____Zip _____
Telephone Number_____Social Security Number _____
I, the undersigned, desire to make my own funeral arrangements in advance, knowing that if I do not make decisions now, my loved ones will have to make them for me some time in the future. I wish to prevent unnecessary stress and confusion at a time when my loved ones should be protected from having to deal with the many details I have outlined on this form.

I wish to be: cremated□; buried above ground (in crypt or mausoleum)□; buried in a grave□

I wish my arrangements to be with a funeral director□memorial society□I am a member of _____memorial society.

I have discussed my funeral arrangements with: a funeral director□; an attorney□; a clergyman□. Name of funeral director_____. Name of attorney_____. Name of clergyman_____.

I desire a coffin in the following price range: $65 to $200 (plain wood)□; $200 to $600□; $600 to $1,000□; $1,000 up□.

I wish my services to be held in a funeral home□; synagogue□; church□.

I desire an open□closed□casket at my services. I desire a military funeral and have made arrangements with:

_____

Instead of a funeral service (with body present), I desire a memorial service (service conducted without the body).

□(A memorial service can be held at home, in a church or synagogue.) I desire flowers.□Please omit flowers.□

Instead of flowers, I would prefer the following in my memory___

_____

341

I desire the following pallbearers:

Name	Address	Telephone	Contacted (yes or no)
_____	_____	_____	_____
_____	_____	_____	_____
_____	_____	_____	_____
_____	_____	_____	_____
_____	_____	_____	_____
_____	_____	_____	_____

Alternates

_____	_____	_____	_____
_____	_____	_____	_____
_____	_____	_____	_____

Honorary Pallbearers

_____	_____	_____	_____
_____	_____	_____	_____
_____	_____	_____	_____

I have arranged for a grave in_____cemetery; I have arranged for burial above ground in a crypt at_____. I have arranged for a vault (check with local cemetery for legal requirements regarding vaults)☐.

Instead of making funeral arrangements, I desire to will my body to a medical school and I have made arrangements as indicated on the attached form (Deed of Disposition of Body for Scientific Purposes). ☐I understand that the medical school will make arrangements for cremation or burial of my body.

I wish to will my body to the following organ and tissue banks:
_____

I wish the following special arrangements for my funeral:_____
_____
_____

Information for obituary:
Full name_____
Birth date_____Birthplace_____
Married to (maiden name)_____on _____
at _____
Father_____Mother_____
Father still living_____? Mother still living _____?
Sons _____
Daughters_____
Brothers_____
Sisters _____
Church affiliation _____
Member of (list organizations) _____
Occupation _____
Former occupation, if retired _____
I am eligible for the following death benefits (Attach necessary
papers regarding death benefits):
    a. Lump sum payment from Social Security □
    b. Payment from Veterans Administration □
    c. Free headstone □
    d. American flag □
    e. Burial in national cemetery □
    f. Insurance plan □
    g. Credit or trade union □
    h. Fraternal organization □
    i. Church □

I have drawn up a will and it is located_____

_____
Signature

_____
Date

_____
Witness

_____
Witness

Appearance*

Appendix D

DEED OF DISPOSITION OF BODY FOR SCIENTIFIC PURPOSES*

Know All Men by These Presents:

That I, Mr. / Miss / Mrs. _____

of _____

do hereby declare it my wish that my body, after my death, shall be used for scientific purposes for the advancement of medical science, teaching, and study.

I do therefore hereby grant and dispose of my body to_____; I hereby authorize and direct any physician, hospital, mortuary, or any other person having possession of my body after my death to deliver my body to_____, and I authorize the medical faculty to use said body for such purposes as it deems most useful to medical science, including tissue and organ transplantation.

I understand it is necessary that the family or estate of the donor defray the transportation and professional service fees of the funeral director, in making the body available for scientific study.

Should an urgent need exist at another medical school,_____may temporarily transfer my body there.___YES___NO

IN WITNESS WHEREOF I have hereunto affixed my signature this_____day of_____, 19___ at _____

_____

Signed by the donor and the following two witnesses in the presence of each other:

Signature of Donor

Date of Birth _____

Social Security Number:

_____
Witness

_____
Witness

NOTE: This is a sample form. Check with the facility where you plan to will your body for actual deed form. Also, check with the same facility to ascertain if your organs might be suitable for transplanting.

344

A LIVING WILL*

*To My Family, My Physician, My Lawyer,
and All Others Whom It May Concern*

Death is as much a reality as birth, growth, maturity, and old age—it is the one certainty of life. If the time comes when I can no longer take part in decisions for my own future, let this statement stand as an expression of my wishes and directions, while I am still of sound mind.

If at such a time the situation should arise in which there is no reasonable expectation of my recovery from extreme physical or mental disability, I direct that I be allowed to die and not be kept alive by medications, artificial means, or "heroic measures." I do, however, ask that medication be mercifully administered to me to alleviate suffering even though this may shorten my remaining life.

This statement is made after careful consideration and is in accordance with my strong convictions and beliefs. I want the wishes and directions here expressed carried out to the extent permitted by law. Insofar as they are not legally enforceable, I hope that those to whom this Will is addressed will regard themselves as morally bound by these provisions.

Signed _____

Date _____

Witness _____

Witness _____

Copies of this request have been given to _____

*Reprinted with permission from Concern For Dying, 250 West 57th Street, New York, NY 10019. Ellen J. Savette, Administrative Assistant.

To Make Best Use of Your LIVING WILL

1. Sign and date before two witnesses. (This is to insure that you signed of your own free will and not under any pressure.)
2. If you have a doctor, give him a copy for your medical file and discuss it with him to make sure he is in agreement.

   Give copies to those most likely to be concerned "if the time comes when you can no longer take part in decisions for your own future." Enter their names on the Living Will. Keep the original nearby, easily and readily available.
3. Above all discuss your intentions with those closest to you, NOW.
4. It is a good idea to look over your Living Will once a year and redate it and initial the new date to make it clear that your wishes are unchanged.

   Additional materials available to contributors:

   Questions and Answers About the Living Will

   Selected articles and case histories

   A bibliography

   Information on films

   The Concern for Dying newsletter is a quarterly publication reporting the most recent developments in the field of death and dying. It contains announcements of upcoming educational conferences, workshops and symposia, as well as reviews of current literature. The Newsletter is sent to anyone who contributes $5.00 or more annually to the Concern for Dying.

A mini-will, a condensed version of the Living Will which can be carried in a wallet in case of accident or emergency, will be sent upon receipt of a contribution.

For information, call: 212 246-6962.

Important

Declarants may wish to add specific statements to the Living Will to be inserted in the space provided for that purpose above the signature. Possible additional provisions are suggested below:

1. a) I appoint _____to make binding decisions concerning my medical treatment.

   or

   b) I have discussed my views as to life-sustaining measures with the following who understand my wishes

   _____

   _____

2. Measures of artificial life support in the face of impending death that are especially abhorrent to me are:
   a) Electrical or mechanical resuscitation of my heart when it has stopped beating.
   b) Nasogastric tube feedings when I am paralyzed and no longer able to swallow.
   c) Mechanical respiration by machine when my brain can no longer sustain my own breathing.
   d) _____

3. If it does not jeopardize the chance of my recovery to a meaningful and sentient life or impose an undue burden on my family, I would like to live out my last days at home rather than in a hospital.

4. If any of my tissues are sound and would be of value as transplants to help other people, I freely give my permission for such donation.

A LIVING WILL FOR CHRISTIANS

To My Loved Ones, Pastor, Physician(s), Attorney, and/or Hospital:

I,_____, believe as a Christian that at no time are we human beings outside our Father's care, whether living or dead, and that even the sparrow does not fall in death without our Father's knowledge (Matthew 10:29). Therefore, if death is inevitable for me, I do not consider it a defeat. I ask for honesty and compassion from those persons who are caring for me and I insist that I be permitted to play a part in my own destiny by helping to make my own decisions and preparations.

If I am no longer able to make decisions about my life and death, and there is no expectation of my recovery, I ask that I be allowed to die. I do not want to be kept alive through artificial life-support systems or other measures. If there is no hope for my recovery, I do not want life-support systems attached to my body in the first place, and then there will be no controversy about who should remove the system or when it should be done. I do not want my life ended through any form of injections or similar measures, but neither do I want my dying to be prolonged needlessly, causing unnecessary grief for my loved ones.

I request that drugs be administered to me as needed to alleviate my suffering, if this becomes necessary, even though these measures may hasten my death.

I realize this Will is not legally binding, but my signature attests to my own beliefs and wishes and I ask that the contents be honored.

Signed_____

Date_____

Witnesses:_____

Name, Address, and Telephone

_____

Name, Address, and Telephone

I have given copies of this Will to:

_____

348